ZB Spelling Connections

J. Richard Gentry, Ph.D.

Series Author

J. Richard Gentry, Ph.D.

Editorial Development: Cottage Communications

Art and Production: Brown Publishing Network

Design: Bill Smith Studio

Photography: George C. Anderson Photography: cover image; © Jeff Hunter/Getty Images, Inc.: p. 12; © George Shelley/CORBIS: p. 14; © PhotoDisc/Getty Images, Inc.: p. 19; © Daniel Barillot/Masterfile: p. 36; © Strauss/Curtis/CORBIS: p. 44; © John and Lisa Merrill/CORBIS: p. 46; © Dennis MacDonald/PhotoEdit: p. 57; © Alistair Duncan/Getty Images, Inc.: p. 60; © Frank Lukasseck/age fotostock: p. 74; © Gary Braasch/Getty Images, Inc.: p. 76; © R. Kimball/Photex/zefa/CORBIS: p. 84; © Banana Stock/age fotostock: p. 103; © Craig Tuttle/CORBIS: p. 107; © Royalty-free/Masterfile: p. 111; © Amwell/Getty Images, Inc.: p. 120; © David Young-Wolff/PhotoEdit: p. 122; © Christina Krutz/age fotostock: p. 127; © Richard Cummins/SuperStock: p. 128; © David Ward/Getty Images, Inc.: p. 136; © Brand X Pictures/Getty Images, Inc.: p. 143; © Richard Koek/Getty Images, Inc.: p. 157; © Herve Bruhat/RAPHO/Imagestate: p. 166; © Tom Vezo/Peter Arnold: p. 169; © Mark Raycrof/Minden Pictures: p. 176; © John Kelly/Getty Images, Inc.: p. 182; © Nancy Sheehan/PhotoEdit: p. 185; © Barbara Stitzer/PhotoEdit: p. 196; © BIOS/Peter Arnold: p. 199; © Peter Beck/CORBIS: p. 206; © Digital Vision/SuperStock: p.219; © Thinkstock Images/PictureQuest: p. 222; © Liane Cary/age fotostock: p. 242; © CORBIS/Jim Sugar: p. 253; © ArenaPal/Topham/The Image Works: p. 261; © Digital Vision/Getty Images, Inc.: p. 277; © Royalty-free/CORBIS: pp. 324, 341, 356; © Richard Cummins/age fotostock: p. 329; © StockByte/PictureQuest: p. 333; © gkphotography/Alamy: p. 337; © Danilo Donadoni/age fotostock: p. 344; © Martin Rugner/age fotostock: p. 348; © Pixtal/age fotostock: p. 352; © Arthur Morris/CORBIS: p. 360; © Ariel Skelley/CORBIS: p. 365; © Brand X Pictures/PictureQuest: p. 367; © Michael Martini/Stock Image/PictureQuest: p. 372; © Michael S. Nolan/age fotostock: p. 376.

Illustrations: Erin Mauterer: pp. 17, 25, 27, 31, 35, 41, 77, 89, 114, 152, 160, 195, 203, 223, 238, 265, 286, 290, 293, 294, 299, 303, 304, 311; Paul Weiner: pp. 23, 38, 52, 58, 73, 79, 81, 146, 198, 214, 244, 252, 257, 268.

The following references were used in the development of the **Word Study** activities included on the **Review** pages:

Ayto, John. *Arcade Dictionary of Word Origins: The Histories of More Than 8,000 English-Language Words*. New York: Arcade Publishing, Little, Brown, and Company, 1990.

Barnhart, Robert K., ed. *The Barnhart Dictionary of Etymology: The Core Vocabulary of Standard English*. New York: The H.W. Wilson Company, 1988.

Makkai, Adam, ed. *A Dictionary of American Idioms*. New York: Barron's Educational Series, Inc., 1987.

Rheingold, Howard. *They Have a Word for It: A Lighthearted Lexicon of Untranslatable Words and Phrases*. Los Angeles: Jeremy P. Tarcher, Inc., 1988.

Terban, Marvin. *Time to Rhyme: A Rhyming Dictionary*. Honesdale, PA: Wordsong, Boyds Mills Press, 1994.

ISBN-13: 978-0-7367-4681-6

ISBN-10: 0-7367-4681-1

Zaner-Bloser, Inc., P.O. Box 16764, Columbus, Ohio 43216-6764 (1-800-421-3018)
www.zaner-bloser.com
Printed in the United States of America   07 08 09 10 330 5 4 3 2

Table of Contents

Spelling Study Strategy

LOOK > SAY > COVER > SEE > WRITE > CHECK

1 **Look** at the word.

2 **Say** the letters in the word. Think about how each sound is spelled.

3 **Cover** the word with your hand or close your eyes.

4 **See** the word in your mind. Spell the word to yourself.

5 **Write** the word.

6 **Check** your spelling against the spelling in the book.

8 Steps
When Taking a Test

1 **Get** ready for the test. Make sure your paper and pencil are ready.

2 **Listen** carefully as your teacher says each word and uses it in a sentence. Don't write before you hear the word **and** the sentence.

3 **Write** the word carefully. Make sure your handwriting is easy to read. If you want to print your words, ask your teacher.

4 **Use** a pen to correct your test. Look at the word as your teacher says it.

5 **Say** the word aloud. Listen carefully as your teacher spells the word. Say each letter aloud. Check the word one letter at a time.

6 **Circle** any misspelled parts of the word.

7 **Look** at the correctly written word. Spell the word again. Say each letter out loud.

8 **Write** any misspelled word correctly.

7 Steps
When Writing a Paper

1. **Think** of the exact word you want to use.

2. **Write** the word, if you know how to spell it.

3. **Say** the word to yourself, if you are not sure how to spell it.

4. **Picture** what the word looks like when you see it written.

5. **Write** the word.

6. **Ask** yourself whether the word looks right.

7. **Check** the word in a dictionary if you are not sure.

Spelling and Thinking

short a

1. _____
2. _____
3. _____
4. _____
5. _____
6. _____
7. _____
8. _____
9. _____

short i

10. _____
11. _____
12. _____
13. _____
14. _____
15. _____

READ the Basic Words 👀 Watch out for easily misspelled words!

1. land	*land*	The farmer planted corn on his **land**.
👀 **2.** stick	*stick*	Kayla used a big **stick** as a bat.
3. plan	*plan*	Dad will help us **plan** our vacation.
4. trip	*trip*	Our class went on a **trip** to the zoo.
5. stand	*stand*	Please **stand** in this line.
6. act	*act*	My sister likes to **act** in plays.
👀 **7.** thing	*thing*	What is that **thing** on your desk?
8. last	*last*	John spent his **last** dollar on pizza.
👀 **9.** lift	*lift*	This box is too heavy to **lift**.
10. band	*band*	The **band** plays music at games.
11. grand	*grand*	Lisa won the **grand** prize.
12. swim	*swim*	Shana likes to **swim** in the pool.
13. stamp	*stamp*	Please put a **stamp** on this letter.
14. list	*list*	Write the words in a short **list**.
15. sand	*sand*	Many beaches are covered by **sand**.

⊚ **Review**		⊚ **Challenge**	
16. bat	18. miss	20. brick	22. gadget
17. fan	19. win	21. dancer	23. skill

SORT the Basic Words

Each word on the spelling list has the **short a** sound or the **short i** sound.

1–9. Write the words that have the **short a** sound.

10–15. Write the words that have the **short i** sound.

REMEMBER the Spelling Strategy

Remember that the **short a** sound you hear in **plan** is spelled **a**. The **short i** sound you hear in **trip** is spelled **i**.

Spelling and Phonics

Ending Sounds

1–5. Write the Basic Words that rhyme with **and**. Circle the consonant cluster at the end of each rhyming word.

Word Structure

6. Change the first letter of **fast** to make this Basic Word.

7. Change the first letter of **mist** to make this Basic Word.

8. Change the first two letters of **sting** to make this Basic Word.

Sound and Letter Patterns

9–10. Write Basic Words by adding the missing letters.

sw__m st__ck

Using the Dictionary

11–15. The words in a dictionary are in a-b-c order. Look at the first letter of each word below. Write these words in a-b-c order.

plan   trip   lift   act   stamp

◆ ◆ ◆

Dictionary Check Be sure to check the a-b-c order of the words in your **Spelling Dictionary**.

Ending Sounds

1.

2.

3.

4.

5.

Word Structure

6.

7.

8.

Sound and Letter Patterns

9.

10.

Using the Dictionary

11.

12.

13.

14.

15.

Spelling and Reading

Solve the Analogies

1.
2.
3.
4.
5.

Complete the Meanings

6.
7.
8.
9.
10.

Complete the Story

11.
12.
13.
14.
15.

land	stick	plan	trip	stand
act	thing	last	lift	band
grand	swim	stamp	list	sand

Solve the Analogies Write a Basic Word to complete each analogy.

1. **Beginning** is to **first** as **end** is to _____.
2. **Ship** is to **water** as **car** is to _____.
3. **Song** is to **sing** as **play** is to _____.
4. **Worm** is to **crawl** as **fish** is to _____.
5. **Small** is to **tiny** as **large** is to _____.

Complete the Meanings Write the Basic Word that fits each clue.

6. Taylor likes to _____ on her head.
7. Pablo can _____ the large stone.
8. This postcard needs a _____.
9. Throw this dry _____ on the fire.
10. Kim plays drums in a _____.

Complete the Story Write Basic Words from the box to complete the story.

After school let out, the Lee family decided to __11.__ a vacation. Kim and Nucha made a __12.__ of places they wanted to visit. They each wrote down one __13.__ they hoped to do. All of the Lees wanted to build castles of __14.__. Where do you think the Lees will go on their __15.__?

sand
plan
trip
thing
list

Spelling and Writing

 Proofread a Letter

To show where changes are needed, you can use **proofreading marks**. The symbol ⊜ means make a capital letter. The symbol ⊘ means make a small letter. Proofread the letter below for eight misspelled words. Then rewrite the letter. Write the spelling words correctly and make the corrections shown by the proofreading marks.

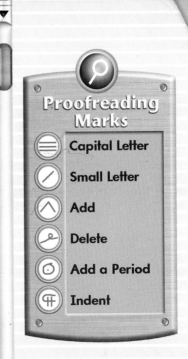

Dear Parents,

    Come help Clean up the lan of Grannd Park. We plann to take a tripp there on the lasst day of school at 10:00 a.m. there is a lisst of things to do. You can pick up Each big stik and lift up every heavy theng.

           Mr. Bell's Third grade Class

More Practice Write and sort the Basic Words.

Write a Letter

Pretend that your class is cleaning up a park. Write a letter to your parents. Ask them to help. Be sure to tell where and when the cleanup takes place. Tell what kind of help you need from grown-ups. Use as many spelling words as you can.

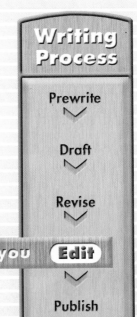

Writing Process
Prewrite
Draft
Revise
Edit
Publish

Proofread your writing as you Edit

When you finish writing your draft, proofread your paper for errors in spelling, grammar, capitalization, and punctuation. Use the **Spelling Dictionary** to check spelling if you are not sure.

Review

Review

Complete the Sentences

1.

2.

3.

4.

Answer the Questions

5.

6.

7.

8.

More Than One Meaning

1.

bat	fan	miss	win

Complete the Sentences Write a Review Word to complete each sentence.

1. People use a _____ to keep cool on warm summer days and nights.
2. If you _____ the bus, you can walk to school.
3. Eric got a ball and a _____ for his birthday.
4. The best speller will _____ the spelling bee.

Answer the Questions Write the Review Word that answers each question.

5. What is the opposite of **lose**?
6. What can you turn on to keep a room cool?
7. What is the opposite of **catch**?
8. What do you use to hit a baseball?

Word Study: More Than One Meaning

Write the one Review Word that fits both of these meanings:

- something that moves air for cooling
- someone who really likes something a lot

◎ Challenge

| brick | dancer | gadget | skill |

Word Clues Write a Challenge Word that matches each clue.

1. Any small kitchen tool can be called this.
2. The Big Bad Wolf could not blow down the house built of this.
3. If you are this, you move your body to the rhythm of the music.
4. A writer needs this to write well.

Complete the Sentences Write a Challenge Word to complete each sentence.

5. The wall around the playground was made of _____.
6. Because she has great _____ in basketball, the coach asked her to help the younger students.
7. The _____ in the ballet was dressed as a swan.
8. My mother found a _____ in the drawer, and she doesn't know what it is!

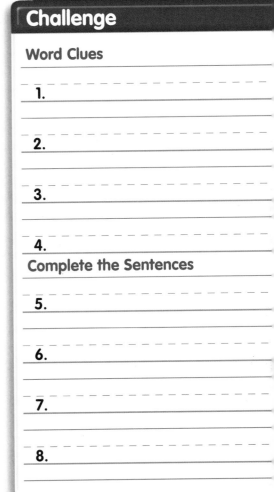

Challenge

Word Clues

1.
2.
3.
4.

Complete the Sentences

5.
6.
7.
8.

Do you think you've mastered the Spelling Strategy? Take the CHAMPION CHALLENGE on page 286!

Spelling and Technology

Spelling and Technology

How a Computer Works

1.

2.

3.

4.

How a Computer Works

A computer has many parts. To work on a computer, you must give it commands. The chart below shows some computer parts and computer commands.

Computer Parts	Computer Commands
disk	open
screen	close
mouse	print
speakers	save

Learn these words for computer parts and commands.

disk	mouse	print	save

Write the word from the box that completes each sentence. Underline words that contain the **short i** sound.

1. I use my _____ to move around the screen.
2. I _____ my work so I can come back to it later.
3. My computer stores my work on a _____.
4. I will _____ my work onto a piece of paper.

Content Words

Link to **Math:** Numbers

Write the Content Word that is the answer.

fifteen	sixteen	seventeen	eighteen

1. six + ten = _____

2. eight + ten = _____

3. five + ten = _____

4. seven + ten = _____

Link to **Science:** Trees

Write the name of each leaf.

oak	maple	elm	birch

5. o_____ **6.** e_____ **7.** m_____ **8.** b_____

Link to **The Spelling Strategy**

Circle the two Content Words you wrote that contain the **short i** sound.

Content Connection: Science

Search the Internet to find out more about trees. You might look at **www.oplin.org/tree**. Write three common names of trees. Write two kinds of fruits from trees.

Content Words

Math: Numbers

1. _____

2. _____

3. _____

4. _____

Science: Trees

5. _____

6. _____

7. _____

8. _____

Spelling and Thinking

short o

1. _____
2. _____
3. _____
4. _____
5. _____
6. _____

short e

7. _____
8. _____
9. _____
10. _____
11. _____
12. _____
13. _____
14. _____
15. _____

READ the Basic Words 👀 Watch out for easily misspelled words!

👀 **1.** crop	*crop*	Ms. Lutz is harvesting her bean **crop**.
2. test	*test*	Joni passed her spelling **test**.
3. clock	*clock*	Is the time on this **clock** correct?
👀 **4.** spent	*spent*	Dana **spent** her lunch money on candy.
5. drop	*drop*	Ben felt a **drop** of rain on his head.
6. left	*left*	Mary writes with her **left** hand.
7. sled	*sled*	The **sled** slid on the ice.
8. plot	*plot*	He grows peas in his garden **plot**.
9. spend	*spend*	Juan and Shawn **spend** summers at camp.
👀 **10.** west	*west*	The sun sets in the **west**.
11. block	*block*	He carved a dog from a **block** of wood.
12. tent	*tent*	Clowns rode on horses in the circus **tent**.
13. desk	*desk*	Shanita likes to study at her **desk**.
14. flock	*flock*	The **flock** of birds flew south in the fall.
15. nest	*nest*	The crow laid an egg in its **nest**.

◎ **Review**		◎ **Challenge**	
16. cot	18. send	20. colony	22. letters
17. nod	19. tell	21. kept	23. socket

SORT the Basic Words

1–6. Write the words that have the **short o** sound spelled **o**.

7–15. Write the words that have the **short e** sound spelled **e**.

REMEMBER the Spelling Strategy

Remember that the **short o** sound you hear in **drop** is spelled **o**. The **short e** sound you hear in **desk** is spelled **e**.

Spelling and Phonics

Ending Sounds

1–3. Write the Basic Words that rhyme with **rock**. Circle the two consonants at the end of each word.

4–5. Write the Basic Words that rhyme with **went**. Circle the two consonants at the end of each word.

Word Structure

6. Replace the first letter of **bend** with two consonants to make this Basic Word.

7. Replace the vowel in **drip** to make this Basic Word.

Sound and Letter Patterns

8–10. Write Basic Words by adding the missing letters.

cr__p

de__k

plo__

Using the Dictionary

Write the Basic Words with these meanings:

11. a platform with runners that slide over snow

12. an examination or trial

13. the direction in which the sun sets

14. opposite of right

15. a place built by birds

Word Structure

6.

7.

Sound and Letter Patterns

8.

9.

10.

Using the Dictionary

11.

12.

13.

14.

15.

crop	test	clock	spent	drop
left	sled	plot	spend	west
block	tent	desk	flock	nest

Complete the Rhymes

1.

2.

3.

Replace the Words

4.

5.

6.

7.

8.

9.

Complete the Paragraph

10.

11.

12.

13.

14.

15.

Complete the Rhymes Read each sentence below. Write a Basic Word to complete each rhyme.

1. I did my very <u>best</u> and scored a 100 on my _____.

2. The henhouse had a <u>theft</u>. Only a few eggs were _____.

3. The skunk looked east, then north and south. Finally the <u>pest</u> ran _____.

Replace the Words Write the Basic Word that could best replace each underlined word or words.

4. He carved a horse from a <u>solid piece</u> of wood.

5. The <u>group</u> of birds flew south for the winter.

6. That farmer's main <u>plant</u> is corn.

7. Please <u>leave</u> off the books at the library.

8. This <u>section</u> of land will make a good garden.

9. My friends and I like to camp out in a <u>cloth house</u>.

Complete the Paragraph Write the Basic Word that belongs in each blank.

Many people __10.__ time enjoying hobbies. My grandfather builds things from wood. Last year he built a __11.__, a __12.__, and a __13.__. My grandmother likes to watch birds. This spring she __14.__ a lot of time watching some robins build their __15.__.

nest
spend
spent
clock
sled
desk

Spelling and Writing

 Proofread a Journal Entry

The symbol ⊕ means **add**. The symbol ⊘ means **take out**, or delete. First, proofread the journal entry below for eight misspelled words. Then rewrite the entry. Write the spelling words correctly and make the corrections shown by the proofreading marks.

> *September 10*
>
> *a̲my and I went camping. When we got to the*
> *camp, we felt a dropp of rain. We set up our tint*
> *next t̶o̶ to a cropp of corn. Next we spint some time*
> *fishing. Then we watched a flok of crows eat corn.*
> *We didn't see a nesst. Before we went to sleep, I*
> *told a story with a scary plott. f̲inally we set our*
> *cluck to get ^up early the next day.*

More Practice Write and sort the Basic Words.

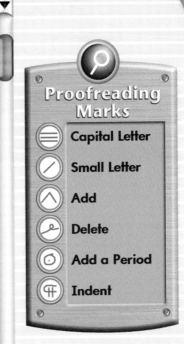

Proofreading Marks

≡	Capital Letter
/	Small Letter
∧	Add
⊘	Delete
⊙	Add a Period
¶	Indent

NARRATIVE

Write a Journal Entry

Write a journal entry about anything you wish, such as something you did today, something exciting that happened at school, or something that happened on the way to school. Begin by writing today's date. Tell what happened in the order that it happened. Use as many spelling words as you can.

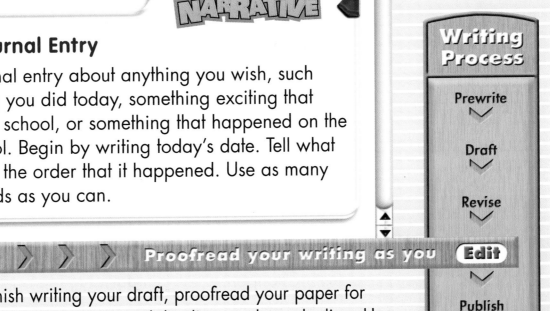

Writing Process

Prewrite
⌄
Draft
⌄
Revise
⌄

Proofread your writing as you Edit

⌄
Publish

When you finish writing your draft, proofread your paper for errors in spelling, grammar, capitalization, and punctuation. Use the **Spelling Dictionary** to check spelling if you are not sure.

◎ Review

Review

Complete the Sentences

1.

2.

3.

4.

Replace the Words

5.

6.

7.

8.

Make a New Word

1.

cot	nod	send	tell

Complete the Sentences Write a Review Word to complete each sentence.

1. Please _tell_ me again what you need from the store.

2. Eric sleeps on a _cot_ when he stays at my house.

3. I will _send_ you a postcard from camp.

4. Did you _nod_ your head?

Replace the Words Write the Review Word that could replace the underlined word or words in each sentence.

5. People usually move their heads up and down to mean "yes."

6. I never talk about my friends' secrets.

7. The woman wants to ship a birthday package to her son overseas.

8. She curled up on the bed for a nap.

Word Study: Make a New Word

• You can use a word chain to make a new word. Change the letter in **dark type** in each word, in order, to make a new word. Write the Review Word that completes this word chain: le**f**t, le**n**t, **l**end, _____.

◎ Challenge

colony	kept	letters	socket

Word Clues Write a Challenge Word that matches each clue.

1. The first English settlers created this in America in 1607. *colony*

2. This can hold a plug or a light bulb. *socket*

3. Your friends might send you these if you move to a new home. *letters*

4. If you did not return *kept* something, you probably did this with it.

Solve the Analogies Write a Challenge Word to complete each analogy.

5. **Cheap** is to **costly** as **threw out** is to ____.

6. **Draw** is to **pictures** as **write** is to *letters*.

7. **Ship** is to **boat** as **settlement** is to *live*.

8. **Blanket** is to **quilt** as **outlet** is to ____.

Do you think you've mastered the Spelling Strategy? Take the CHAMPION CHALLENGE on page 287!

Challenge

Word Clues

1.

2.

3.

4.

Solve the Analogies

5.

6.

7.

8.

Spelling and Technology

Spelling and Technology

Computer Actions

1.

2.

3.

4.

Computer Actions

Does your computer stay in one place, or do you carry it around? Many people work in one place on a desktop computer. Other people carry a laptop computer.

Desktop and laptop computers have the same features. They have menus, or lists of choices. One menu choice is **help**. Other menu choices are **font type** and **size**.

Learn these words for making choices with computers.

desktop	font	help	menu

Write the word from the box that matches each clue.

1. I am a list of choices. *menu*

2. I make words on a screen look different. *font*

3. I am a computer that stays in one place. *desktop*

4. I can show you how to solve problems.

Circle the word that has a **short e** and a **short o** sound. Draw one line under the words that contain just the **short e** sound. Draw two lines under the word that contains just the **short o** sound. *help*

Content Words

Science: Birds

Write the name of each bird.

owl	robin	crow	hawk

1.    **2.**    **3.**    **4.**

Link to **Language Arts:** Past-Tense Verbs

Write the past-tense verb that fits each sentence.

slept	slid	swam	sang

5. The car _slid_ on the ice.

6. The boy _swam_ in the pool.

7. She _sang_ the song as loudly as she could.

8. The bear _slept_ in its den until spring.

Link to **The Spelling Strategy**

Circle the Content Word you wrote that has the **short o** sound. Underline the Content Word you wrote that has the **short e** sound.

Content Connection: Science

 Learn more about birds at www.aviary.owls.com. Choose three kinds of birds. Write their names, and write one sentence about each one.

Content Words

Science: Birds

1. _____

2. _____

3. _____

4. _____

Language Arts: Past-Tense Verbs

5. _____

6. _____

7. _____

8. _____

Spelling and Thinking

short u spelled u

1.

2.

3.

4.

5.

6.

7.

8.

9.

short u spelled o

10.

11.

12.

13.

14.

15.

READ the Basic Words 👀 Watch out for easily misspelled words!

1.	lunch	*lunch*	Domingo ate **lunch** at noon.
👀 2.	until	*until*	We stroked the cat **until** it purred.
👀 3.	cover	*cover*	What is on the **cover** of your book?
4.	buzz	*buzz*	Tamika heard some bees **buzz**.
5.	become	*become*	Joel wants to **become** a teacher.
6.	stuff	*stuff*	We will **stuff** the old pillow.
7.	nothing	*nothing*	The gift she made cost **nothing**.
8.	dull	*dull*	We can shine these **dull** coins.
9.	month	*month*	February is the shortest **month**.
10.	study	*study*	People **study** to learn.
11.	love	*love*	Karen has a **love** for pets.
12.	uncle	*uncle*	An **uncle** is a parent's brother.
13.	cuff	*cuff*	The **cuff** of the sleeve was dirty.
👀 14.	none	*none*	She ate the apples and left us **none**.
15.	under	*under*	Is the baseball **under** the bed again?

◎ Review

16. cup   18. jump
17. dust   19. rub

◎ Challenge

20. button   22. summit
21. hunter   23. trust

SORT the Basic Words

1–9. Write the words that spell the **short u** sound **u**.

10–15. Write the words that spell the **short u** sound **o**.

REMEMBER the Spelling Strategy

Remember that the **short u** sound can be spelled in different ways: **u** in **lunch** and **o** in **become**.

Spelling and Phonics

Beginning Sounds

1–3. Write the Basic Words that begin with the **short u** sound.

Sound and Letter Patterns

4–7. Write the Basic Words that end with two consonants that are the same. Circle the two consonants.

8–9. Write the one-syllable Basic Words that end with two different consonants that work together to spell one sound. Circle the two consonants.

Word Structure

10. Replace the first two letters in **diver** to make a Basic Word.

11. Add one letter to **one** to make a Basic Word.

 Using the Dictionary

Write the word in each pair that comes first in the dictionary.

12. uncle, study   **14.** nothing, under

13. become, buzz   **15.** lunch, love

◆ ◆ ◆

Dictionary Check Be sure to check the a-b-c order of the words in your **Spelling Dictionary**.

Beginning Sounds

1. _____

2. _____

3. _____

Sound and Letter Patterns

4. _____

5. _____

6. _____

7. _____

8. _____

9. _____

Word Structure

10. _____

11. _____

Using the Dictionary

12. _____

13. _____

14. _____

15. _____

lunch	until	cover	buzz	become
stuff	nothing	dull	month	study
love	uncle	cuff	none	under

Solve the Analogies Write a Basic Word to complete each analogy.

1. **Dog** is to **bark** as **bee** is to _____.
2. **Night** is to **day** as **sharp** is to _____.
3. **Out** is to **in** as **over** is to _____.
4. **Mother** is to **father** as **aunt** is to _____.
5. **Morning** is to **breakfast** as **noon** is to _____.
6. **Game** is to **practice** as **test** is to _____.
7. **Ten** is to **zero** as **many** is to _____.

Complete the Sentences Write the Basic Word that belongs in each sentence.

8. Latoya's birthday is next _____.
9. Rob sewed a button on the _____ of his shirt.
10. Babies _____ being cuddled.

Complete the Story Write the Basic Words from the box to complete the story.

Dave has __11.__ fond of his new black shoes. He lost one shoe and did not want to go to school __12.__ he found it. Under his dresser he found socks, toys, and lots of other __13.__, but no shoe. There was __14.__ at all under his bed. Finally, he lifted the __15.__ off his bed and there it was!

nothing
until
cover
become
stuff

Solve the Analogies

1. _____
2. _____
3. _____
4. _____
5. _____
6. _____
7. _____

Complete the Sentences

8. _____
9. _____
10. _____

Complete the Story

11. _____
12. _____
13. _____
14. _____
15. _____

Spelling and Writing

 Proofread a Paragraph

The symbol ⊚ means **add a period**. The symbol ⊞ means **indent**. Proofread the paragraph below for eight misspelled words. Then rewrite the paragraph. Write the spelling words correctly and make the corrections shown by the proofreading marks.

⊞ My best friend and I ate lonch in the park. We could hear ̷Bees buz as we ate. Then we went home and played games untill three. a̲f̲terward, we had to stody. Sometimes we do nothin but sit and talk undr a maple tree. That is fun, too. We lov to do lots of stuf together⊚

More Practice Write and sort the Basic Words.

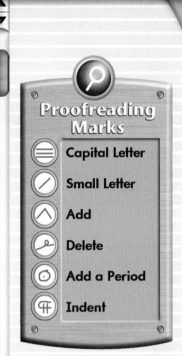

Proofreading Marks

≡	Capital Letter
/	Small Letter
∧	Add
℘	Delete
⊚	Add a Period
⊞	Indent

NARRATIVE

Write a Paragraph

Write a paragraph about some things you did with a friend. Take these steps before you begin: Make a list of activities you do that are fun, and choose one thing to write about. Write down some words to remind you of what you want to include in your paragraph. Write a rough draft using your notes. Use as many spelling words as you can.

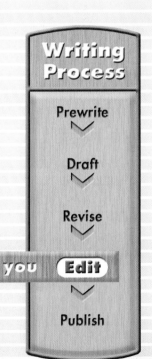

Writing Process

Prewrite
⌄
Draft
⌄
Revise
⌄

❯ ❯ ❯ ❯ ❯ **Proofread your writing as you** **Edit**
⌄
Publish

When you finish writing your draft, proofread your paper for errors in spelling, grammar, capitalization, and punctuation. Use the **Spelling Dictionary** to check spelling if you are not sure.

◎ Review

Review

Complete the Sentences

1.
_____

2.
_____

3.
_____

4.
_____

Word Groups

5.
_____

6.
_____

7.
_____

8.
_____

Suffixes

1.
_____

cup	dust	jump	rub

Complete the Sentences Write the Review Word to complete each sentence.

1. Mica drank milk from the _____.

2. Did you see the tiger _____ its back against the tree?

3. I like to help my father clean the _____ off of the furniture.

4. My cat likes to _____ on the top of the table.

Word Groups Write the Review Word that belongs in each group.

5. leap, hurdle, _____

6. mug, glass, _____

7. touch, stroke, _____

8. dirt, powder, _____

Word Study: Suffixes

● The **-er** suffix can be added to a verb to name a person who does something. For example, a **baker** is someone who bakes. Write the Challenge Word that has the **-er** suffix and means "a person who hunts."

 **Challenge**

button	hunter	summit	trust

Matching Write a Challenge Word that matches each meaning.

1. the highest point of something
2. an animal who chases another animal for food
3. a round object that fastens clothes together
4. to believe in another

Complete the Paragraph Write Challenge Words to complete the paragraph.

The __5.__ was searching for a lion in the thick jungle. He reached the __6.__ of a small hill and stopped to rest. He unfastened the top __7.__ of his shirt to cool off. He wasn't sure he was going in the right direction, but he decided to __8.__ his guide, who had drawn a map for him.

Challenge

Matching

1.

2.

3.

4.

Complete the Paragraph

5.

6.

7.

8.

 Do you think you've mastered the Spelling Strategy? Take the CHAMPION CHALLENGE on page 288!

Spelling and Technology

Spelling and Technology

Computer Commands

1. _____

2. _____

3. _____

4. _____

Computer Commands

You must tell your computer what to do. You can switch it on, open files, and store your work. You can back up your work, or make an extra copy of it. When you are finished using the computer, you can put it to sleep or shut it down.

Learn these words for telling your computer what to do.

back up	open	shut down	store

Four terms from the box are not spelled correctly in this paragraph. Write the terms correctly. Underline the terms that contain a **short u** sound.

Sit down at your computer. Now opin your word processing program. Type your report. Select Save from time to time. This tells your computer to stor your work. You may also want to bak op your work by making an extra copy and saving it on a disk. When you are done, you can shout don the computer.

Content Words

Content Words

Science: Beekeeping

1. _____
2. _____
3. _____
4. _____

Language Arts: Onomatopoeia

5. _____
6. _____
7. _____
8. _____

 Link to **Science:** Beekeeping

Write the Content Word that fits each blank.

| bees | clover | honey | beeswax |

The __1.__ gather nectar from flowers and make __2.__. The wax made by the bees to build their honeycombs is called __3.__. You might see bees gathering nectar in a field of __4.__.

Link to **Language Arts:** Onomatopoeia

Write the Content Word that names the sound each of these might make.

| hiss | click | bang | beep |

5. a snake
6. a car horn

7. a slamming door
8. horse's hoofs

Link to **The Spelling Strategy**

Circle the letter that spells the **short u** sound in one of the Content Words you wrote.

Content Connection: Science

Search the Internet to find out more about bees. You might look at www.honey.com. Click on **Kids**. Be prepared to give a report on some things you learned about honeybees.

Spelling Connections Online
www.zaner-bloser.com

Spelling and Thinking

READ the Basic Words 👀 Watch out for easily misspelled words!

👀	**1.** proud	*proud*	I am **proud** of myself for getting an A.
	2. boil	*boil*	Water will **boil** when it gets very hot.
	3. loud	*loud*	The music was too **loud** for my ears.
👀	**4.** house	*house*	The Carters live in a large **house**.
	5. join	*join*	Roberto wants to **join** the scouts.
	6. cloud	*cloud*	We saw a dark **cloud** in the sky.
	7. sound	*sound*	The loud ringing **sound** made me jump.
👀	**8.** voice	*voice*	The singer had a beautiful **voice**.
	9. oil	*oil*	Fish is often fried in **oil**.
	10. round	*round*	Put the cake batter in the **round** pan.
	11. point	*point*	Please sharpen the **point** of this pencil.
	12. south	*south*	North is the opposite of **south**.
	13. found	*found*	Tamika **found** her lost money.
	14. soil	*soil*	Some plants need rich **soil** to grow well.
	15. ground	*ground*	It is hard to dig in the frozen **ground**.

/ou/

7.

8.

9.

10.

11.

12.

13.

14.

15.

Review

16. bounce   18. count
17. coin   19. shout

Challenge

20. aloud   22. mouth
21. choice   23. noise

SORT the Basic Words

Each word on the spelling list has the vowel sound in **oil** or in **loud**.

1–6. Write the words that have the /**oi**/ sound.

7–15. Write the words that have the /**ou**/ sound.

REMEMBER the Spelling Strategy

Remember that the /**oi**/ sound you hear in **oil** is spelled **oi**. The /**ou**/ sound you hear in **loud** is spelled **ou**.

Rhyming Words

1–3. Write **oil** and the Basic Words that rhyme with **oil**.

4–6. Write **loud** and the Basic Words that rhyme with **loud**. Circle the words you wrote that begin with a consonant cluster.

7–10. Write **sound** and the Basic Words that rhyme with **sound**. Circle the word you wrote that begins with a consonant cluster.

Word Structure

11. Change one letter in **mouse** to make a Basic Word.

12. Change one letter in **paint** to make a Basic Word.

13. Change one letter in **mouth** to make a Basic Word.

 Using the Dictionary

14. Write the Basic Word that would come last in the dictionary.

15. Write the Basic Word that would come after **house** but before **loud** in the dictionary.

◆ ◆ ◆

Dictionary Check Be sure to check your answers in your **Spelling Dictionary**.

Rhyming Words

1.

2.

3.

4.

5.

6.

7.

8.

9.

10.

Word Structure

11.

12.

13.

Using the Dictionary

14.

15.

proud	boil	loud	house	join
cloud	sound	voice	oil	round
point	south	found	soil	ground

Solve the Analogies Write a Basic Word to complete each analogy.

1. **Box** is to **square** as **ball** is to _____.
2. **East** is to **west** as **north** is to _____.
3. **Whisper** is to **quiet** as **yell** is to _____.
4. **Cold** is to **freeze** as **hot** is to _____.
5. **Find** is to **found** as **grind** is to _____.

Replace the Words Write the Basic Word that could best replace each underlined word or words.

6. Shall we study at my <u>home</u>?
7. The teacher's <u>tone</u> was cheerful.
8. He wants to <u>become a member of</u> the math club.

Complete the Paragraph Write the Basic Words from the box that complete the paragraph.

Judy Kane was __9.__ to be the Science Fair winner. Her model showed how rainwater goes from a __10.__ in the sky, to the earth, and back again. She used arrows to __11.__ to the water soaking into some sandy __12.__. She rubbed salad __13.__ on the grass to make it look wet. She even __14.__ a way to make the __15.__ of rain!

sound
point
oil
proud
found
soil
cloud

Solve the Analogies

1.
2.
3.
4.
5.

Replace the Words

6.
7.
8.

Complete the Paragraph

9.
10.
11.
12.
13.
14.
15.

Spelling and Writing

Proofread an Article

First, proofread the article below for eight misspelled words. Then rewrite the article. Write the spelling words correctly and make the corrections shown by the proofreading marks.

¶A tornado is a column of air that is shaped like a a funnel. The funnel dips down from a clout. At the poynt where the funnel touches the gound, it stirs up soyl and other objects⊙ A Tornado can sounnd like a lowd train. A tornado can destroy a howse. Cars have been fownd upside down. Tornadoes are a great Danger.

More Practice Write and sort the Basic Words.

Write an Article

Write an article about a thunderstorm or a snowstorm. The information must be true. Before you start writing, fold a sheet of paper into three columns to list your ideas. Label each column with one of these headings: See, Hear, Feel. Include the information in your columns as you write your article. Use as many spelling words as you can.

> > > > > Proofread your writing as you **Edit**

When you finish writing your draft, proofread your paper for errors in spelling, grammar, capitalization, and punctuation. Use the **Spelling Dictionary** to check spelling if you are not sure.

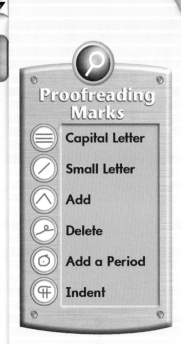

Proofreading Marks

≡	Capital Letter
/	Small Letter
∧	Add
⌒	Delete
⊙	Add a Period
¶	Indent

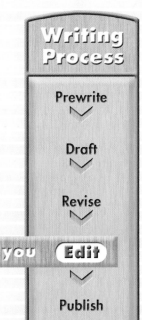

Writing Process

Prewrite

Draft

Revise

Edit

Publish

◎ Review

Complete the Paragraph

_____
1. _____

_____
2. _____

_____
3. _____

_____
4. _____

Complete the Sentences

_____
5. _____

_____
6. _____

_____
7. _____

_____
8. _____

bounce	coin	count	shout

Complete the Paragraph Write Review Words to complete the paragraph.

 James took the small, round __1.__ out of his pocket. He dropped it and watched it __2.__ on the playground. The other kids began to __3.__ at him to pick it up. They needed to __4.__ all of their money to see if they had enough to buy a gift for Mr. Chen.

Complete the Sentences Write a Review Word to complete each sentence.

5. He had trouble hearing me in the storm, so I had to _____.

6. Did you _____ the number of stars in the flag?

7. We watched the ball _____ across the street.

8. The _____ slipped through a small hole in my pocket.

Challenge

aloud	choice	mouth	noise

Word Clues Write a Challenge Word that matches each clue.

1. The dentist often asks you to open this wide to check your teeth.
2. If you read a book this way, everyone can hear you.
3. You have this if you can pick something.
4. This is the name of a loud sound.

Complete the Sentences Write a Challenge Word to complete each sentence.

5. She put the grape in her _____ while her sister wasn't looking.
6. Our class reads each story _____ so that we can enjoy listening.
7. When the baby is asleep, we try not to make too much _____.
8. If I have a _____, I prefer chocolate to vanilla.

Challenge

Word Clues

1. _____

2. _____

3. _____

4. _____

Complete the Sentences

5. _____

6. _____

7. _____

8. _____

 Do you think you've mastered the Spelling Strategy? Take the CHAMPION CHALLENGE on page 289!

Spelling and Technology

Spelling and Technology

Main Computer Parts

1. _____

2. _____

3. _____

4. _____

Main Computer Parts

Your computer is sometimes called hardware. Hardware includes the memory, processing unit, and input and output units. Your mouse is an input unit. Your screen is an output unit.

Your computer uses software. Software is a set of instructions for word processing, games, going online, and more. You load software onto your computer.

Learn these words for computer parts.

hardware	input	output	software

A. Add the missing word part to write a word from the box. Underline the word that has the /**ou**/ sound.

1. hard___   3. soft___

2. in___   4. out___

B. Learn more about computer parts at www.kids-online.net/learn/click/table.html. Find the meanings of these terms: microprocessor, motherboard, and RAM. Write your own definition of these terms. Then use each term correctly in a sentence.

Content Words

Write the Content Word that completes each sentence.

weather	sunny	cloudy	hail

1. Some people say that snowy _____ is bad.
2. Ice that falls from the sky is called _____.
3. When the sun does not shine, the day is _____.
4. It hardly ever rains on a _____ day.

Link to **Math:** Ordinal Numbers

Look at the picture. Write the Content Word that completes each sentence.

fifth	seventh	sixth	eighth

5. The clown is _____ in line.
6. The boy with the airplane is _____ in line.
7. The girl holding the ball is _____ in line.
8. The man in the blue shirt is _____ in line.

Link to **The Spelling Strategy**

Circle the Content Word you wrote that contains the /**ou**/ sound.

Content Connection: Math

Search the Internet to find out more about numbers. You might play a math game at **www.playkidsgames.com**. Click on **math games**. Write the name of the game you played.

Line starts here.

Content Words

Science: Weather

1. _____

_____

2. _____

_____

3. _____

_____

4. _____

Math: Ordinal Numbers

5. _____

_____

6. _____

_____

7. _____

_____

8. _____

ew

1. _____
2. _____
3. _____
4. _____
5. _____
6. _____

oo

7. _____
8. _____
9. _____
10. _____
11. _____
12. _____
13. _____
14. _____
15. _____

Spelling and Thinking

READ the Basic Words 👀 Watch out for easily misspelled words!

1. crew	*crew*	A **crew** of workers fixed the street.
2. loose	*loose*	His **loose** baby tooth fell out.
3. news	*news*	The good **news** is that he won the race.
👀 4. school	*school*	Kurt left his books at **school**.
5. drew	*drew*	Shandra **drew** a picture of Alex.
👀 6. knew	*knew*	She **knew** that lying was wrong.
7. smooth	*smooth*	The shirt felt **smooth** and soft.
8. pool	*pool*	He swam in the deep **pool**.
9. shoot	*shoot*	Can I **shoot** a picture of you?
10. threw	*threw*	Michael **threw** the garbage out.
11. roof	*roof*	A worker fixed the leaking **roof**.
12. fool	*fool*	The clown acted like a silly **fool**.
13. chew	*chew*	She asked us to **chew** our food slowly.
👀 14. balloon	*balloon*	The **balloon** floated into the sky.
15. choose	*choose*	We will **choose** a color for the walls.

◎ Review

16. blew   18. grew
17. boot   19. noon

◎ Challenge

20. dew   22. review
21. loop   23. toot

SORT the Basic Words

1–6. Write the words that have the /o͞o/ sound spelled **ew**.

7–15. Write the words that have the /o͞o/ sound spelled **oo**.

REMEMBER the Spelling Strategy

Remember that the /o͞o/ sound can be spelled in different ways: **oo** in **pool** and **ew** in **chew**.

Sounds and Letters

1–5. Write the Basic Words that end with the /$\overline{oo}$/ sound. Circle the word that begins with a silent consonant.

6–8. Write **pool** and the Basic Words that rhyme with **pool**. Circle the letters that spell the /$\overline{oo}$/ sound.

Word Structure

9. Replace the first letter in **moose** to make a Basic Word.

10. Replace the last letter in **root** to make this Basic Word.

11. Replace one letter in **short** to make a Basic Word.

12. Add one letter to the word **chose** to make a Basic Word.

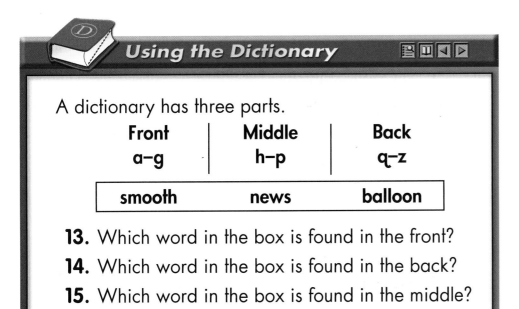

Using the Dictionary

A dictionary has three parts.

Front a–g	Middle h–p	Back q–z
smooth	news	balloon

13. Which word in the box is found in the front?

14. Which word in the box is found in the back?

15. Which word in the box is found in the middle?

Sounds and Letters

1.

2.

3.

4.

5.

6.

7.

8.

Word Structure

9.

10.

11.

12.

Using the Dictionary

13.

14.

15.

crew	loose	news	school	drew
knew	smooth	pool	shoot	threw
roof	fool	chew	balloon	choose

Solve the Analogies Write a Basic Word to complete each analogy.

1. **Dull** is to **sharp** as **rough** is to _____.
2. **Touch** is to **feel** as **pick** is to _____.
3. **Eyes** are to **see** as **teeth** are to _____.
4. **Sleep** is to **bed** as **swim** is to _____.
5. **Thick** is to **thin** as **tight** is to _____.
6. **Box** is to **lid** as **house** is to _____.
7. **Joke** is to **cheer** as **trick** is to _____.

balloon	news	school	crew
shoot	knew	drew	threw

Complete the Sentences Write a Basic Word from the box to complete each sentence.

8. Marcy went to _____ on Monday.
9. John Glenn was part of the space shuttle's _____.
10. We heard important _____.
11. The scientists will _____ a rocket into space.
12. Our class _____ pictures of a space capsule.
13. Did the hot air _____ drift above the trees?
14. Martin _____ the ball through the hoop.
15. Mr. Debbs's class _____ about the test.

Solve the Analogies

1.
2.
3.
4.
5.
6.
7.

Complete the Sentences

8.
9.
10.
11.
12.
13.
14.
15.

Proofread a News Story

First, proofread the news story below for eight misspelled words. Then rewrite the story. Write the spelling words correctly and make the corrections shown by the proofreading marks.

¶ In our schol, we get a baloon every time we read a book. One day, we put air into all the balloons. Then we let them lose to ~~to~~ fly away over the roff. The ~~S~~ky was filled with colors. Then we wrote nooz stories and droow pictures. my teacher will chews five stories from my class to read out loud. Who knu reading a book could lead to so much fun ^

More Practice Write and sort the Basic Words.

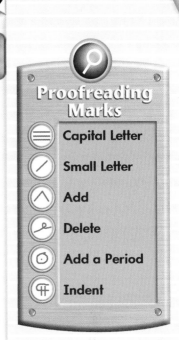

Proofreading Marks

≡	Capital Letter
/	Small Letter
∧	Add
✌	Delete
⊙	Add a Period
¶	Indent

Write a News Story

Write a news story about something special that happened at your school. Include information about what happened, where and when it happened, and how and why it happened. Use as many spelling words as you can.

Writing Process

Prewrite
∨
Draft
∨
Revise
∨
Edit
∨
Publish

> > > > > Proofread your writing as you **Edit**

When you finish writing your draft, proofread your paper for errors in spelling, grammar, capitalization, and punctuation. Use the **Spelling Dictionary** to check spelling if you are not sure.

Review

Review

Rhyming Words

1.

2.

3.

4.

Word Groups

5.

6.

7.

8.

| blew | boot | grew | noon |

Rhyming Words Write a Review Word that rhymes with the underlined word.

1. I lost my <u>suit</u>, but I found my _____.
2. The light of the <u>moon</u> cannot be seen at _____.
3. It started out with a <u>few</u>, but then the crowd _____.
4. The leaves <u>flew</u> as the wind _____.

Word Groups Write the Review Word that belongs in each group.

5. shoe, sandal, _____
6. wind, movement, _____
7. larger, older, _____
8. midnight, morning, _____

Challenge

dew	loop	review	toot

Word Clues Write the Challenge Word that matches each clue.

1. To tie your shoes, you need to make one of these.

2. Before you take a test, it is best to do this.

3. This can sometimes be found early in the morning on grass.

4. A car makes this sound with a horn.

Complete the Sentences Write a Challenge Word to complete each sentence.

5. Although the train was still far away, we could hear the _____ of its whistle.

6. Kerry pulled the rope through the _____ to finish tying the knot.

7. His shoes were soaked with _____ because he walked across the field to school.

8. I need to _____ my spelling words before the quiz!

Challenge

Word Clues

1. _____

2. _____

3. _____

4. _____

Complete the Sentences

5. _____

6. _____

7. _____

8. _____

Do you think you've mastered the Spelling Strategy? Take the **CHAMPION CHALLENGE** on page 290!

Spelling and Technology

Spelling and Technology

Creating a Document

1. _____

2. _____

3. _____

4. _____

Creating a Document

Computers make it easy to create reports, letters, and other documents. Word processing software makes this possible. It is usually the software that computer users want most.

Read these instructions. Think about the meaning of the words in dark print.

> Do you want to write a paragraph, a report, or a letter? Start by opening the word processing **program** and creating a new, blank **document**. As you input your text, use **Zoom** to make the document larger or smaller. The **Tools** menu lets you revise and check your work. You can move words around, check spelling, or find a better word.

| document | program | Tools | Zoom |

Write the word from the box to complete each sentence. Underline the words that have the /o͞o/ sound spelled **oo**.

1. You need a special _____ to make a video.

2. The small type is hard to read, so you use _____ to make it larger.

3. The _____ menu helps you move words around and check spelling.

4. A book report is one kind of _____.

Content Words

Link to **Science:** Plants

Write the Content Word that fits each definition.

greenhouse	roots	seedling	bloom

1. A young plant grown from a seed is a _____.
2. The parts of the plant that are usually underground are its _____.
3. The flower of a plant is also called a _____.
4. A house built mostly of glass to control the temperature and help plants grow is a _____.

Link to **Math:** Relationships

Write the Content Word that belongs in each blank.

numbers	less	equal	greater

5. Five is _____ than four.
6. We count using _____.
7. Four is _____ than seven.
8. The sides of a square are _____.

Link to **The Spelling Strategy**

Circle the letters that spell the /o͞o/ sound in two of the Content Words you wrote.

Content Connection: Science

 Search the Internet to find out more about plants. Try http://library.thinkquest.org/3715 to find information on how plants grow. Write one fact you learned.

Content Words

Science: Plants

1. _____

2. _____

3. _____

4. _____

Math: Relationships

5. _____

6. _____

7. _____

8. _____

Spelling Connections Online
www.zaner-bloser.com

Assessment and Review

Unit 1

1. _____
2. _____
3. _____

Unit 2

4. _____
5. _____
6. _____

Unit 3

7. _____
8. _____
9. _____

Unit 4

10. _____
11. _____
12. _____

Unit 5

13. _____
14. _____
15. _____

ASSESSMENT

Units 1–5

Each Assessment Word in the box fits one of the spelling strategies you have studied over the past five weeks. Read the spelling strategies. Then write each Assessment Word under the unit number it fits.

● Unit 1

1–3. The **short a** sound you hear in **plan** is spelled **a**. The **short i** sound you hear in **trip** is spelled **i**.

● Unit 2

4–6. The **short o** sound you hear in **drop** is spelled **o**. The **short e** sound you hear in **desk** is spelled **e**.

● Unit 3

7–9. The **short u** sound can be spelled in different ways: **u** in **lunch** and **o** in **become**.

● Unit 4

10–12. The **/oi/** sound you hear in **oil** is spelled **oi**. The **/ou/** sound you hear in **loud** is spelled **ou**.

● Unit 5

13–15. The **/ōo/** sound can be spelled in different ways: **oo** in **pool** and **ew** in **chew**.

fund
stout
groom
damp
troop
son
hound
track
ton
coop
bent
shock
toil
lend
trim

REVIEW

Unit 1: **Short a, Short i**

> plan   stick   grand   stamp   list   act   trip

Write the spelling word that goes with each clue.

1. Add **l** to **pan**.

2. Add **t** to **sick**.

3. Add **r** to **tip**.

4. Change **e** to **t** in **ace**.

5. Change **nd** to **mp** in **stand**.

6. Change **n** to **s** in **lint**.

7. Change **st** to **gr** in **stand**.

REVIEW

Unit 2: **Short o, Short e**

> drop   spend   clock   spent   nest   desk   block

Write a spelling word for each clue.

8. You have one. Your teacher has one. You may be seated at it right now.

9. It might be made of wood. It has several sides. You can stack one on top of another.

10. It has hands, but never washes them. There is probably one in your room.

11. It is made of twigs, but birds call it home.

Write a spelling word to complete each sentence.

12. By Thursday, Jake had _____ his week's allowance.

13. If I save my money, I will have $2.00 to _____.

14. Be careful not to _____ the glasses.

Unit 1

1. _____

2. _____

3. _____

4. _____

5. _____

6. _____

7. _____

Unit 2

8. _____

9. _____

10. _____

11. _____

12. _____

13. _____

14. _____

1.

2.

3.

4.

5.

6.

7.

8.

9.

10.

11.

12.

13.

14.

REVIEW

Unit 3: Short u

| none | until | love | nothing | study | buzz | under |

Write the spelling word for each clue.

1. This word rhymes with **dove**.
2. This word rhymes with **does**.
3. This word rhymes with **thunder**.
4. This word rhymes with **sun**.
5. This word ends in **ing**.
6. This word rhymes with **muddy**.
7. This word means "up to the time."

REVIEW

Unit 4: ou, oi

| point | house | voice | ground | south | loud | join |

Write a spelling word to complete each sentence. The word you write will rhyme with the underlined word.

8. The <u>crowd</u> at the game gave a _____ cheer for their team.
9. "Please make your <u>choice</u>," said the clerk with a kind _____.
10. Flip a <u>coin</u> to decide which team you will _____.
11. The doctor asked me to _____ to the <u>joint</u> that hurt.
12. Can I go _____ to reach the <u>mouth</u> of the river?
13. We found a <u>mouse</u> had made its _____ in the woodpile.
14. I <u>found</u> my book lying on the _____.

Unit 5: ew, oo

threw   school   knew   choose

balloon   roof   news

Write the spelling word that completes each sentence.

1. Throw the ball the way I _____ it to you.

2. I know you thought I _____ what to do.

3. That story is really old _____.

4. The string on my yellow _____ broke.

5. It floated high up over the _____ of the house.

6. Everyone in my class at _____ saw it go.

7. You may _____ any color you like.

GAME

Spelling Study Strategy

Circle Dot

Find a partner. Each partner should write a list of 15 spelling words. Then trade lists. Your partner should read one word from your list aloud. You write that word.

When you finish, your partner should spell the word aloud. As your partner says each letter, make a dot under each correct letter. If you have a letter that is not correct, draw a circle under the letter. If you have left out a letter, make a little circle to show where it should have been. The circles will show where you have trouble. Write the word again and check the spelling. Take turns as you play **Circle Dot**.

Unit 5

1.

2.

3.

4.

5.

6.

7.

Writer's Workshop

Practice Activity

A.

1.

2.

3.

4.

5.

B.

6.

7.

8.

9.

10.

Grammar, Usage, and Mechanics

Kinds of Sentences

There are four kinds of sentences. Each ends with a special mark.

Telling Sentence:	My friend will come, too.
Asking Sentence:	Have you met her?
Command:	Move over, please.
Sentence That Shows Strong Feeling:	This is fun!

Practice ACTIVITY

A. What kind of sentence is each one? Write **telling** or **asking** to answer the question.

1. My bus is yellow.
2. Is that your sister?
3. Are you in my class?
4. We can walk home.
5. Our team won the game.

B. What kind of sentence is each one? Write **command** or **feeling** to answer the question.

6. What a funny joke!
7. Wait at the corner.
8. Call your father at work.
9. This juice is great!
10. Bring me the paper, please.

The Writing Process NARRATIVE

Writing a Personal Narrative

Prewriting

Sometimes people write true accounts about experiences they have had. Think about a special time you've had with your friends. What did you do? As you think about your topic, make an outline of your ideas. You can find personal narratives at the library. An adult can help you search for personal narratives on Internet sites such as Kids Reads (www.kidsreads.com).

Drafting

Use your outline to write a personal narrative. Use as many spelling words as possible. If you don't know how to spell a word, make a guess. You will be able to revise your narrative later.

Revising

When you have finished writing, read your narrative from beginning to end. Have you included all of the points in your outline? Now write your final draft.

Editing

Use the editing checklist to proofread your narrative. Be sure to use proofreading marks when you make corrections.

Publishing

Make a copy of your personal narrative, and share it with your readers.

✓ Editing Checklist

Spelling

- ○ I circled words that contain the spelling strategies I learned in Units 1–5.
- ○ I checked the circled words in my Spelling Dictionary.
- ○ I also checked for other spelling errors.

Capital Letters

- ○ Important words in the title
- ○ Beginning of all sentences
- ○ Proper nouns

Punctuation

- ○ Commas, apostrophes, and quotation marks are used correctly.

Grammar, Usage, and Mechanics

- ○ Each sentence ends with the correct punctuation.

Spelling and Thinking

READ the Basic Words 👀 Watch out for easily misspelled words!

1. state	*state*	In which **state** do you live?
👀 **2.** close	*close*	Please **close** the door as you leave.
3. slide	*slide*	The boy went down the water **slide**.
👀 **4.** face	*face*	Tanja drew a happy **face**.
5. globe	*globe*	A **globe** is a round map of the world.
6. pave	*pave*	The workers will **pave** the street.
7. size	*size*	Mary's shoes are the wrong **size**.
8. smoke	*smoke*	My eyes tear when I smell **smoke**.
9. flame	*flame*	The **flame** set the grease on fire.
10. broke	*broke*	The glass **broke** into pieces.
11. prize	*prize*	Carla won first **prize** at the fair.
12. skate	*skate*	Juanita learned to **skate** on ice.
👀 **13.** smile	*smile*	A baby will **smile** when it is happy.
14. plane	*plane*	David went to New York by **plane**.
15. stone	*stone*	The **stone** in her shoe hurt her toe.

⊚ Review
16. cake	18. joke
17. dime	19. mule

⊚ Challenge
20. alive	22. scrape
21. scene	23. tube

SORT the Basic Words

Write the words that have

1–6. the **long a** sound spelled **vowel-consonant-e**.

7–10. the **long i** sound spelled **vowel-consonant-e**.

11–15. the **long o** sound spelled **vowel-consonant-e**.

REMEMBER the Spelling Strategy

Remember that the long vowel sounds you hear in **pave,
size,** and **globe** are spelled **vowel-consonant-e.**

---

long a

1.
2.
3.
4.
5.
6.

long i

7.
8.
9.
10.

long o

11.
12.
13.
14.
15.

Spelling and Phonics

Beginning Sounds

1–6. Write the Basic Words that begin with an **s** and another consonant. Draw a line under the first two consonants.

7–8. Write the Basic Words that begin with a **p** and another consonant. Draw a line under the first two consonants.

Rhyming Words

9. Write a Basic Word that rhymes with **lace**.

10. Write a Basic Word that rhymes with **blame**.

11. Write a Basic Word that rhymes with **cave**.

 Using the Dictionary

The dictionary uses letters and symbols to stand for the sounds in words. Look at these dictionary letters and symbols. Say each word, then write the Basic Word. Use the pronunciation key in your **Spelling Dictionary**.

12. /brōk/

13. /sīz/

14. /glōb/

15. /klōz/

Beginning Sounds

1. _____

2. _____

3. _____

4. _____

5. _____

6. _____

7. _____

8. _____

Rhyming Words

9. _____

10. _____

11. _____

Using the Dictionary

12. _____

13. _____

14. _____

15. _____

Spelling and Reading

state	close	slide	face	globe
pave	size	smoke	flame	broke
prize	skate	smile	plane	stone

Solve the Analogies Write a Basic Word to complete each analogy.

1. **Bottle** is to **cap** as **door** is to _____.
2. **Toes** is to **foot** as **nose** is to _____.
3. **Square** is to **cube** as **round** is to _____.
4. **Water** is to **swim** as **ice** is to _____.
5. **Land** is to **car** as **air** is to _____.
6. **Cold** is to **ice** as **hot** is to _____.

Use the Clues Write the Basic Word for each clue.

7. I rise through a chimney.
8. I can also be called a rock.
9. I am given as a reward.
10. I am something your face can do.
11. I am often found on a playground.

Complete the Paragraph Write the Basic Words from the box that complete the paragraph.

state	broke	pave	size

Workers came to the road to fill and __12.__ a hole. The __13.__ of the hole was large. Heavy trucks used the road so much that the surface __14.__ up. The government of our __15.__ pays for road repair.

Solve the Analogies

1.

2.

3.

4.

5.

6.

Use the Clues

7.

8.

9.

10.

11.

Complete the Paragraph

12.

13.

14.

15.

Spelling and Writing

 Proofread Interview Questions

First, proofread the interview questions below for eight misspelled words. Then rewrite the questions. Write the spelling words correctly and make the corrections shown by the proofreading marks.

1. How did you learn to skayte so well?
2. did you slyde often when you practiced?
3. Did you hit a stoan when you broak your leg?
4. Did you ever fall on your fase?
5. how did you feel when you lost the prise at the stat meet?
6. Do you travel to Meets by car, bus, or plain?

More Practice Write and sort the Basic Words.

Write Interview Questions

Pretend you are going to interview a sports figure. Write some questions you would like to ask, such as how the person became interested in the sport, why the person likes the sport, and what special prizes the person has received. Be sure to leave some space after each question for the answer. Use as many spelling words as you can.

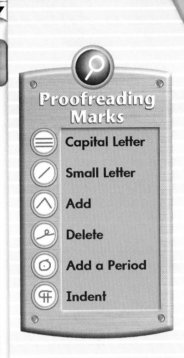

Proofreading Marks

- ≡ Capital Letter
- / Small Letter
- ∧ Add
- ⌐ Delete
- ⊙ Add a Period
- ⌗ Indent

Writing Process

- Prewrite
- Draft
- Revise

> > > > > **Proofread your writing as you** **Edit**

- Publish

When you finish writing your draft, proofread your paper for errors in spelling, grammar, capitalization, and punctuation. Use the **Spelling Dictionary** to check spelling if you are not sure.

⊚ Review

Review

Word Clues

1. _____

2. _____

3. _____

4. _____

Solve the Analogies

5. _____

6. _____

7. _____

8. _____

cake	dime	joke	mule

Word Clues Write the Review Word that matches each clue.

1. I have candles on me for your birthday.
2. I look like a horse with long ears.
3. I am a silvery coin.
4. People laugh when you tell this.

Solve the Analogies Write a Review Word to complete each analogy.

5. **Foot** is to **person** as **hoof** is to _____.
6. **Play** is to **music** as **tell** is to _____.
7. **Five** is to **nickel** as **ten** is to _____.
8. **Fruit** is to **apple** as **dessert** is to _____.

Challenge

alive	scene	scrape	tube

Complete the Sentences Write the Challenge Word that completes each sentence.

1. Is there any glue left in this _____?

2. The kitten that got lost is _____ and well.

3. Please _____ the ice off the window so I can see.

4. My class will perform the first _____ of the play at noon.

Replace the Words Write the Challenge Word that could replace the underlined word in each sentence.

5. Inside the bicycle tire is a <u>cylinder</u> filled with air.

6. The best <u>part</u> of the play was when the king found his lost daughter.

7. Jerry's fish are still <u>living</u>, although he forgot to feed them yesterday.

8. If you <u>scratch</u> your knee, you may need a bandage.

Do you think you've mastered the Spelling Strategy? Take the CHAMPION CHALLENGE on page 291!

Spelling and Technology

Spelling and Technology

Saving Your Work

1.

2.

3.

4.

Saving Your Work

How do you make a document? It's easy! Open a word processing program. Type in your first draft and name it. Now it is a file. You might also put your file into a folder. You can keep related files in the same folder. If you have many files, this will help you find a particular document later.

Study this sequence chain. Think about the meaning of the words in dark print.

Write a **draft**.

↓

Give your draft a **name**.

↓

Select a **folder** for your work.

↓

Hit Save to make a **file**.

Learn these words for writing on a computer.

draft	file	folder	name

Follow the directions to write a word from the box. Underline the words that have the **vowel-consonant-e** pattern.

1. game – g + n = ___

2. folded – ed + er = ___

3. drag – g + ft = ___

4. fin – n + le = ___

Content Words

Link to **Fine Arts:** Drawing

Write the Content Words that complete the paragraph.

| sketch | scribble | doodle | trace |

Miss Stall gave Tim some thin paper and asked him to __1.__ a copy of a picture in a book. Tim drew a rough __2.__ of it instead. He also decided to __3.__ notes to himself about the picture. Finally, he decided just to __4.__ on some scrap paper.

Link to **Science:** Respiratory System

Write the Content Word that matches each clue.

| heart | living | beat | breath |

5. A plant or animal that is not dead is this.

6. This is an organ in your body that pumps blood.

7. This means "to pound again and again."

8. This can be seen in cold weather.

Link to **The Spelling Strategy**

Circle the letters that spell the **long a** vowel sound in one of the Content Words you wrote.

Content Connection: Fine Arts

Search the Internet to find out more about drawing. You can go to www.draw3d.com. Click **Enter**, then **Drawing Lessons**. Ask an adult to help you complete a lesson. Share your drawing with the class.

Content Words

Fine Arts: Drawing

1. _____

2. _____

3. _____

4. _____

Science: Respiratory System

5. _____

6. _____

7. _____

8. _____

Spelling Connections Online
www.zaner-bloser.com

Spelling and Thinking

ai

1.
2.
3.
4.
5.
6.
7.
8.
9.

ay

10.
11.
12.
13.
14.
15.

READ the Basic Words 👀 Watch out for easily misspelled words!

1.	aid	*aid*	A map is a useful **aid** on a trip.
2.	pay	*pay*	How much did you **pay** for the pen?
3.	chain	*chain*	Tina wears a golden **chain**.
4.	mail	*mail*	Did you **mail** my letter?
5.	tray	*tray*	Put the glasses on the **tray**.
6.	paint	*paint*	We will **paint** my room yellow.
7.	maybe	*maybe*	If we try, **maybe** we will win.
8.	plain	*plain*	I like to wear **plain** shirts.
9.	lay	*lay*	Please **lay** my crayons down.
10.	main	*main*	We went to the **main** building.
👀 11.	always	*always*	Is he **always** late?
12.	pail	*pail*	Another word for **pail** is bucket.
👀 13.	laid	*laid*	The hen **laid** an egg.
14.	away	*away*	Please throw **away** the empty box.
👀 15.	paid	*paid*	Did you get **paid** for the work?

◎ Review

16. braid
17. play
18. spray
19. train

◎ Challenge

20. holiday
21. railway
22. remain
23. waist

SORT the Basic Words

1–9. Write the words in which the **long a** sound is spelled **ai**.

10–15. Write the words in which the **long a** sound is spelled **ay**.

REMEMBER the Spelling Strategy

Remember that the **long a** sound can be spelled in different ways: **ai** in **paint** and **ay** in **tray**.

Ending Sounds

1–3. Write **aid** and the Basic Words that rhyme with **aid**.

4–5. Write **mail** and the Basic Word that rhymes with **mail**.

6–8. Write **main** and the Basic Words that rhyme with **main**.

Word Structure

9. Add the letter **a** to **way** to make this Basic Word.

10. Add the letters **be** to **may** to make this Basic Word.

11. Add the letters **al** to **ways** to make this Basic Word.

12. Drop one letter from **play** to make this Basic Word.

 Using the Dictionary

To find a word that has an ending added, you must look up the base word. Write the word you would look up to find the meaning of each of these words.

13. trays **14.** paying **15.** painted

Dictionary Check Be sure to check the base words in your **Spelling Dictionary**.

Ending Sounds

1.

2.

3.

4.

5.

6.

7.

8.

Word Structure

9.

10.

11.

12.

Using the Dictionary

13.

14.

15.

aid	pay	chain	mail	tray
paint	maybe	plain	lay	main
always	pail	laid	away	paid

Word Groups Read each set of words. Add the Basic Word that belongs in each group.

1. tub, bucket, _____
2. never, sometimes, _____
3. common, simple, _____
4. crayon, marker, _____
5. plate, platter, _____
6. letters, packages, _____
7. probably, perhaps, _____

pay   lay   laid   away   chain   paid   aid   main

Complete the Sentences Write the Basic Word from the box that completes each sentence.

8. Will you help me put _____ these games?
9. Please _____ the blanket on the bed.
10. I will come as soon as I _____ for my paper and brushes.
11. Tom has already _____ for his supplies.
12. Someone _____ a book on my chair.
13. Our projects will be shown in the _____ hallway.
14. My mobile is the one hanging from a _____.
15. Glasses may _____ your sight.

Word Groups

1.

2.

3.

4.

5.

6.

7.

Complete the Sentences

8.

9.

10.

11.

12.

13.

14.

15.

Spelling and Writing

Proofread a Paragraph

First, proofread the paragraph below for eight misspelled words. Then rewrite the paragraph. Write the spelling words correctly and make the corrections shown by the proofreading marks.

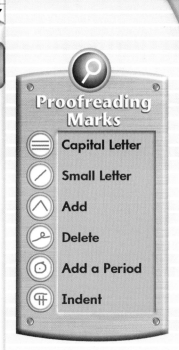
Proofreading Marks

☰	Capital Letter
/	Small Letter
∧	Add
✄	Delete
⊙	Add a Period
¶	Indent

Buy by catalog!

¶You can send awway for many items by mael. You might want to Ørder some paynt or a gold chayne or a useful traye. There are allways people to help you with y~~our~~ your order. Call the maine number for help. When Ɨt comes time to paye, the company will send you a bill⊙

More Practice Write and sort the Basic Words.

DESCRIPTIVE

Write a Paragraph

Write a paragraph about something you would like to send away for. It might be something to wear that you saw in a catalog, or a videotape or DVD advertised on TV. Name the item. Describe the color, size, style, and price. Tell your reader why you want that item. Use as many spelling words as you can.

Writing Process

Prewrite
ᐯ
Draft
ᐯ
Revise
ᐯ
Publish

> > > > > **Proofread your writing as you** **Edit**

When you finish writing your draft, proofread your paper for errors in spelling, grammar, capitalization, and punctuation. Use the **Spelling Dictionary** to check spelling if you are not sure.

Review

Review

Complete the Sentences

1.

2.

3.

4.

Complete the Paragraph

5.

6.

7.

8.

Homophones

1.

braid	play	spray	train

Complete the Sentences Write a Review Word to complete each sentence.

1. The _____ from the garden hose soaked my new clothes.
2. The _____ pulled slowly into the station.
3. Terry is wearing her hair in a _____.
4. Everyone in my class likes to _____ soccer and basketball.

Complete the Paragraph Write the Review Words to complete the paragraph.

Every Saturday morning, Lexi's mother would fix her hair in a __5.__. Then Lexi would buy her ticket for the __6.__ to Grandma's town, which was a few miles away. Lexi loved to work in Grandma's garden. She would help Grandma direct the __7.__ of the sprinklers, dig out weeds, and plant new flowers. Then they would __8.__ a game of hide-and-seek behind the tall corn and tomato plants.

Word Study: Homophones

Words that sound alike but have different spellings and meanings are **homophones**. **Won** and **one** are homophones. Write the Challenge Word that is a homophone for **waste**.

 Challenge

holiday	railway	remain	waist

Word Clues Write a Challenge Word that matches each clue.

1. This is the part of the body around which a belt is worn.

2. This is another word for **stay**.

3. This is another word for **railroad**.

4. This is a day when people celebrate something special.

Complete the Sentences Write a Challenge Word to complete each sentence.

5. The man put his hand on his dance partner's _____ to guide her.

6. Her favorite _____ is Thanksgiving.

7. Many people helped build the _____ that crossed the United States.

8. He wanted to _____ at the beach for another week, but he had to go back to school.

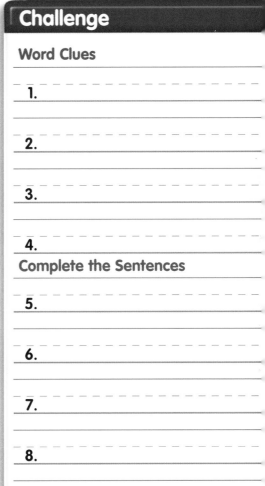

Challenge

Word Clues

1. _____

2. _____

3. _____

4. _____

Complete the Sentences

5. _____

6. _____

7. _____

8. _____

 Do you think you've mastered the Spelling Strategy? Take the CHAMPION CHALLENGE on page 292!

Spelling and Technology

Drawing and Painting a Picture

1. _____

2. _____

3. _____

4. _____

Spelling and Technology

Drawing and Painting a Picture

A computer does more than help you write. It also helps you draw and paint. You can make shapes, diagrams, pictures, charts, and other graphics.

Learn these words for drawing and painting.

bucket	gray	paint	pattern

Read this paragraph. Write the missing words. Underline the words that spell the **long a** sound **ai** or **ay**.

    Do you want to draw? Click on a pencil tool. You can create a __1.__ in black, white, or __2.__. You can then fill it in with black, white, or gray designs. If you click on a brush tool, you will be ready to __3.__. Dip your brush in a __4.__ of red or blue. Start your picture!

Content Words

Link to **Science:** Water

Write a Content Word that matches each clue.

bay	ocean	gulf	beach

1. This is a huge body of salt water.
2. This is the sandy shore of a body of water.
3. This body of water rhymes with the word **way**.
4. This body of water is partly closed in by land. It is usually larger than a bay.

Link to **Social Studies:** Government

Write the Content Word that completes each sentence.

cities	towns	duty	worker

5. Someone who does a job is known as a _____.
6. Places with many buildings and people are _____.
7. All citizens should do their _____ and vote.
8. Places that are smaller than cities are _____.

Link to **The Spelling Strategy**

Circle the letters that spell the **long a** sound in one of the Content Words you wrote.

Content Connection: Social Studies

Search the Internet to find out more about government. Try www.worldalmanacforkids.com. Click on **Explore** and then on **States**. Click on your state and then on **Government and Politics**. Write at least one fact you learned.

Content Words

Science: Water

1. _____

2. _____

3. _____

4. _____

Social Studies: Government

5. _____

6. _____

7. _____

8. _____

Spelling Connections Online
www.zaner-bloser.com

Spelling and Thinking

READ the Basic Words 👀 Watch out for easily misspelled words!

1. sheep	*sheep*	Farmers keep **sheep** for their wool.
2. dream	*dream*	All people **dream** during sleep.
3. street	*street*	The **street** has much traffic.
4. east	*east*	The sun rises in the **east**.
5. treat	*treat*	Do you **treat** your pet dog well?
6. mean	*mean*	Scaring the child was a **mean** trick.
👀 7. wheels	*wheels*	Bicycle **wheels** vary in size.
8. peace	*peace*	The treaty brought **peace** to the land.
9. real	*real*	The book is about a **real** event.
10. cheese	*cheese*	Milk is used to make **cheese**.
11. leave	*leave*	Sometimes I **leave** early for school.
12. stream	*stream*	A river is a large **stream**.
👀 13. sweet	*sweet*	This candy tastes **sweet**.
👀 14. teacher	*teacher*	My **teacher** helps me learn.
15. heat	*heat*	Fire creates **heat**.

◉ Review
16. bean   18. need
17. clean   19. seem

◉ Challenge
20. beetle   22. reason
21. degree   23. steam

SORT the Basic Words

1–5. Write the words that have the **long e** sound spelled **ee**.

6–15. Write the words that have the **long e** sound spelled **ea**.

REMEMBER the Spelling Strategy

Remember that the **long e** sound can be spelled in different ways: **ea** in **treat** and **ee** in **street**.

ee

1.
2.
3.
4.
5.

ea

6.
7.
8.
9.
10.
11.
12.
13.
14.
15.

Spelling and Phonics

Sound Patterns

1–6. Write the Basic Words that begin with one consonant. Circle the letters that spell the **long e** sound.

Letter Patterns

Write Basic Words by adding the missing letters.

7. st___eam   **9.** e___st

8. stre___t   **10.** trea___

Beginnings and Endings

Match the beginnings of the Basic Words in the first column with their endings in the second column. Write the Basic Words.

11. wh   eam

12. sw   eels

13. dr   eet

Using the Dictionary

One word in each sentence is the dictionary respelling for a Basic Word. Write the Basic Word.

14. Warm blankets are made from the wool of /shēp/.

15. Milk is added to make /chēz/.

Sound Patterns

1.

2.

3.

4.

5.

6.

Letter Patterns

7.

8.

9.

10.

Beginnings and Endings

11.

12.

13.

Using the Dictionary

14.

15.

73

Spelling and Reading

sheep	dream	street	east	treat
mean	wheels	peace	real	cheese
leave	stream	sweet	teacher	heat

Complete the Sentences Read each sentence below. Write the Basic Word that completes each sentence.

1. On cold days I turn on the _____ when I get home.

2. I like to eat crackers with _____.

3. My _____ explained the problem to us.

Answer the Questions Write a Basic Word to answer each question.

4. What word names a farm animal?

5. What is the opposite of **imaginary**?

6. What parts of a bicycle are round?

7. What do we do while we are asleep?

8. What is the opposite of **west**?

9. What is the opposite of **kind**?

Complete the Story Write the Basic Words from the box that best complete the story.

stream	leave	treat	street	peace	sweet

I like to get lots of exercise and eat healthy foods. When I __10.__ school at the end of the day, I carefully cross the busy __11.__ . I enjoy the __12.__ and quiet of the __13.__ that flows near my house. When I get home, my favorite __14.__ is a piece of __15.__ fruit.

Complete the Sentences

1.

2.

3.

Answer the Questions

4.

5.

6.

7.

8.

9.

Complete the Story

10.

11.

12.

13.

14.

15.

Spelling and Writing

Proofread a Recipe

First, proofread the recipe below for eight misspelled words. Then rewrite the recipe. Write the spelling words correctly and make the corrections shown by the proofreading marks.

tomato Sandwich

- bread
- tomato
- sweat butter or low-fat spread
- 1 slice cheeze

1. Have a grownup slice the tomato and toast the bread. Be careful of the heet.
2. Put tomato on a slice of buttered Toast.
3. add reel cheese, salt, and pepper.
4. Put the second slice of buttered toast on top.

Now enjoy your dreem treate in pease. Don't leeve the sandwich alone or someone might eat it!

More Practice Write and sort the Basic Words.

Write a Recipe

A recipe gives step-by-step directions. Write a recipe for your favorite snack. Name the snack and list the ingredients. Number the steps to tell what to do first, second, third, and so on. Use as many spelling words as you can.

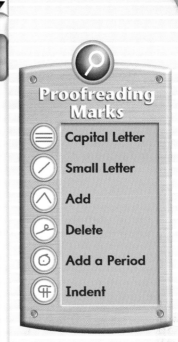

Proofreading Marks

☰	Capital Letter
/	Small Letter
∧	Add
⚮	Delete
⊙	Add a Period
⌗	Indent

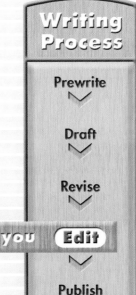

Writing Process

Prewrite
⌄
Draft
⌄
Revise
⌄

> > > > > **Proofread your writing as you** **Edit**

⌄
Publish

When you finish writing your draft, proofread your paper for errors in spelling, grammar, capitalization, and punctuation. Use the **Spelling Dictionary** to check spelling if you are not sure.

Review

Review

Complete the Paragraph

1. _____

2. _____

3. _____

4. _____

Complete the Sentences

5. _____

6. _____

7. _____

8. _____

bean	clean	need	seem

Complete the Paragraph Write the Review Words to complete the paragraph.

Maria looked around the __1.__ kitchen. She wrote a list of what she would __2.__ to buy from the grocery store. She wanted to make soup for dinner with a special kind of __3.__ . It might __4.__ like a strange dish for her to cook, but she knew her parents loved it.

Complete the Sentences Write a Review Word to complete each sentence.

5. A _____ is a seed that is used for food.

6. We _____ to go home because it is getting very late.

7. Polar bears _____ to enjoy playing in ice-cold water.

8. Dogs have to be washed, but cats lick themselves _____.

⊚ Challenge

beetle	degree	reason	steam

Word Clues Write the Challenge Word that matches each of these clues.

1. It is a type of insect.
2. Water becomes this when it boils.
3. This is a unit used to measure heat.
4. This word rhymes with **treason**.

Word Groups Write the Challenge Word that belongs in each group.

5. temperature, measure, _____
6. vapor, water, _____
7. insect, bug, _____
8. purpose, why, _____

Do you think you've mastered the Spelling Strategy? Take the CHAMPION CHALLENGE on page 293!

Challenge

Word Clues

1. _____

2. _____

3. _____

4. _____

Word Groups

5. _____

6. _____

7. _____

8. _____

Spelling and Technology

Spelling and Technology

Computer Spreadsheets

1. _____

2. _____

3. _____

4. _____

Computer Spreadsheets

One common computer program allows you to make spreadsheets. Spreadsheets are tables. They can help you show, find, and organize a lot of information. For example, they can add and subtract rows of numbers or change numbers into charts.

cell	**grid**	**screen**	**spreadsheet**

Write words from the box to complete the paragraph. Underline any words that have a **long e** sound.

Ana opens the __1.__ program on her computer. She studies what appears on the __2.__. A very large __3.__, or empty table, appears there. She will write labels for the columns and rows of the table. Each column and row is made up of many boxes. Ana will fill in each box, called a __4.__, with numbers.

Content Words

Link to **Social Studies:** Culture

Write the Content Word for each definition.

adobe	culture	pueblo	customs

1. a village of stone buildings
2. a sun-dried brick
3. the special practices that people follow at Thanksgiving and other times
4. all the things that make a group unique, including language, foods, religion, and music

Link to **Health:** Nutrition

Write a Content Word for each picture.

meals	vegetables	meats	grains

5.
6.
7.
8.

Link to **The Spelling Strategy**

Circle the letters that spell the **long e** sound **ea** in two of the Content Words you wrote.

Content Connection: Social Studies

Search the Internet to find out more about a culture. You might look at www.indianpueblo.org. Report on something you learned.

Content Words

Social Studies: Culture

1. _____
2. _____
3. _____
4. _____

Health: Nutrition

5. _____
6. _____
7. _____
8. _____

Spelling and Thinking

READ the Basic Words 👀 Watch out for easily misspelled words!

1.	night	*night*	We sleep during the **night**.
2.	bright	*bright*	I like to wear **bright** colors.
3.	find	*find*	Can you **find** my lost keys?
4.	light	*light*	The **light** helps us see in the dark.
5.	wild	*wild*	Deer are **wild** animals.
👀 6.	high	*high*	The kite flew **high** in the sky.
7.	blind	*blind*	Some **blind** people use dogs as guides.
8.	fight	*fight*	People who **fight** get hurt.
9.	sight	*sight*	The glasses improved her **sight**.
10.	kind	*kind*	The **kind** boy helps sick birds.
👀 11.	sign	*sign*	We will cross at a stop **sign**.
👀 12.	knight	*knight*	A **knight** fought for his king.
13.	mild	*mild*	I eat only **mild** cheese.
14.	right	*right*	He draws with his **right** hand.
15.	sigh	*sigh*	A **sigh** is a long deep breath.

Review
16. ivory   18. shiny
17. lion   19. tiger

Challenge
20. libraries   22. slight
21. might   23. title

SORT the Basic Words

1–6. Write the spelling words in which the **long i** sound is spelled **i**.

7–15. Write the spelling words in which the **long i** sound is spelled **igh**.

REMEMBER the Spelling Strategy

Remember that the **long i** sound can be spelled in different ways: **i** in **kind** and **igh** in **sigh**.

i

1.

2.

3.

4.

5.

6.

igh

7.

8.

9.

10.

11.

12.

13.

14.

15.

Spelling and Phonics

Ending Sounds

1. Write the Basic Word that rhymes with **wild**. Circle the two consonants at the end of the word.

2. Write the Basic Word that rhymes with **sigh**. Circle the silent consonants.

Sound and Letter Patterns

3. Write the Basic Word that begins with a silent consonant. Circle the silent consonant.

4. Write the Basic Word that begins with a consonant cluster and ends with **t**.

5–9. Write **night**. Change the first letter to write four more Basic Words.

10–12. Write the Basic Words that end with **nd**. Circle the letters that spell the **long i** sound.

Using the Dictionary

Find **sigh, sign,** and **wild** in your **Spelling Dictionary**. Write the Basic Word that goes with each meaning.

13. not tamed; not cultivated; living or growing in a natural condition

14. a long, deep breathing sound

15. a notice or board with writing on it

Ending Sounds

1.

2.

Sound and Letter Patterns

3.

4.

5.

6.

7.

8.

9.

10.

11.

12.

Using the Dictionary

13.

14.

15.

night	bright	find	light	wild
high	blind	fight	sight	kind
sign	knight	mild	right	sigh

Find the Opposites

1.
_____
2.
_____
3.
_____
4.
_____
5.

Complete the Sentences

6.
_____
7.
_____
8.
_____
9.
_____
10.
_____
11.

Complete the Story

12.
_____
13.
_____
14.
_____
15.

Find the Opposites Write the Basic Word that is the opposite in meaning of each of these words.

1. low

2. left

3. day

4. seeing clearly

5. heavy

Complete the Sentences Write the Basic Word that completes each sentence.

6. The directions on the road _____ helped us find our way.

7. The army had to _____ for freedom.

8. What _____ of story do you like to read?

9. The museum has a suit of armor worn by a _____.

10. The forests were a beautiful _____.

11. Do you like your chili hot or _____?

Complete the Story Write the Basic Words from the box that best complete the story.

sigh	wild	bright	find

Jamaal was exploring a __12.__, sunny field. He hoped to __13.__ butterflies. Instead, he saw a raccoon. He gave a __14.__ of relief when the __15.__ animal ran the other way.

Spelling and Writing

 Proofread a Paragraph

First, proofread the paragraph below for eight misspelled words. Then rewrite the paragraph. Write the spelling words correctly and make the corrections shown by the proofreading marks.

¶ Our country is a land of many amazing sytes. Some are are natural wonders. Many people fynd the grand Canyon and Yellowstone National Park beautiful with their wonderful landscapes and wilde rivers. Some people like the Everglades with its milde winter temperatures. Others like the highe Rocky mountains. Still others like the Underground Carlsbad Caverns, where it is always nite, except when there is brite lyte.

More Practice Write and sort the Basic Words.

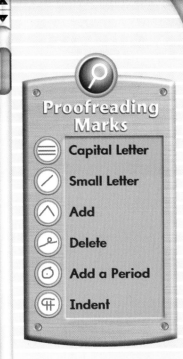

Proofreading Marks

≡	Capital Letter
/	Small Letter
∧	Add
✎	Delete
⊙	Add a Period
¶	Indent

 NARRATIVE

Write a Paragraph

A topic sentence gives the main idea of a paragraph. Detail sentences give specific facts about the main idea. Write a paragraph about a day in the life of a busy student. You could also write about a funny thing that happened to you yesterday. Use as many spelling words as possible.

Writing Process

Prewrite
∨
Draft
∨
Revise
∨

> > > > > Proofread your writing as you **Edit**

∨
Publish

When you finish writing your draft, proofread your paper for errors in spelling, grammar, capitalization, and punctuation. Use the **Spelling Dictionary** to check spelling if you are not sure.

◎ Review

Review

Word Clues

1.

2.

3.

4.

Solve the Analogies

5.

6.

7.

8.

Coined Words

1.

ivory	lion	shiny	tiger

Word Clues Write the Review Word that matches each clue.

1. A male one of these has a mane.
2. A very large wild cat that has black stripes is known by this name.
3. A new penny is said to be this.
4. This is another name for an elephant's tusks.

Solve the Analogies Write a Review Word to complete each analogy.

5. **Herd** is to **cow** as **pride** is to _____.
6. **Black** is to **white** as **ebony** is to _____.
7. **Spot** is to **leopard** as **stripe** is to _____.
8. **Rich** is to **wealthy** as **glossy** is to _____.

Word Study: Coined Words

● A **coined word** is made up to name something new. **Liger** is a coined word. It names an animal whose parents are two different kinds of big cats. One parent is a lion. Can you guess what animal the other parent is? Write the Review Word that names it.

◎ Challenge

libraries	might	slight	title

Complete the Sentences Write a Challenge Word to complete each sentence.

1. The name of an article or a book is its _____.
2. You can borrow books and many other items from _____.
3. We _____ go to the zoo tomorrow.
4. There is a _____ error in that sentence.

Complete the Paragraph Write the Challenge Words to complete the paragraph.

Emilio is a real book lover. He likes to visit __5.__ in every town he goes to. He looks at the __6.__ and description of each book before choosing what to read. Emilio thinks that someday he __7.__ open his own bookstore! Unfortunately, he has only a __8.__ interest in business.

 Do you think you've mastered the Spelling Strategy? Take the CHAMPION CHALLENGE on page 294!

Spelling and Technology

Making a Drawing

1. _____

2. _____

3. _____

4. _____

Spelling and Technology

Making a Drawing

Would you like to draw a happy face on the computer? You can use drawing and painting tools. Use the curve line tool to draw a face. Add a smile, too. Then make two dots for eyes. If you wish, you can click on a brush icon to add color.

If you don't want to draw a face, make a smiley. A smiley looks like **:)**. It means "happy."

Learn these words. Each one has something to do with drawing.

curve	fill color	icon	smiley

Write the word from the box that best replaces the underlined words. Underline any word that has a **long i** sound.

1. Click on the <u>little picture</u> showing a brush.

2. Choose the <u>color for the entire inside of your shape</u>.

3. You must use different tools for a straight line or a <u>rounded line</u>.

4. You can also use the keyboard to make a <u>symbol that means "happy."</u>

Content Words

Link to Math: Operations

Write a Content Word that matches each clue.

math	multiply	subtract	divide

1. the opposite of **divide**
2. the opposite of **add**
3. the opposite of **multiply**
4. a shortened form of the word **mathematics**

Link to Social Studies: Careers

Write the Content Word that names the worker you might find in each of these places.

pilot	driver	firefighter	clerk

5. at an airport
6. at a shopping center
7. in a bus
8. at a burning building

Link to The Spelling Strategy

Circle the letters that spell the **long i** sound **i** or **igh** in two of the Content Words you wrote.

Content Connection: Social Studies

 Search the Internet to find out more about careers. You might look at www.bls.gov/kl2. Click on an area that interests you. Write two or three careers in that area.

Content Words

Math: Operations

1. _____
2. _____
3. _____
4. _____

Social Studies: Careers

5. _____
6. _____
7. _____
8. _____

Spelling Connections Online
www.zaner-bloser.com

Spelling and Thinking

ow

1.

2.

3.

4.

5.

6.

7.

oa

8.

9.

10.

11.

12.

13.

o

14.

15.

READ the Basic Words 👀 Watch out for easily misspelled words!

1.	snow	*snow*	The new **snow** is white and fresh.
	2.	load	*load*	The mule has a heavy **load** on its back.
👀	**3.**	almost	*almost*	I am **almost** nine years old.
	4.	row	*row*	We **row** the boat across the lake.
	5.	soak	*soak*	I **soak** my sore foot in hot water.
👀	**6.**	window	*window*	The **window** lets in a lot of light.
	7.	foam	*foam*	Wind makes **foam** appear on the water.
	8.	most	*most*	I am friends with **most** of the girls.
	9.	flow	*flow*	Does this river **flow** into the ocean?
	10.	goat	*goat*	We get milk and cheese from a **goat**.
	11.	throw	*throw*	Please **throw** me the ball.
	12.	float	*float*	I can **float** on the water.
	13.	blow	*blow*	The guards will **blow** their trumpets.
👀	**14.**	below	*below*	Your coat is **below** mine in the pile.
	15.	soap	*soap*	Wash with warm water and **soap**.

◎ **Review**		◎ **Challenge**	
16. coat	18. grow	20. coast	22. pillow
17. follow	19. road	21. fold	23. solo

SORT the Basic Words

1–7. Write the words with the **long o** sound spelled **ow**.

8–13. Write the words with the **long o** sound spelled **oa**.

14–15. Write the words with the **long o** sound spelled **o**.

REMEMBER the Spelling Strategy

Remember that the **long o** sound can be spelled **ow** in **blow, oa** in **float,** and **o** in **most**.

Spelling and Phonics

Rhyming Groups

Write the Basic Word that belongs in each rhyming group.

1. toad, road, _____
2. home, roam, _____
3. hope, rope, _____
4. joke, woke, _____

Word Structure

Replace the underlined letters in each word to make a Basic Word.

5. r<u>ed</u>
6. fl<u>oor</u>
7. fla<u>g</u>
8. go<u>od</u>
9. thr<u>ee</u>
10. bl<u>ue</u>
11. sna<u>p</u>
12. m<u>ore</u>

Using the Dictionary

Your dictionary shows a • between syllables of entry words. Write these words with a • between the syllables.

13. almost   14. below   15. window

Dictionary Check Be sure to check the syllables in your **Spelling Dictionary**.

Rhyming Groups

1. _____
2. _____
3. _____
4. _____

Word Structure

5. _____
6. _____
7. _____
8. _____
9. _____
10. _____
11. _____
12. _____

Using the Dictionary

13. _____
14. _____
15. _____

snow	load	almost	row	soak
window	foam	most	flow	goat
throw	float	blow	below	soap

Replace the Words Write the Basic Word that could best replace the underlined word or words.

Replace the Words

1.
2.
3.
4.
5.
6.

1. We are just about ready to start studying for the spelling bee.
2. Please put these desks in a straight line.
3. We stood on the bridge and looked at the river under us.
4. Tim will pitch the trash into the can.
5. Maria helped us pile the wood into the back of the large truck.
6. The sink was filled with bubbles.

Complete the Sentences Write a Basic Word to complete each sentence.

Complete the Sentences

7.
8.
9.
10.
11.
12.
13.
14.
15.

7. That shirt will come clean if we _____ it overnight.
8. Use a lot of _____ on your dirty hands.
9. Do you think our raft will _____?
10. The wind began to _____ hard as the hurricane got closer to the coast.
11. A _____ has horns and hooves.
12. This stream will _____ into the river.
13. This _____ will melt soon.
14. Which class in your school has the _____ students in it?
15. The baseball went through the _____ and shattered the glass.

Spelling and Writing

 ### Proofread Directions

First, proofread the directions below for eight misspelled words. Then rewrite the directions. Write the spelling words correctly and make the corrections shown by the proofreading marks.

⌐ *Jumping in a wave is fun. to have the moast fun, do it right. Wait until the wave is almoast ready to crash. Then dive into it. To do this, thro yourself into the wave just belo its top. Make sure you go against the flowe of the water. keep your mouth shut and bloe air out through your nose. Then just flote as you soke in the water.*

More Practice Write and sort the Basic Words.

Write Directions

Think of something you like to do or know how to do well. It might be delivering newspapers, making a sandwich, or grooming a horse. Before writing your draft, list all the steps to take. Write the steps in the correct order. Use as many spelling words as you can.

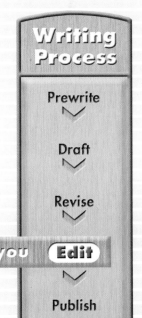

Proofreading Marks

≡	Capital Letter
/	Small Letter
∧	Add
ℯ	Delete
⊙	Add a Period
⌐	Indent

Writing Process

Prewrite
⌄
Draft
⌄
Revise
⌄
Edit
⌄
Publish

> > > > > **Proofread your writing as you** **Edit**

When you finish writing your draft, proofread your paper for errors in spelling, grammar, capitalization, and punctuation. Use the **Spelling Dictionary** to check spelling if you are not sure.

◎ Review

coat	follow	grow	road

Word Clues Write a Review Word for each clue.

1. This word has two syllables and a double consonant in its spelling.

2. This word rhymes with **toad**.

3. This word has a /**k**/ sound, but it does not have the letter **k** in its spelling.

4. This word begins with two consonants together and rhymes with **throw**.

Replace the Words Write the Review Word that could replace the underlined word or words in each sentence.

5. Put on your jacket, and let's go play in the snow!

6. Our family drove east on the highway.

7. When the tomato vines get bigger, she will tie them to stakes for support.

8. I don't know where I'm going, so I will go after you.

Word Study: Shades of Meaning

When words mean almost the same thing, we say they have different **shades of meaning**. For example, **munch** and **bite** name different ways to chew. Write the Review Word that fits with the meaning of these words: **highway, street, ____**.

Challenge

coast	fold	pillow	solo

Solve the Analogies Write a Challenge Word to complete each analogy.

1. **Table** is to **plate** as **bed** is to _____.
2. **Two** is to **duet** as **one** is to _____.
3. **Mix** is to **stir** as **bend** is to _____.
4. **Marsh** is to **swamp** as **shoreline** is to _____.

Complete the Sentences Write a Challenge Word to complete each sentence.

5. John will play a saxophone _____ at the jazz concert.
6. There are many seafood restaurants along the _____.
7. He lay his head on the _____ and fell asleep.
8. Janine helps her brother _____ the laundry.

Challenge

Solve the Analogies

1.

2.

3.

4.

Complete the Sentences

5.

6.

7.

8.

Do you think you've mastered the Spelling Strategy? Take the CHAMPION CHALLENGE on page 295!

Spelling and Technology

Spelling and Technology

Computer Formats

1.

2.

3.

4.

Computer Formats

A computer lets you place words on a page in many ways. This placement of words on a page is called the **format**. You can move the borders, add headings, or change the size and shape of the words. To do that, first highlight the word or words you want to change. Then select the new look, such as bold or italic, and click the correct button on the format bar or ruler.

You need to know these words about formats:

bold	**case**	**font style**	**italic**

A. Write the word that names each format below. Underline the word that has a **long o** sound.

  1. This is how I look.

  2. *Do you like the way I look?*

  3. I can look like **this**, **this**, or this!

  4. I can look THIS WAY or that way.

B. Ask an adult to help you view different fonts on a word processor. Pick a font you like, such as Times or Arial. Type a letter to a friend using this font.

Content Words

Link to **Math:** Measurement

Write the Content Word that answers each question.

gallon	pint	pound	measure

1. Which is a unit of weight?
2. Which means "to find the size of something"?
3. Which equals four quarts?
4. Which equals two cups?

Link to **Social Studies:** Geography

Write the Content Word that fits each meaning.

highland	grassland	desert	lowland

5. an area of land lower than the land around it
6. a dry region, sometimes covered with sand
7. an area of land higher and more hilly than the land around it
8. open land that is covered with grass

Link to **The Spelling Strategy**

Circle the letters that spell the **long o** sound in one of the Content Words you wrote.

Content Connection: Math

Search the Internet to find out more about measurement. Try this site: www.aaamath.com. Click on **Measurement** and **U.S. Volumes.** Play a game or learn a fact. Write the name of the game or the fact.

Content Words

Math: Measurement

1. _____

2. _____

3. _____

4. _____

Social Studies: Geography

5. _____

6. _____

7. _____

8. _____

Spelling Connections Online
www.zaner-bloser.com

Assessment and Review

Unit 7

1.

2.

3.

Unit 8

4.

5.

6.

Unit 9

7.

8.

9.

Unit 10

10.

11.

12.

Unit 11

13.

14.

15.

ASSESSMENT

Units 7–11

Each Assessment Word in the box fits one of the spelling strategies you have studied over the past five weeks. Read the spelling strategies. Then write each Assessment Word under the unit number it fits.

Unit 7

1–3. The long vowel sounds you hear in **pave, size,** and **globe** are spelled **vowel-consonant-e**.

Unit 8

4–6. The **long a** sound can be spelled in different ways: **ai** in **paint** and **ay** in **tray**.

Unit 9

7–9. The **long e** sound can be spelled in different ways: **ea** in **treat** and **ee** in **street**.

Unit 10

10–12. The **long i** sound can be spelled in different ways: **i** in **kind** and **igh** in **sigh**.

Unit 11

13–15. The **long o** sound can be spelled **ow** in **blow, oa** in **float,** and **o** in **most**.

stripe
bail
cream
bind
groan
sold
thigh
bead
bait
brave
fellow
rind
creep
sway
grove

REVIEW

Unit 7: Vowel-Consonant-e

| broke | smile | close | state | face | stone | size |

Write the spelling words by taking the **-ing** off the words below and adding the final **e**.

1. smiling   **3.** facing

2. closing   **4.** sizing

Write the spelling word that completes the sentence.

5. The plate _____ when I dropped it.

6. The _____ of California is on the west coast of the United States.

7. Another word for **rock** is _____.

REVIEW

Unit 8: Long a: ai, ay

| always | chain | laid | maybe | mail | pay | main |

Write the spelling word that rhymes with each word.

8. day   **9.** braid   **10.** baby

Find the word that is misspelled in each sentence. Write the word correctly.

11. I alwaz try to help a friend in trouble.

12. The magazine was delivered with our mayle.

13. The mayn gate of the garden was locked.

14. The swing fell when the chian broke.

Unit 7

1. _____
2. _____
3. _____
4. _____
5. _____
6. _____
7. _____

Unit 8

8. _____
9. _____
10. _____
11. _____
12. _____
13. _____
14. _____

1.

2.

3.

4.

5.

6.

7.

8.

9.

10.

11.

12.

13.

14.

REVIEW

Unit 9: Long e: ee, ea

real   teacher   street   wheels   east   heat   stream

Write the spelling word that completes the sentence.

1. The sun comes up in the _____.

2. I could see many fish in the clear _____.

3. That moving truck has many _____.

4. In front of my school is a wide _____.

5. The fruit in that picture looks almost _____.

6. The reading _____ gave them each a book.

7. The fire gave out a lot of _____.

REVIEW

Unit 10: Long i: i, igh

bright   mild   kind   right   night   sign   high

Write the spelling word that completes the sentence.

8. My uncle likes his chili hot and spicy instead of _____.

9. There is a "For Sale" _____ in front of that house.

10. I am not afraid to jump off the _____ diving board.

Write the spelling word that means the opposite of the underlined word in these sentences.

11. The clerk had a <u>mean</u> look on her face.

12. This is the <u>day</u> I have been waiting for.

13. Warren got every question on the test <u>wrong</u>.

14. The <u>dim</u> light of the moon lighted the path.

Unit 11: Long o: ow, oa, o

almost snow float window below goat soap

Write the spelling word that means about the same as the word or words below.

1. to drift on water   **2.** under   **3.** nearly

Write the spelling word that completes each sentence.

4. The cold rain will soon turn to _____.

5. Farmer Olson kept a prize _____ at his farm.

6. Be careful not to slip on the _____ in the shower.

7. Open the _____ to let in some fresh air.

WORD SORT
Spelling Study Strategy

Sorting by Vowel Spelling Patterns

Write spelling words on small cards. Then sort the words by spelling pattern. Share your words with a partner.

1. Make stacks of words in which **ow** or **oa** spells **long o**.

2. Make stacks of words in which **ai** or **ay** spells **long a**.

3. Make stacks of words in which **ee** or **ea** spells **long e**.

4. Make stacks of words in which **i** or **igh** spells **long i**.

5. Make stacks of words in which **vowel-consonant-e** spells **long a** or **long o**.

Unit 11

1. _____
2. _____
3. _____
4. _____
5. _____
6. _____
7. _____

Writer's Workshop

Grammar, Usage, and Mechanics

Singular and Plural Nouns

A **singular noun** names one person, place, or thing.

The **girl** has a **cat**.

The **boat** has a **sail**.

A **plural noun** names more than one person, place, or thing.

The **girls** own many **cats**.

These **boats** have many **sails**.

Many plural nouns are formed by adding an **-s** to the end of the singular noun.

Practice ACTIVITY

A. Write the singular noun used to make each plural below.

1. teachers   **3.** nights   **5.** streets

2. stones   **4.** windows   **6.** prizes

B. Each sentence has one plural noun. Write the plural nouns.

7. My dog has blue eyes.

8. The students left the classroom.

9. Dry your hands with this towel.

10. Look at the flowers on that tree!

Practice Activity

A.
_____

1.
_____

2.
_____

3.
_____

4.
_____

5.
_____

6.
_____

B.
_____

7.
_____

8.
_____

9.
_____

10.
_____

The Writing Process **NARRATIVE**

Writing a Friendly Letter

Prewriting

Writing a friendly letter is a fun way to share information. You can write a letter to a friend, a family member, or a key pal. Think about some exciting news you could share with this person. Make a list of the events in order.

Drafting

Use your list of events to write a friendly letter. Make sure your letter has all five parts: heading, greeting, body, closing, and signature. Use as many spelling words as possible.

Revising

When you have finished your first draft, read your letter from beginning to end. Check to see if you have included all of the events on your list. Did you include all five parts of a friendly letter? Now, write your final draft.

Editing

Use the editing checklist to proofread your letter. Be sure to use proofreading marks when you make corrections.

Publishing

Make a copy of your friendly letter. Ask an adult to help you address and mail your letter.

✔ Editing Checklist

Spelling

○ I circled words that contain the spelling strategies I learned in Units 7–11.

○ I checked the circled words in my Spelling Dictionary.

○ I also checked for other spelling errors.

Capital Letters

○ Important words in the heading, greeting, body, closing, and signature

Punctuation

○ Each sentence ends with the correct punctuation.

Grammar, Usage, and Mechanics

○ Each singular noun names one person, place, or thing.

○ Each plural noun has the correct ending.

sh, ch, tch, th, wr, ck

end with ck or tch

1. _____
2. _____
3. _____
4. _____

wr, ch, sh, or th

5. _____
6. _____
7. _____
8. _____
9. _____
10. _____
11. _____
12. _____
13. _____
14. _____
15. _____

Spelling and Thinking

READ the Basic Words 👀 Watch out for easily misspelled words!

	1.	shape	*shape*	A square is a **shape** with four sides.
	2.	church	*church*	Many people go to a **church** or temple.
👀	3.	watch	*watch*	Let's **watch** the game on television.
	4.	father	*father*	My **father** taught me to throw a ball.
👀	5.	wrap	*wrap*	We **wrap** the gifts in pretty paper.
	6.	check	*check*	Put a **check** mark next to each word.
	7.	finish	*finish*	I will **finish** the book tonight.
	8.	sharp	*sharp*	That knife has a very **sharp** edge.
👀	9.	mother	*mother*	My **mother** showed me how to bat.
	10.	write	*write*	I will **write** an e-mail message to you.
	11.	catch	*catch*	Throw the ball, and I will **catch** it.
	12.	chase	*chase*	Do not let the dog **chase** the cat.
	13.	shall	*shall*	I **shall** call you in the morning.
	14.	thick	*thick*	This **thick** coat will keep you warm.
	15.	wrote	*wrote*	Nan **wrote** me a letter yesterday.

Review

16. bench
17. chin
18. shine
19. thank

Challenge

20. chuckle
21. scratches
22. shower
23. wrinkle

SORT the Basic Words

1–4. Write the words that end with **ck** or **tch**.

5–15. Write the words that are spelled with **wr**, **ch**, **sh**, or **th**.

REMEMBER the Spelling Strategy

Two consonants together can spell a single sound: **wr** in **wrap** and **ck** in **thick**. Two or more consonants can spell new sounds called **consonant digraphs: ch** in **chase**, **sh** in **shape**, **th** in **mother**, and **tch** in **watch**.

Spelling and Phonics

Sound and Letter Patterns

Write the Basic Words by adding the missing letters.

1. __ __ ape

2. cat __ __

3. __ __ ote

4. c __ e __ __

5. __ __ i __ k

Word Clues

Write a Basic Word for each clue.

6. This word rhymes with **harp**.

7. male parent

8. Change one letter in **shell** to make this word.

9. It rhymes with **face**.

10. female parent

11. You see the word **fin** in this word.

12. It begins and ends with the same two letters.

 Using the Dictionary

The words in a dictionary are in a-b-c order.

13–15. Write these words in a-b-c order.

    wrap   watch   write

◆ ◆ ◆

Dictionary Check Be sure to check the a-b-c order of the words in your **Spelling Dictionary**.

Sound and Letter Patterns

1.

2.

3.

4.

5.

Word Clues

6.

7.

8.

9.

10.

11.

12.

Using the Dictionary

13.

14.

15.

shape	church	watch	father	wrap
check	finish	sharp	mother	write
catch	chase	shall	thick	wrote

Complete the Story

1.

2.

3.

4.

5.

6.

7.

8.

Complete the Rhymes

9.

10.

11.

12.

13.

14.

15.

Complete the Story Write the Basic Words to complete the story.

"What time __1.__ I meet you on Sunday?" Jenny asked.

Mike said, "I forgot to tell you. My __2.__ and __3.__ will drop me off there after __4.__."

"Great!" said Jenny. "That will give me time to __5.__ my morning chores. I also have to __6.__ my little cousin for a while."

Mike said, "I will be there at 10 o'clock __7.__. I will __8.__ it down so that I don't forget!"

Complete the Rhymes Write a Basic Word that fits each sentence. The Basic Word will rhyme with the underlined word.

9. Let Jim read the <u>note</u>. I don't know what she _____.

10. Please check the <u>latch</u>. Did you hear it _____?

11. Look at this <u>grape</u>. It has a funny _____.

12. Which sweater would you <u>pick</u>? I think this one is too _____.

13. Is there a bug on my <u>neck</u>? Would you please _____?

14. I must pick up the <u>pace</u>. I am falling behind in the _____.

15. First, loosen the <u>flap</u>. Then tear off the _____.

Spelling and Writing

Proofread a Poem

First, proofread the poem below for nine misspelled words. Then rewrite the poem. Write the spelling words correctly and make the corrections shown by the proofreading marks.

just Fishing

I rap a worm around a sharpe hook.

I drop it in the bubbling brook.

I chek my wach: it's 9 A.M.

I hope I get a catsch and finnish by 10.

Shal I sleep? Shall i rite?

Big, thik fish, please take take a bite.

More Practice Write and sort the Basic Words.

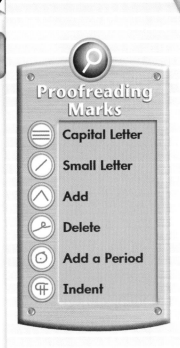

Proofreading Marks

☰	Capital Letter
/	Small Letter
∧	Add
℘	Delete
⊙	Add a Period
¶	Indent

DESCRIPTIVE

Write a Poem

Write a poem about a sport or hobby you enjoy. The lines of the poem do not have to rhyme. Be sure to tell where, when, and how you enjoy the hobby. Use details about what you see, do, taste, touch, hear, or smell. Use as many spelling words as you can.

Writing Process

Prewrite
⌄
Draft
⌄
Revise
⌄
Edit
⌄
Publish

〉 〉 〉 〉 〉 **Proofread your writing as you** **Edit**

When you finish writing your draft, proofread your paper for errors in spelling, grammar, capitalization, and punctuation. Use the **Spelling Dictionary** to check spelling if you are not sure.

◎ Review

Review

Word Clues

1. _____

2. _____

3. _____

4. _____

Complete the Sentences

5. _____

6. _____

7. _____

8. _____

Anagrams

1. _____

bench	chin	shine	thank

Word Clues Write a Review Word for each clue.

1. This word begins like **shoe** and ends like **line**.
2. This word begins like **boy** and ends like **lunch**.
3. This word rhymes with **win**.
4. This word begins like **thin** and rhymes with **sank**.

Complete the Sentences Write a Review Word to complete each sentence.

5. Paolo wanted to _____ his friend for the birthday card.
6. The basketball players sat on the _____, waiting to play in the game.
7. When the rain stops, the sun will _____.
8. Eva fell down and got a bruise on her _____.

Word Study: Anagrams

● **Anagrams** are words that have all the same letters, but the letters are in a different order in each word. **Slip** and **lips** are anagrams. Write the Review Word that is an anagram of **inch**.

 Challenge

| chuckle | scratches | shower | wrinkle |

Word Meanings Write a Challenge Word that is related in meaning to each pair of words.

1. cuts, scrapes
2. storm, downpour
3. fold, crease
4. laugh, giggle

Answer the Questions Write a Challenge Word to answer each question.

5. When there are many clouds, what might happen?
6. What would you get if you walked through thorny bushes?
7. What is another word for **laugh**?
8. If clothes are not hung or folded neatly, what do you see?

Challenge

Word Meanings

1. _____

2. _____

3. _____

4. _____

Answer the Questions

5. _____

6. _____

7. _____

8. _____

Do you think you've mastered the Spelling Strategy? Take the CHAMPION CHALLENGE on page 296!

Spelling and Technology

Spelling and Technology

Computer Searches

1. _____

2. _____

3. _____

4. _____

Computer Searches

There are two main ways to perform a search. One way is by using a type of index. First, you type in a search word. Then you see a list of topics. Choosing a topic brings up a list of Web pages. The other way is by using a search tool. You type in a search word and then see a list of Web pages.

Learn these words for doing searches.

bookmark	browse	scan	search

Read this paragraph. Find four words with missing letters. Write a word from the box by adding the missing letters. Underline the word that is spelled with **ch**.

To find information, you need to do a sear__ __. Type a word or phrase in the box. Your computer will return results. You can s __ a __ these for the information you want. Choose a topic or a page. Explore or br __ __ se what is there. Would you like to come back to this page another day? Then b__ __ kmark it.

Content Words

Link to **Science:** Human Body

Write the Content Word for each definition.

lips	wrist	thumb	tongue

1. part of the mouth used in tasting and swallowing food
2. part of the face that surrounds the mouth
3. the shortest, thickest finger
4. part of the arm that joins the hand

Link to **Social Studies:** Family

Write Content Words to complete the paragraph.

brother	family	sister	chores

I have one __5.__ named Jed. I have one __6.__ named Leah. There are no other children in my __7.__ . We all like to play together, but we never do __8.__ together.

Link to **The Spelling Strategy**

Circle the **th** or the **ch** in three of the Content Words you wrote.

Content Connection: Science

 Search the Internet to find out more about the human body. Try www.kidshealth.org/kid. Click on **My Body**. Write two facts you learned.

Content Words

Science: Human Body

1. _____

2. _____

3. _____

4. _____

Social Studies: Family

5. _____

6. _____

7. _____

8. _____

Spelling Connections Online
www.zaner-bloser.com

Spelling and Thinking

/j/ sound

1. _____

2. _____

3. _____

4. _____

/s/ sound

5. _____

6. _____

7. _____

8. _____

9. _____

10. _____

11. _____

12. _____

13. _____

14. _____

15. _____

READ the Basic Words 👀 Watch out for easily misspelled words!

👀	**1.** change	*change*	I will **change** into my baseball clothes.
👀	**2.** fence	*fence*	There is a **fence** around the pool.
	3. space	*space*	We use this **space** as a gym.
	4. age	*age*	Letifa is now ten years of **age**.
	5. center	*center*	My desk is in the **center** of the room.
	6. large	*large*	We ordered a **large** pizza.
👀	**7.** since	*since*	I have been able to swim **since** I was five.
	8. price	*price*	The **price** of the book is ten dollars.
	9. page	*page*	Read to the bottom of the **page**.
	10. ice	*ice*	The **ice** will melt when it warms up.
	11. dance	*dance*	Mom and Dad **dance** at the party.
	12. pencil	*pencil*	This **pencil** has no eraser.
	13. slice	*slice*	Please cut me a **slice** of bread.
	14. place	*place*	This is a nice **place** to visit.
	15. city	*city*	We take the bus into the **city**.

Review

16. nice
17. orange
18. race
19. spice

Challenge

20. bridge
21. cellar
22. engine
23. piece

SORT the Basic Words

1–4. Write the words that have the /**j**/ sound.

5–15. Write the words that have the /**s**/ sound.

REMEMBER the Spelling Strategy

The /**j**/ sound in **age** is spelled **g,** followed by **e**. The /**s**/ sound in **ice** and **city** is spelled **c**. The **c** is followed by **e** (**ice**) or by **i** (**city**).

Spelling and Vocabulary

Sound and Letter Patterns

Write the Basic Word for each clue.

1. It begins with the **long a** sound.
2. It has the sound of **s** twice and contains the word **in**.
3. It begins with the **long i** sound.
4. It rhymes with **chance**.
5. It has four letters and two syllables.
6. It has the **/s/** sound in its second syllable.
7. It has one syllable and the **short e** sound.

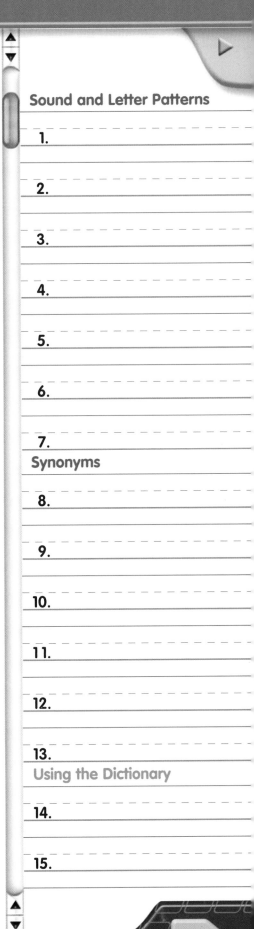

Synonyms

Write the spelling word that is a synonym for each of these words.

8. middle
9. cost
10. big
11. put
12. cut
13. area

Using the Dictionary

The two words at the top of a dictionary page are called **guide words**. The guide word at the left is the first entry word on that page. The guide word at the right is the last entry word on that page. Write the Basic Word that would be on the same page as these guide words.

14. over • pepper   15. cavity • children

Sound and Letter Patterns

1. _____
2. _____
3. _____
4. _____
5. _____
6. _____
7. _____

Synonyms

8. _____
9. _____
10. _____
11. _____
12. _____
13. _____

Using the Dictionary

14. _____
15. _____

change	fence	space	age	center
large	since	price	page	ice
dance	pencil	slice	place	city

Use the Clues Write the Basic Word that fits each clue.

1. This word can describe an elephant.
2. This is where to find the planets and stars.
3. This names one piece of bread.
4. This means "from then until now."
5. This is a small part of a book.
6. This names a very large town.
7. This is on a package for sale or in a bar code.
8. This word names a waltz or a tango.
9. This word names a country, building, or park.

Complete the Riddles Write a Basic Word to answer each riddle.

10. What runs all around a field but never moves? a f_____
11. What goes up and never comes down? a_____
12. What is the hardest thing about learning to skate? the i_____
13. What makes a point but never says a word? a p_____
14. Why did the woman have her pocketbook open? She was expecting some c_____ in the weather.
15. Why is a nose always in the middle of a face? It's the c_____.

Use the Clues

1. _____
2. _____
3. _____
4. _____
5. _____
6. _____
7. _____
8. _____
9. _____

Complete the Riddles

10. _____
11. _____
12. _____
13. _____
14. _____
15. _____

Spelling and Writing

 Proofread a Letter

First, proofread the letter below for eight misspelled words. Then rewrite the letter. Write the spelling words correctly and make the corrections shown by the proofreading marks.

Dear neighbors,

Let's make the playground a better plase for Children! We can chang this larje spase into a great park for the sity. The fens needs to be Fixed also, sinse it fell down in May. We'll meet in the senter of the playground on Sunday.

yours truly,
Mark Jackson

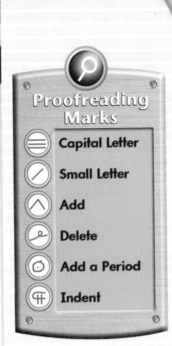

Proofreading Marks

≡	Capital Letter
/	Small Letter
∧	Add
℘	Delete
⊙	Add a Period
⁋	Indent

More Practice Write and sort the Basic Words.

 **PERSUASIVE**

Write a Letter

What change would you like to make in your school, neighborhood, or town? Write a letter to friends asking for help. Include what needs changing, what your plans are, and why others might want to help. Use as many spelling words as you can.

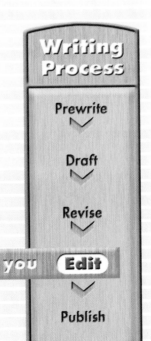

Writing Process

Prewrite
⌄
Draft
⌄
Revise
⌄
Publish

> > > > > **Proofread your writing as you** **Edit**

When you finish writing your draft, proofread your paper for errors in spelling, grammar, capitalization, and punctuation. Use the **Spelling Dictionary** to check spelling if you are not sure.

◎ Review

Review

Solve the Analogies

1.

2.

3.

4.

Complete the Sentences

5.

6.

7.

8.

| nice | orange | race | spice |

Solve the Analogies Write a Review Word that completes each analogy.

1. **Vine** is to **grape** as **tree** is to _____.
2. **Ugly** is to **pretty** as **mean** is to _____.
3. **Rose** is to **flower** as **pepper** is to _____.
4. **Home** is to **apartment** as **contest** is to _____.

Complete the Sentences Write a Review Word to complete each sentence.

5. Julius eats one _____ every day to get his vitamin C.
6. The woman added a red _____ to her chili as she cooked.
7. The kids we met at the park were so _____.
8. My favorite track-and-field event is the relay _____.

Challenge

bridge	cellar	engine	piece

Complete the Sentences Write a Challenge Word that completes each sentence.

1. Please lift the hood of the car so that I can look at the _____.
2. May I cut a _____ of cornbread for you?
3. This large _____ connects northern California to San Francisco.
4. We store potatoes in the _____.

Complete the Paragraph Write Challenge Words to complete the paragraph.

Ellen drove across the __5.__ toward home. The __6.__ of her car hummed softly, and she turned the radio up. She was eager to have a __7.__ of her mom's homemade pie when she got home. But first, she would have to unload the groceries into the __8.__ .

 Do you think you've mastered the Spelling Strategy? Take the CHAMPION CHALLENGE on page 297!

Challenge

Complete the Sentences

1.

2.

3.

4.

Complete the Paragraph

5.

6.

7.

8.

Spelling and Technology

Internet Seach Engines

1. _____

2. _____

3. _____

4. _____

Spelling and Technology

Internet Search Engines

All Internet searches begin with a search engine. You tell the engine one or more key words about a topic. The search engine then matches your words with words in certain Web sites. Some engines will match only the exact phrase you type into the search box. Others will find pages that contain any of the words as well as the exact phrase.

These terms will help you with your searches.

engine: program that helps you find the information you want

interface: what you see on a computer screen

exact phrase: the words you use to search, exactly as you type them in

Web page: part of a Web site with its own file name

engine interface exact phrase Web page

Write the term from the box that completes each sentence. Underline the words with the /j/ sound. Circle the word with the /s/ sound.

1. I opened my search _____.

2. I typed in this _____: "Fourth of July."

3. The _____ showed text and graphics.

4. I visited another _____ on the same site.

Content Words

Link to **Science:** Animals

Write the Content Word that matches each description.

camel	giraffe	zebra	elephant

1. a humped desert animal that carries loads

2. a large animal with stripes

3. an animal with a long neck, long legs, and short horns

4. the largest land animal

Link to **Math:** Graphing

Write the Content Word or words that complete each sentence.

graph	circle	bar	pictograph

5. A pie chart is round like a _____.

6. When you draw pictures to show items in a chart, you are making a _____.

7–8. A chart that shows information with blocks of different lengths is a _____ _____.

Link to **The Spelling Strategy**

Circle the letter that spells the /**s**/ sound in one of the Content Words you wrote.

Content Connection: Science

 Search the Internet to find out more about animals. Try www.kidsplanet.org. Click on **Wild Games**. Play one of the games. Write its name.

Content Words

Science: Animals

1. _____

2. _____

3. _____

4. _____

Math: Graphing

5. _____

6. _____

7. _____

8. _____

Spelling Connections Online
www.zaner-bloser.com

sh, ch, tch, ng

1.
2.
3.
4.
5.
6.
7.
8.
9.
10.
11.
12.

br, cl, nk

13.
14.
15.

Spelling and Thinking

READ the Basic Words 👀 Watch out for easily misspelled words!

1.	shook	*shook*	I **shook** the juice before pouring it.
2.	flash	*flash*	I just saw a **flash** of lightning.
👀 3.	speech	*speech*	The mayor made a long **speech**.
4.	think	*think*	I like to **think** before I answer.
5.	strong	*strong*	We are **strong** enough to lift this.
👀 6.	cloth	*cloth*	That coat is made from heavy **cloth**.
7.	brook	*brook*	The water in the **brook** is cold.
👀 8.	stitch	*stitch*	One **stitch** will not hold the button.
9.	string	*string*	The cat chases the ball of **string**.
10.	scratch	*scratch*	Please **scratch** my back.
11.	fresh	*fresh*	This bread is **fresh** and tasty.
12.	spring	*spring*	I will play baseball in the **spring**.
13.	switch	*switch*	Use the **switch** to turn on the light.
14.	stretch	*stretch*	We want to **stretch** if we sit for too long.
15.	splash	*splash*	Jim made a big **splash** in the pool.

Review

16. bring
17. clap
18. store
19. trash

Challenge

20. flight
21. station
22. strange
23. thunder

SORT the Basic Words

1–12. Write the words with the **sh, ch, tch,** or **ng** digraph.

13–15. Write the words with the consonant clusters **br, cl,** or **nk**.

REMEMBER the Spelling Strategy

Consonant digraphs are two or more consonants together that spell one new sound: **sh** in **shook**.

Consonant clusters are two or more consonants together that make more than one sound: **br** in **brook**.

Spelling and Phonics

Word Structure

1. Change the last two letters in **flame** to make a Basic Word.

2. Delete one letter and change one letter in **strange** to make a Basic Word.

3. Change the last three letters in **scraped** to make a Basic Word.

4. Change one letter in **stitch** to make another Basic Word.

Word Groups

Write the Basic Word that belongs in each group.

5. imagine, remember, believe, _____

6. rope, thread, _____

7. winter, summer, fall, _____

8. stream, creek, _____

9. new, clean, _____

10. talk, lecture, sermon, _____

Using the Dictionary

The words in a dictionary are in a-b-c order.

11–15. Write these words in a-b-c order.

stretch	splash
shook	stitch
cloth	

Dictionary Check Be sure to check the a-b-c order of the words in your **Spelling Dictionary**.

Word Structure

1.

2.

3.

4.

Word Groups

5.

6.

7.

8.

9.

10.

Using the Dictionary

11.

12.

13.

14.

15.

shook	flash	speech	think	strong
cloth	brook	stitch	string	scratch
fresh	spring	switch	stretch	splash

Solve the Analogies Write a Basic Word to complete each analogy.

1. **Mountain** is to **hill** as **river** is to _____.
2. **Tiny** is to **huge** as **stale** is to _____.
3. **Evening** is to **morning** as **fall** is to _____.
4. **Take** is to **took** as **shake** is to _____.
5. **Eye** is to **sight** as **tongue** is to _____.
6. **Easy** is to **difficult** as **weak** is to _____.
7. **Sentence** is to **write** as **idea** is to _____.

Complete the Sentences Write a Basic Word to complete each sentence.

8. Use a soft _____ to wipe down the car.
9. Did you see the _____ when you took the picture?
10. Can you _____ your arms up to the ceiling?
11. I got a _____ on my elbow from falling down.
12. The doctor sewed one _____ in Jimmy's finger.
13. We will _____ schools in sixth grade.
14. You can tie the package with _____.
15. Please don't _____ me. I don't want to get wet!

Solve the Analogies

1.
2.
3.
4.
5.
6.
7.

Complete the Sentences

8.
9.
10.
11.
12.
13.
14.
15.

Spelling and Writing

🔍 Proofread a Paragraph

First, proofread the paragraph below for eight misspelled words. Then rewrite the paragraph. Write the spelling words correctly and make the corrections shown by the proofreading marks.

¶ *We hiked up Sugar Mountain on a warm, clear sping day. We followed the the rushing barook to the top. We saw fish splassh in the water.The sun was hot, and there was a storng, frech breeze. We smelled the deep green Pine trees. We stayed away from the branches so they wouldn't scrach us. after the hike, I thingk we were all ready to strech out for a nap.*

More Practice Write and sort the Basic Words.

Write a Paragraph

Think of something you saw at a fair or a festival that you can describe. Write a paragraph about it. Include details about size, shape, and color. Include words that tell about what you saw, heard, smelled, touched, or tasted. Use as many spelling words as you can.

> > > > > Proofread your writing as you **Edit**

When you finish writing your draft, proofread your paper for errors in spelling, grammar, capitalization, and punctuation. Use the **Spelling Dictionary** to check spelling if you are not sure.

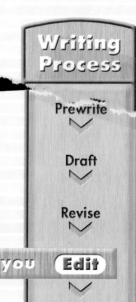

Proofreading Marks

☰	Capital Letter
/	Small Letter
∧	Add
✎	Delete
⊙	Add a Period
¶	Indent

Writing Process

Prewrite
∨
Draft
∨
Revise
∨

Publish

◎ Review

Review

Word Clues

1. _____
2. _____
3. _____
4. _____

Complete the Sentences

5. _____
6. _____
7. _____
8. _____

bring	clap	store	trash

Word Clues Write a Review Word for each clue.

1. It begins like **stop** and ends like **more**.
2. It rhymes with **crash**.
3. It has a /**k**/ sound but no letter **k**.
4. It begins like **brand** and ends like **sing**.

Complete the Sentences Write a Review Word to complete each sentence.

5. We helped pick up _____ on the beach.
6. Don't forget to _____ your shoes for gym class tomorrow.
7. The audience began to _____ loudly after the concert.
8. Tom is a cashier at the _____ on Fifth Avenue.

 **Challenge**

| flight | station | strange | thunder |

Challenge

Complete the Paragraph

1.

2.

3.

4.

Answer the Questions

5.

6.

7.

8.

Complete the Paragraph Write Challenge Words to complete the paragraph.

   When we went to bed, we were excited about our trip the next day. But when we woke up in the morning, the sky was a __1.__ gray color. It wasn't long until we heard a clap of __2.__. We turned on the local radio __3.__. We found out that the airport was closed. Our __4.__ to Orlando would not leave today.

Answer the Questions Write a Challenge Word to answer each question.

5. What might you hear during a storm?
6. What is another word for **odd**?
7. What do you call a trip taken by plane?
8. Where might you hear a radio show?

 Do you think you've mastered the Spelling Strategy? Take the CHAMPION CHALLENGE on page 298!

Spelling and Technology

Spelling and Technology

Search Terms

1. _____

2. _____

3. _____

4. _____

Search Terms

A suffix is a word part that is added to the end of a word. You can do a search with or without a suffix. You can also search using the singular or plural form of a word. For example, if you want to find out about camping, you can type in **camping**. You can also type in **camp** or **camps**.

plural	singular	spelling	suffix

A. Write the word that completes each sentence. Underline the words with the **/ng/** sound.

1. The **es** ending in the search term **buses** makes the word _____.

2. In the search term **fishing**, the **ing** ending is a _____.

3. The search term **airport** is _____.

4. Be sure to use the correct _____ when inputting search terms!

B. Learn more about safe Internet searching at this site: www.wowusa.com/KidsOnline. Click on **Internet 101**. Choose one of the topics listed. Write three tips you learned.

Content Words

Link to **Science:** Ocean Life

Write the Content Word that matches each description.

| starfish | whale | shark | octopus |

1. a sea animal that is shaped like a star
2. a sea animal with a soft body and eight arms
3. the largest of all animals on land or sea
4. a large ocean fish with sharp teeth

Link to **Math:** Numbers

Write the Content Word that can replace the number or set of numbers in each sentence.

| twenty-four | fifty-nine | thirty-two | sixty-one |

5. I got 59 trading cards for my birthday.
6. There are 61 third graders in our school.
7. My Aunt Sharon is 10 + 10 + 4 years old.
8. My Uncle Jed is 10 + 10 + 10 + 2 years old.

Link to **The Spelling Strategy**

Circle the **sh** or **wh** digraph in three of the Content Words you wrote.

Content Connection: Math

You can learn more about numbers at www.kidsnumbers.com. Play an addition game. Write its name.

Content Words

Science: Ocean Life

1. _____

2. _____

3. _____

4. _____

Math: Numbers

5. _____

6. _____

7. _____

8. _____

Spelling Connections Online
www.zaner-bloser.com

Spelling and Thinking

READ the Basic Words 👀 Watch out for easily misspelled words!

schwa more than once

1.

2.

schwa in first syllable

3.

4.

5.

6.

7.

8.

9.

10.

schwa in last syllable

11.

12.

13.

14.

15.

1. afraid	afraid	Is Cindy **afraid** of that big dog?
2. around	around	Let's run **around** the block.
👀 **3.** upon	upon	We looked **upon** a strange sight.
4. never	never	You should **never** call people names.
5. open	open	May I **open** my presents now?
6. animal	animal	The **animal** has four legs and a tail.
7. ever	ever	Will we **ever** get there?
8. about	about	This book is **about** a hidden cave.
👀 **9.** again	again	We will visit Grandpa **again** tonight.
10. another	another	Take **another** look at what you wrote.
👀 **11.** couple	couple	That **couple** has three children.
12. awake	awake	Are you **awake** at seven o'clock?
13. over	over	I climbed **over** the tall fence.
14. asleep	asleep	My dog is **asleep** on his bed.
15. above	above	The light switch is **above** the desk.

Review

16. model   18. seven
17. planted   19. wagon

Challenge

20. agree   22. tractor
21. alarm   23. water

SORT the Basic Words

Write the words that have

1–2. more than one **schwa** sound.

3–10. just one **schwa** sound, in the first syllable.

11–15. just one **schwa** sound, in the last syllable.

REMEMBER the Spelling Strategy

Remember that the **schwa** sound can be spelled: **a** in **about**, **u** in **upon**, and **e** in **over**.

Spelling and Vocabulary

Sound and Letter Patterns

Write the Basic Words by adding the missing letters.

1. __ pon
2. ev __ r
3. __ bo __ t
4. __ sl __ ep
5. __ ro __ nd
6. __ ga __ n
7. co __ pl __
8. n __ v __ r

Rhyming Words

9. Write the Basic Word that rhymes with **braid**.
10. Write the Basic Word that rhymes with **clover**.
11. Write the Basic Word that rhymes with **take**.
12. Write the Basic Word that rhymes with **love**.
13. Write the Basic Word that rhymes with **mother**.

Using the Dictionary 🖳 ⏻ ◀ ▶

Look at these dictionary respellings. Say each word. Write the Basic Word for each dictionary respelling.

14. /ăn′ ə məl/   15. /ō′ pən/

◆ ◆ ◆

Dictionary Check Be sure to check the respellings in your **Spelling Dictionary**.

Sound and Letter Patterns

1.
2.
3.
4.
5.
6.
7.
8.
Rhyming Words
9.
10.
11.
12.
13.
Using the Dictionary
14.
15.

Complete the Sentences

1. _____
2. _____
3. _____
4. _____
5. _____
6. _____
7. _____

Complete the Story

8. _____
9. _____
10. _____
11. _____
12. _____
13. _____
14. _____
15. _____

afraid	around	upon	never	open
animal	ever	about	again	another
couple	awake	over	asleep	above

Complete the Sentences Write a Basic Word that fits each sentence.

1. I would like _____ glass of milk.

2. Have you _____ met my parents?

3. I will leave the door _____ for you.

4. The ball sailed right _____ the wall.

5. Your name is on the list, right _____ mine.

6. I have seen that movie, but I would like to see it _____.

7. My friends and I should be ready to go in a _____ of minutes.

Complete the Story Write Basic Words to complete the story.

Yesterday, I went to the Stone Zoo. I had __8.__ been there before. I had heard all __9.__ it, though. Everyone said it was a great place to visit. I wanted to see my favorite __10.__, the lion. We had studied lions and other wild creatures in school. I was worried he would be __11.__ when I got there. But he was wide __12.__! When he stood __13.__ a rock and roared, I felt a little __14.__. I was glad there was a high fence all __15.__ his area.

Spelling and Writing

 ## Proofread an E-Mail Message

First, proofread the e-mail message below for eight misspelled words. Then rewrite the message. Write the spelling words correctly and make the corrections shown by the proofreading marks.

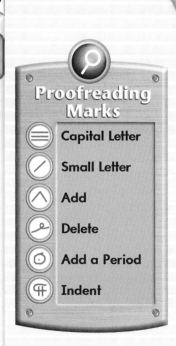

Proofreading Marks

≡	Capital Letter
/	Small Letter
∧	Add
⤺	Delete
⊙	Add a Period
¶	Indent

To: SteinJ@mail.net.com

From: Joshboy27@kids.net

Subject: My Baseball Team

Dear Uncle Jake∧

I had anothur great year in baseball. The regular

Season is overr. My team is in the playoffs agen in

a cupple of weeks. My Team nevur, evur gives up.

See you at Lum Field uround noon. after the game,

I will tell you abowt our season⊙

Your nephew,

josh

More Practice Write and sort the Basic Words.

Write an E-Mail Message

Invite a friend or an adult to come see you in a game, play, or other event. Include the day, the time, and the place. Use as many spelling words as you can.

Writing Process

Prewrite
⌄
Draft
⌄
Revise
⌄
Edit
⌄
Publish

Proofread your writing as you

When you finish writing your draft, proofread your paper for errors in spelling, grammar, capitalization, and punctuation. Use the **Spelling Dictionary** to check spelling if you are not sure.

◎ **Review**

Review

Word Clues

_____

1. _____

2. _____

3. _____

4. _____

Complete the Sentences

5. _____

6. _____

7. _____

8. _____

Idioms

1. _____

model	planted	seven	wagon

Word Clues Write the Review Word that matches each clue.

1. This word has the **schwa** sound spelled **o**.

2. This word ends with the **schwa** sound and the letter **l**.

3. This word rhymes with **chanted**.

4. This word has a **short e** sound and the **schwa** sound spelled **e**.

Complete the Sentences Write a Review Word to complete each sentence.

5. The farmer loaded vegetables into the _____.

6. Mrs. Wendell _____ yellow flowers in her yard this year.

7. There are _____ days in a week.

8. The _____ of the ship is only 10 inches long.

Word Study: Idioms

● An **idiom** is a saying that doesn't mean what the words in it say. **Raining cats and dogs** means that it is raining very hard. Write one Challenge Word to finish all these sayings: **in deep _____; in hot _____; tread _____.**

Challenge

agree	alarm	tractor	water

Word Groups Write the Challenge Word that belongs in each group.

1. mower, plow, thresher, _____

2. soil, air, _____

3. nod, say yes, _____

4. bell, beeper, buzzer, _____

Complete the Paragraph Write the Challenge Words to complete the paragraph.

The three men heard the __5.__ sound loudly and ran out to the fields. Fire was burning through the dry corn stalks and getting close to the __6.__, which was parked near the barn! They all ran to get __7.__ to put out the fire. When it was finally out, the men could not __8.__ on what had started the fire.

Do you think you've mastered the Spelling Strategy? Take the CHAMPION CHALLENGE on page 299!

Challenge

Word Groups

1.

2.

3.

4.

Complete the Paragraph

5.

6.

7.

8.

Spelling and Technology

Spelling and Technology

Web Home Pages

1.

2.

3.

4.

Web Home Pages

How do you get to a Web site? You type in its address, or URL. Often, you will visit the home page of a site before you visit other pages. The home page is the main page. From there it is usually easy to reach all the other pages.

When you reach a Web page, you may want to make it bigger. You do this by clicking on a corner. Then you drag the edge until the page fills your screen.

| corner | home page | site | URL |

Write a word from the box for each clue. Underline the word with the **schwa** sound.

1. I am the address of a site on the Web.

2. I am the main page of a Web site.

3. I am a location on the Web.

4. I am part of a page that you can click and drag.

Content Words

Link to **Language Arts:** Time

Write the Content Word that answers each question.

tomorrow	tonight	yesterday	today

1. What is the day that came before today?
2. What is the day that will come after today?
3. What do you call the day you are in right now?
4. What is today when the sun goes down?

Link to **Science:** Animal Names

Write the Content Word that matches each clue.

beaver	rabbit	raccoon	skunk

5. animal with sharp teeth that builds dams
6. animal with markings that look like a mask
7. animal that defends itself with a bad smell
8. animal that has long ears and soft fur

Link to **The Spelling Strategy**

Circle the letter that spells the **schwa** sound in two of the Content Words you wrote.

Content Connection: Science

You can find more animal names at **www.nationalzoo.si.edu**. Click on **Kids**. Write the names of animals you find.

Content Words

Language Arts: Time

1. _____

2. _____

3. _____

4. _____

Science: Animal Names

5. _____

6. _____

7. _____

8. _____

Spelling Connections Online
www.zaner-bloser.com

one syllable

1.

2.

3.

4.

5.

6.

7.

8.

two syllables

9.

10.

11.

12.

13.

14.

15.

Spelling and Thinking

READ the Basic Words 👀 Watch out for easily misspelled words!

👀 **1.** friend   *friend*   I play with my **friend** Jonathan.

2. very   *very*   That is a **very** tall building.

👀 **3.** people   *people*   Many **people** wait in line for tickets.

4. your   *your*   I will give you **your** present.

5. after   *after*   We have gym **after** lunch.

👀 **6.** busy   *busy*   The **busy** woman worked two jobs.

7. other   *other*   What **other** books have you read?

8. were   *were*   We **were** sleeping when Abe visited.

9. should   *should*   You **should** take off your hat in school.

10. once   *once*   I will ask you this just **once**.

11. would   *would*   No one **would** do such a mean thing.

12. sure   *sure*   Are you **sure** you forgot the key?

13. little   *little*   The **little** boy cried for his mom.

14. every   *every*   Ted ate **every** bite of his dinner.

15. could   *could*   We **could** ride our bikes to the park.

◎ **Review**	
16. any	18. myself
17. does	19. said

◎ **Challenge**	
20. between	22. however
21. either	23. though

SORT the Basic Words

1–8. Write the words with one syllable.

9–15. Write the words with two syllables. Draw a line between the syllables.

REMEMBER the Spelling Strategy

Remember that it is important to learn the spellings of words that writers often misspell.

Word Analysis

Write the Basic Word for each clue.

1. This word is inside **another**.
2. It has the /**sh**/ sound and ends with a vowel.
3. In this word, the letters **ie** spell the **short e** sound.
4. It begins with **sh** and rhymes with **could**.
5. It has the /**k**/ sound but no letter **k**.
6. It sounds the same as the word **wood**.
7. It has two syllables. Both begin with the same consonant.

Word Groups

Write the Basic Word that belongs in each group.

8. all, each, _____
9. really, a lot, _____
10. later, behind, _____
11. small, tiny, _____
12. twice, never, _____
13. my, his, her, their, _____

Using the Dictionary

Write the Basic Word that would be on the same page as these guide words.

14. weigh • work
15. bunny • caterpillar

Dictionary Check Be sure to check the a-b-c order of the words in your **Spelling Dictionary**.

Word Analysis

1.
2.
3.
4.
5.
6.
7.

Word Groups

8.
9.
10.
11.
12.
13.

Using the Dictionary

14.
15.

friend	very	people	your	after
busy	other	were	should	once
would	sure	little	every	could

Complete the Paragraph

1.

2.

3.

4.

5.

6.

7.

8.

Complete the Paragraph Write the Basic Words to complete the paragraph.

You __1.__ read about Clara Barton in __2.__ history books. During her lifetime, Clara Barton was a __3.__ woman. She was a teacher, a nurse, and the founder of the American Red Cross. During the Civil War, she __4.__ go out on the battlefield while soldiers __5.__ still shooting at each __6.__. Even after the war ended, she knew she __7.__ do more to help __8.__. That is when she started the American Red Cross.

Replace the Words

9.

10.

11.

12.

13.

14.

15.

Replace the Words Replace the underlined part of each sentence with a Basic Word.

9. Heather was <u>certain</u> that she had won.
10. Rico is <u>quite</u> proud of his garden.
11. I forgot to study for my spelling test just <u>one time</u>.
12. John is a <u>person I know and like</u>.
13. He knocked on <u>each</u> door.
14. That <u>small</u> dog has a big bark!
15. We will eat dessert <u>following</u> dinner.

Spelling and Writing

 ## Proofread a Poem

First, proofread the poem below for eight misspelled words. Then rewrite the poem. Write the spelling words correctly and make the corrections shown by the proofreading marks.

A Kinder Place to Live

I think peeple shood be kind.

I know if if they wer we woud find

This world a verry nice place to live,

if we cood all just Learn to give.

Affter you try this onse, you will see

That the world is a happier place to be.

More Practice Write and sort the Basic Words.

Write a Personal Narrative

What have you done to make the world a kinder or better place to live? Tell about something you have done that helped someone. Include how you got the chance to help and what you did. Write how you were helpful to the person. Use as many spelling words as you can.

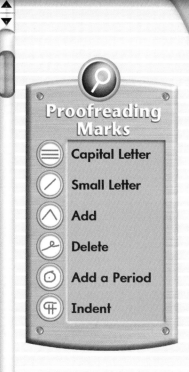

Proofreading Marks

≡	Capital Letter
/	Small Letter
∧	Add
✐	Delete
⊙	Add a Period
¶	Indent

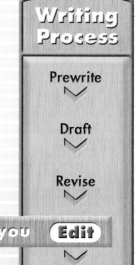

Writing Process

Prewrite

Draft

Revise

Edit

Publish

 Proofread your writing as you Edit

When you finish writing your draft, proofread your paper for errors in spelling, grammar, capitalization, and punctuation. Use the **Spelling Dictionary** to check spelling if you are not sure.

◎ Review

Review

Solve the Analogies

1. _____

2. _____

3. _____

4. _____

Complete the Paragraph

5. _____

6. _____

7. _____

8. _____

Writer's Tip

1. _____

any	does	myself	said

Solve the Analogies Write a Review Word to complete each analogy.

1. **You** is to **yourself** as **me** is to _____.

2. **Mark** is to **ark** as **many** is to _____.

3. **Go** is to **goes** as **do** is to _____.

4. **Ask** is to **asked** as **say** is to _____.

Complete the Paragraph Write the Review Words to complete the paragraph.

My sister never asks for __**5.**__ help with her homework. She always __**6.**__ it by herself when she gets home. She __**7.**__ that she works better by herself. But I thought to __**8.**__ that sometimes it is good to ask for help.

Word Study: Writer's Tip

• Good writers use a variety of words instead of using the same word over and over. Write the Review Word that is an overused synonym for **told, exclaimed,** and **answered**.

Challenge

between	either	however	though

Word Clues Write the Challenge Word that fits each clue.

1. This word has one syllable.
2. This word has three syllables.
3. This word has two syllables and the **schwa** sound.
4. This word has the **long e** sound in the second syllable.

Complete the Sentences Write a Challenge Word to complete each sentence.

5. _____ she likes to paint, Amina did not sign up for art class.
6. Marco stood _____ the tall trees and looked up at the blue sky.
7. The student was late to class; _____, he had a very good reason.
8. We can choose _____ chicken or fish for dinner tonight.

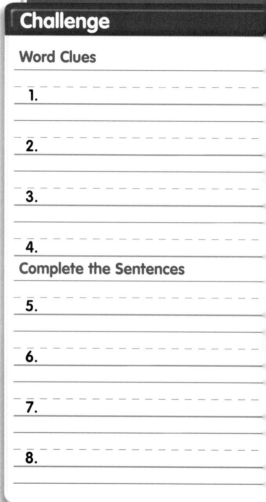

Challenge

Word Clues

1.
2.
3.
4.

Complete the Sentences

5.
6.
7.
8.

Do you think you've mastered the Spelling Strategy? Take the **CHAMPION CHALLENGE** on page 300!

enrichment

Spelling and Technology

Spelling and Technology

Make a Web Search More Exact

1. _____

2. _____

3. _____

4. _____

Make a Web Search More Exact

How can you be sure your search gives you the information you want? There are ways to make a search more exact. Look at these search boxes. They show a phrase with a plus or minus sign.

Select Search Category:	Web	Images	Video
Search the Web:	map USA + Alaska		Search

This search tells the engine that your results must include the word **Alaska**.

Select Search Category:	Web	Images	Video
Search the Web:	map USA − Hawaii		Search

This search tells the engine that your results should not include the word **Hawaii**.

Learn these words for making a search more exact.

minus	narrow	phrase	plus

Write a word from the box for each dictionary respelling.

1. /frāz/   **3.** /mī′ nəs/

2. /plŭs/   **4.** /năr′ ō/

Content Words

Link to **Language Arts:** Titles

Write the Content Word that completes each sentence.

Miss	Mrs.	Mr.	Ms.

1. The man's name tag said _____ Chang.
2. Carol believes that all women should have the same title. She calls herself _____ O'Roarke.
3. Mr. Diaz introduced his wife, _____ Diaz.
4. Amy Li is not married and calls herself _____ Li.

Link to **Social Studies:** Geography

Write the Content Word that matches each definition.

cliff	steep	peak	ledge

5. rising or falling sharply
6. the pointed top of a mountain
7. a high face of rock
8. a rim or edge

Link to **The Spelling Strategy**

Circle the capital letters in four of the Content Words you wrote.

Content Connection: Social Studies

 Search this Internet site to find out more about geography: www.funbrain.com/where. Play a map game. Write the names of two states or countries that you identify.

Content Words

Language Arts: Titles

1. _____
2. _____
3. _____
4. _____

Social Studies: Geography

5. _____
6. _____
7. _____
8. _____

Spelling Connections Online
www.zaner-bloser.com

Unit 13

1. _____

2. _____

3. _____

4. _____

5. _____

Unit 14

6. _____

7. _____

8. _____

9. _____

Unit 15

10. _____

11. _____

12. _____

Unit 16

13. _____

14. _____

15. _____

Assessment and Review

ASSESSMENT

Units 13–17

Read the spelling strategies below. Then write each Assessment Word under the unit number it fits.

Unit 13

1–5. Two consonants together can spell a single sound: **wr** in **wrap** and **ck** in **thick**. Two or more consonants can spell new sounds called **consonant digraphs: ch** in **chase, sh** in **shape, th** in **mother,** and **tch** in **watch**.

Unit 14

6–9. The /j/ sound in **age** is spelled **g**, followed by **e**. The /s/ sound in **ice** and **city** is spelled **c**. The **c** is followed by **e** (**ice**) or by **i** (**city**).

Unit 15

10–12. Consonant digraphs are two or more consonants together that spell one new sound: **sh** in **shook. Consonant clusters** are two or more consonants together that make more than one sound: **br** in **brook**.

Unit 16

13–15. The **schwa** sound can be spelled: **a** in **about, u** in **upon,** and **e** in **over**.

Unit 17

It is important to learn the spellings of words that writers often misspell.

blush

charm

cage

wren

await

gem

stung

apron

pitch

brace

stack

flood

aside

patch

rage

REVIEW

Unit 13: sh, ch, tch, th, wr, ck

| father | finish | mother | write | shall | watch | check |

Write the spelling word for each meaning.

1. to end
2. to make letters with a pencil or pen
3. a clock for your wrist
4. a mark for record keeping
5. female parent
6. male parent
7. another word for **will**

REVIEW

Unit 14: Consonants: /j/, /s/

| change | place | large | since | dance | age | city |

Write the spelling word that completes each sentence.

8. New York is a _____ city.
9. A _____ is larger than a town.
10. I have been out of school ever _____ I caught this bad cold.
11. It is time to _____ the towels.
12. This is the _____ where you should stand.
13. Most children in our town enter school at the _____ of five or six.
14. I love to _____ to that music.

Unit 13

1.
2.
3.
4.
5.
6.
7.

Unit 14

8.
9.
10.
11.
12.
13.
14.

1. _____

2. _____

3. _____

4. _____

5. _____

6. _____

7. _____

8. _____

9. _____

10. _____

11. _____

12. _____

13. _____

14. _____

REVIEW

Unit 15: Digraphs, Clusters

splash   strong   stretch   think   speech   cloth   shook

Write the spelling word that rhymes with the underlined word and will complete the sentence.

1. After a <u>dash</u>, I made a _____.
2. This stick is <u>long</u> and very _____.
3. I _____ I will throw this in the <u>sink</u>.
4. He <u>took</u> the jar and _____ out the beans.
5. The creature's _____ sounded like a <u>screech</u>!
6. She got up to _____ after she finished her <u>sketch</u>.
7. Oh, no! There's a <u>moth</u> in the _____.

REVIEW

Unit 16: The Schwa Sound

again   another   animal   around   about   open   never

Each spelling word is missing letters. Write each spelling word.

8. ___gain
9. an___m___l
10. ___round
11. ___bout

Write a spelling word for each of these clues.

12. It has two syllables. The first syllable is the **long o** sound.
13. The letter **e** is found in both syllables.
14. The words **not, the,** and **her** can be found in this word.

Unit 17: Words Writers Use

friend	people	once	would	other	were	could

Write the spelling word that completes each sentence.

1. The girls _____ like to go.

2. Many _____ waited for the bus.

3. That person is my good _____.

4. She was sure that she _____ do it.

5. Bring me the _____ book, not that one.

6. Where _____ you going yesterday?

7. Many stories begin with "_____ upon a time."

1. _____
2. _____
3. _____
4. _____
5. _____
6. _____
7. _____

GAME

Spelling Study Strategy

Spelling Tic-Tac-Toe

Practicing spelling words can be fun if you make it into a game.

1. Write your spelling words in a list. Ask your friend to do the same. Trade spelling lists.

2. Draw a tic-tac-toe board on a scrap of paper. Decide who will use **X** and who will use **O**.

3. Ask your partner to call the first word on your spelling list to you. Spell it out loud. If you spell it correctly, make an **X** or an **O** (whichever you are using) on the tic-tac-toe board. If you misspell the word, ask your partner to spell it out loud for you. In that case, you miss your turn.

4. Now call a word from your partner's list. Play until one of you makes "tic-tac-toe."

Writer's Workshop

Practice Activity

A.

1.

2.

3.

4.

5.

B.

6.

7.

8.

9.

10.

Grammar, Usage, and Mechanics

Action Verbs

An **action verb** tells what the subject of a sentence does or did.

Ellen **caught** the ball.

The dog **barked** at the men.

The whistle **blows** at noon.

Practice ACTIVITY

A. Write the action verb in these sentences.

1. Her large dog jumped on the couch.
2. The bell rang earlier than usual today.
3. Fish swam around inside the tank.
4. We planted flowers around the porch.
5. Ben sang in the school choir.

B. Write an action verb from the box to complete each sentence.

| open | catch | shook | dance | write |

6. Juanita will _____ a letter to Dan tomorrow.
7. The stores _____ at noon today.
8. Let's _____ to this music!
9. The wind _____ the tree's branches.
10. He can _____ the baseball.

The Writing Process — DESCRIPTIVE

Writing a Descriptive Paragraph

● Prewriting

Choose a country you would like to visit. Write down words and phrases that describe things you could see, hear, taste, touch, or smell in this place. You can find facts about new places in books at the library. An adult can help you learn about places on Internet sites such as www.geographia.com .

● Drafting

Use your list to write a descriptive paragraph. Describe the place using the five senses. Use as many spelling words as possible.

● Revising

When you have finished your first draft, read your paragraph from beginning to end. Check to make sure that you included many describing words. Now, write your final draft.

● Editing ✓

Use the editing checklist to proofread your paragraph. Be sure to use proofreading marks when you make corrections.

● Publishing

Make a copy of your descriptive paragraph. Include a drawing or map of the place you wrote about and share it with your readers.

✓ Editing Checklist

Spelling

○ I circled words that contain the spelling strategies I learned in Units 13–17.

○ I checked the circled words in my Spelling Dictionary.

○ I also checked for other spelling errors.

Capital Letters

○ Important words in the title

○ Beginning of all sentences

○ Proper nouns

Punctuation

○ Each sentence ends with the correct punctuation.

○ Commas, apostrophes, and quotation marks are used correctly.

Grammar, Usage, and Mechanics

○ Each action verb tells what the subject of a sentence does or did.

Spelling and Thinking

aw

1. _____

2. _____

3. _____

4. _____

5. _____

6. _____

7. _____

o

8. _____

9. _____

10. _____

11. _____

12. _____

13. _____

14. _____

15. _____

READ the Basic Words 👀 Watch out for easily misspelled words!

1. draw	*draw*	I **draw** pictures of my dog.
2. cost	*cost*	The **cost** of that hat is five dollars.
3. dawn	*dawn*	It is dark and chilly at **dawn**.
👀 4. across	*across*	Aaron lives **across** the street.
5. belong	*belong*	Do you **belong** to that club?
6. cross	*cross*	Be careful when you **cross** the street.
7. soft	*soft*	This pillow is very **soft**.
👀 8. crawl	*crawl*	The baby is learning to **crawl**.
9. song	*song*	We will sing a **song** together.
10. boss	*boss*	The **boss** hired her for the new job.
11. straw	*straw*	Sip your drink through this **straw**.
👀 12. lawn	*lawn*	That **lawn** is thick and green.
13. raw	*raw*	Never eat **raw** meat or eggs.
14. lost	*lost*	We **lost** the ball in the woods.
15. law	*law*	Everyone must obey the **law**.

⦿ **Review**	
16. dog	18. moth
17. jaw	19. saw

⦿ **Challenge**	
20. because	22. caught
21. bought	23. haul

SORT the Basic Words

1–7. Write the words that spell the /ô/ sound **aw**.

8–15. Write the words that spell the /ô/ sound **o**.

REMEMBER the Spelling Strategy

Remember that the vowel sound you hear in **song** and **lawn** is spelled in different ways: **o** in **song** and **aw** in **lawn**.

Spelling and Phonics

Word Structure

1. Change one letter in **long** to make a Basic Word.

2. Change the last two letters in **code** to make a Basic Word.

3. Change the last two letters in **crook** to make a Basic Word.

4. Change two letters in **late** to make a Basic Word.

5. Change two letters in **base** to make a Basic Word.

Sounds and Meanings

Write the Basic Word that rhymes with the first word and is a synonym for the second word.

6. stall   creep

7. gone   sunrise

8. saw   uncooked

9. paw   hay

10. saw   sketch

11. paw   rule

Using the Dictionary

Write the Basic Word that would be on the same page as these pairs of guide words.

12. liter • mainly

13. smooth • spring

14. bear • blood

15. about • anything

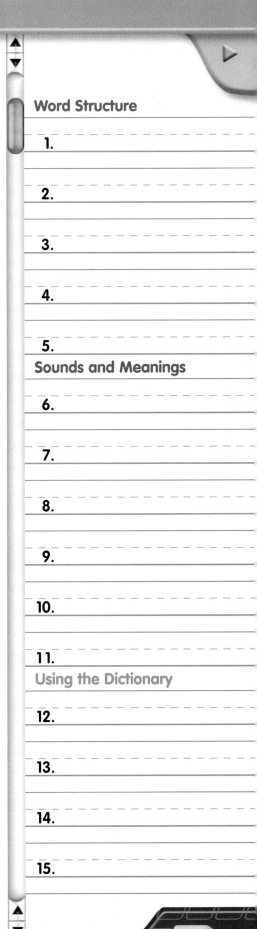

Word Structure

1.

2.

3.

4.

5.

Sounds and Meanings

6.

7.

8.

9.

10.

11.

Using the Dictionary

12.

13.

14.

15.

Spelling and Reading

draw	cost	dawn	across	belong
cross	soft	crawl	song	boss
straw	lawn	raw	lost	law

Solve the Analogies

1.

2.

3.

4.

Complete the Sentences

5.

6.

7.

8.

9.

10.

11.

12.

Replace the Words

13.

14.

15.

Solve the Analogies Write the Basic Word that completes each analogy.

1. Read is to **story** as **sing** is to _____.

2. Student is to **teacher** as **worker** is to _____.

3. Dot is to **i** as _____ is to **t**.

4. Follow is to **rule** as **obey** is to _____.

Complete the Sentences Write the Basic Word that completes each sentence.

5. It is not easy to _____ a map.

6. My horse likes to eat _____ carrots.

7. I saw a scarecrow made of _____.

8. A smile spread _____ his face.

9. Does that scarf _____ to you?

10. Caterpillars _____ very slowly.

11. How much did that flashlight _____?

12. It is Dana's job to mow the _____.

Replace the Words Replace the underlined word with a Basic Word. The Basic Word will mean the opposite of the underlined word.

13. It was easy to dig a hole for the plant in the <u>hard</u>, wet ground.

14. Even though Jacob had no idea where we were, he would not admit he had <u>found</u> his way.

15. I enjoy getting up at <u>sunset</u> and jogging on the beach.

Spelling and Writing

Proofread a Book Report

Proofread the book report below for eight misspelled words. Then rewrite the book report. Write the spelling words correctly and make the corrections shown by the proofreading marks.

¶ You should read <u>Arthur's Pet Business</u>. It is by Marc Brown. He also drause all the pictures. In this book, Arthur wants to get a job⊙ Instead of cutting someone's lawne or babysitting, Arthur becomes his own bowss. He watches pets that belowng to other people. They pay what he says it will cawst. One pet gets lawst. arthur has to crowl around looking for it. He finds the Pet. He also finds something new and saft! This book is fun to read.

More Practice Write and sort the Basic Words.

Write a Book Report

Think of a book you enjoyed. Tell why a friend should read it. Be sure to include the title, the author, and one or more reasons to read the book. Use as many spelling words as you can.

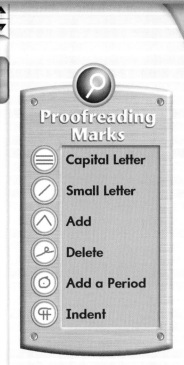

Proofreading Marks

≡	Capital Letter
/	Small Letter
∧	Add
✀	Delete
⊙	Add a Period
¶	Indent

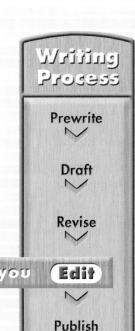

Writing Process

Prewrite
⌄
Draft
⌄
Revise
⌄
Edit
⌄
Publish

> Proofread your writing as you **Edit**

When you finish writing your draft, proofread your paper for errors in spelling, grammar, capitalization, and punctuation. Use the **Spelling Dictionary** to check spelling if you are not sure.

◎ Review

| dog | jaw | moth | saw |

Word Clues Write a Review Word for each clue.

1. This word begins like **job** and ends like **law**.
2. This word rhymes with **hog**.
3. This word begins like **see** and ends like **raw**.
4. This word ends with **th**.

Solve the Analogies Write a Review Word to complete each analogy.

5. **Leopard** is to **panther** as **butterfly** is to _____.
6. **Scale** is to **fish** as **fur** is to _____.
7. **Ring** is to **rang** as **see** is to _____.
8. **Leg** is to **knee** as **face** is to _____.

 **Challenge**

| because | bought | caught | haul |

Word Structure Follow the directions to write a Challenge Word.

1. bite – ite + ought = _____

2. hate – te + ul = _____

3. before – fore + cause = _____

4. catch – tch + ught = _____

Complete the Sentences Write a Challenge Word to complete each sentence.

5. We _____ five fish this weekend at the lake.

6. He doesn't like winter _____ he hates cold weather.

7. Please help me _____ this heavy box up the stairs.

8. After she _____ her lunch, she returned to work.

Challenge

Word Structure

1. _____

2. _____

3. _____

4. _____

Complete the Sentences

5. _____

6. _____

7. _____

8. _____

 Do you think you've mastered the Spelling Strategy? Take the CHAMPION CHALLENGE on page 301!

Spelling and Technology

Spelling and Technology

Answer Your E-Mail

1. _____

2. _____

3. _____

4. _____

Answer Your E-Mail

Got mail? Then it's time to reply.

Suppose you received an e-mail from Max, and he sent a copy to Dan. Here are four ways to reply:

reply all: send your answer to Max and Dan

forward: send Max's message to someone new

cc: send your reply to Max and someone new

bcc: send your reply to Max and someone else without letting Max know

Learn these terms for e-mail.

bcc	cc	forward	reply all

Write the word from the box that matches each clue. Underline the word with the /ô/ sound.

1. I answered Hannah's e-mail and sent a copy to everyone else Hannah wrote to.

2. I answered Hannah and sent a copy to Max, but Hannah doesn't know that.

3. I sent Hannah's message on to Tina.

4. I answered Hannah and sent a copy to Jan.

Content Words

Link to **Language Arts:** Exact Meanings

Write the Content Word that best replaces each group of underlined words.

rushed	paced	dawdled	dashed

1. Rosa <u>took more time than necessary</u> on the way home.
2. The runner <u>went quickly</u> across the finish line.
3. Todd <u>went with sudden speed</u> to the bus station.
4. The lions <u>went back and forth</u> in the cage.

Link to **Health:** Teeth

Write Content Words to complete the paragraph.

cavity	filling	flossing	crown

Proper brushing and __5.__ will keep your teeth and gums healthy. If you do get a __6.__ in the __7.__ of your tooth, the dentist can give you a __8.__.

Link to **The Spelling Strategy**

Circle the letters that spell the /ô/ sound in two of the Content Words you wrote.

Content Connection: Health

Search the Internet to find out more about teeth. You might look at **www.adha.org**. Click on **Kidstuff**. Write a fact you learn there.

Content Words

Language Arts: Exact Meanings

1. _____

2. _____

3. _____

4. _____

Health: Teeth

5. _____

6. _____

7. _____

8. _____

Spelling Connections Online
www.zaner-bloser.com

Spelling and Thinking

READ the Basic Words 👀 Watch out for easily misspelled words!

1.	story	*story*	Please read me that **story**.
2.	wore	*wore*	Jen **wore** a red dress to the party.
3.	north	*north*	We will head **north** to Canada.
👀 4.	board	*board*	That **board** in the floor is loose.
5.	form	*form*	You can **form** the clay into any shape.
6.	corner	*corner*	Turn left at the next **corner**.
7.	warm	*warm*	You can **warm** up by the fire.
8.	score	*score*	Did Penny **score** the winning goal?
👀 9.	morning	*morning*	Dad gets up early each **morning**.
10.	forget	*forget*	I will not **forget** to drink my milk.
👀 11.	before	*before*	We brush our teeth **before** bed.
12.	storm	*storm*	The noise of the **storm** scared Spot.
13.	tore	*tore*	Matt **tore** his new pants in the game.
14.	order	*order*	May I **order** a hamburger?
15.	war	*war*	We fight the **war** against pollution.

◎ Review			◎ Challenge	
16. corn	18. more		20. forest	22. report
17. horse	19. short		21. forty	23. sport

SORT the Basic Words

Write the words that spell the /ôr/ sound

1–4. ore.   13–14. ar.

5–12. or.   15. oar.

REMEMBER the Spelling Strategy

The vowel sound you hear in **form** is spelled in different ways: **or** in **form**, **ore** in **tore**, **oar** in **board**, and **ar** in **warm**.

ore

1.
2.
3.
4.
or
5.
6.
7.
8.
9.
10.
11.
12.
ar
13.
14.
oar
15.

Spelling and Phonics

Sound and Letter Patterns

Write Basic Words by adding the missing letters.

1. w __ re

2. t __ r __

3. f __ r __

4. __ t __ rm

5. sc __ r __

6. c __ rn __ r

Word Meanings

Write the Basic Word that means the opposite of the underlined word in each sentence below.

7. Judy was a soldier when her country was at <u>peace</u>.

8. The train was traveling <u>south</u>.

9. We will leave early in the <u>evening</u>.

10. Mary arrived <u>after</u> everyone else.

11. Did you <u>remember</u> to bring the map?

12. There was a <u>cool</u> breeze blowing across the lake.

Using the Dictionary

The dictionary lists the part of speech for each entry word after the respelling.

> morn•ing /**môr′** nĭng/, *n.*

Write each word with its part of speech.

13. story   **14.** board   **15.** order

Sound and Letter Patterns

1.

2.

3.

4.

5.

6.

Word Meanings

7.

8.

9.

10.

11.

12.

Using the Dictionary

13.

14.

15.

story	wore	north	board	form
corner	warm	score	morning	forget
before	storm	tore	order	war

Name the Categories

1.

2.

3.

4.

Complete the Sentences

5.

6.

7.

8.

9.

10.

11.

12.

13.

14.

15.

Name the Categories Write the Basic Word that could name each item in each group.

1. two to one, 23–14, nine to nothing

2. hot dog and fries, one garden salad

3. "Cinderella," "The Three Little Pigs," "Snow White and the Seven Dwarfs"

4. Main Street and Elm Street, Broadway and 34th Street, Michigan Avenue and Rush Street

Complete the Sentences Write the Basic Word that fits each sentence.

5. Kevin _____ a blue sweater and a new pair of shoes to school today.

6. Julie _____ her jacket on the fence at recess.

7. May we have this _____ to finish building our tree house?

8. The boat was damaged during the _____.

9. The dripping water will _____ icicles when it freezes in the cold weather.

10. Ed did not _____ to put a stamp on the letter.

11. I will give you the book _____ you go.

12. Ryan plays tennis in _____ weather.

13. The train tracks are _____ of our house.

14. I hope to see my grandmother bright and early tomorrow _____.

15. My grandfather fought in that _____.

Spelling and Writing

Proofread a Story Beginning

First, proofread the paragraph below for eight misspelled words. Then rewrite the paragraph. Write the spelling words correctly and make the corrections shown by the proofreading marks.

¶ It was early in the morening when Juanita and Tim headed noarth on their search. they woare their old clothes because a storme was coming. They did not forgett their hats. As they they turned the last coarner at the edge of town, they saw a man running down the street. He kept looking nervously behind him. He tripped and tor his pants. Befor juanita and Tim could say anything, the Man was gone.

More Practice Write and sort the Basic Words.

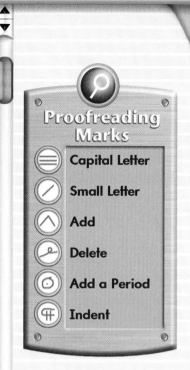

Proofreading Marks

≡	Capital Letter
/	Small Letter
∧	Add
✎	Delete
⊙	Add a Period
¶	Indent

NARRATIVE

Write a Story Beginning

Begin a story in an interesting way. Include a hint of mystery, as the writer does above. Be sure to tell who is in your story and something about the time and place. Write the beginning of the action. Use as many spelling words as you can.

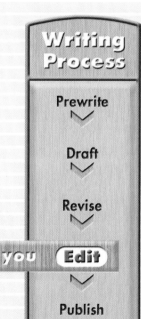

Writing Process

Prewrite

∨

Draft

∨

Revise

∨

Edit

∨

Publish

> > > > > Proofread your writing as you **Edit**

When you finish writing your draft, proofread your paper for errors in spelling, grammar, capitalization, and punctuation. Use the **Spelling Dictionary** to check spelling if you are not sure.

◉ Review

Review

Word Groups

1. _____

2. _____

3. _____

4. _____

Complete the Paragraph

5. _____

6. _____

7. _____

8. _____

Word Roots

1. _____

---

corn	horse	more	short

Word Groups Write a Review Word to complete each group.

1. wheat, rice, _____
2. plus, in addition, _____
3. small, little, _____
4. goat, cow, donkey, _____

Complete the Paragraph Write the Review Words to complete the paragraph.

The rancher got down from his __5.__ and led the animal to the stream. It had only been a __6.__ ride, but the day was hot. He refilled his canteen with __7.__ water, then untied the sack of __8.__ from the animal's back.

Word Study: Word Roots

● **Port** was an old word that meant "to carry back" or "to carry information." Write the Challenge Word that is related to this word root and means "a written account."

Challenge

| forest | forty | report | sport |

Word Structure Replace the underlined letter or letters to write a Challenge Word.

1. Soccer is my favorite s<u>h</u>ort.

2. The teacher asked us to write a rep<u>air</u>.

3. Can you swim across the pool f<u>i</u>fty times?

4. We enjoyed hiking through the <u>ar</u>rest.

Complete the Sentences Write a Challenge Word to complete each sentence.

5. Johan's favorite _____ is skiing.

6. _____ students will go on the trip to New York.

7. Cathy walked through the _____ and listened to the birds.

8. Leo got an excellent grade on his _____.

Challenge

Word Structure

1.

2.

3.

4.

Complete the Sentences

5.

6.

7.

8.

Do you think you've mastered the Spelling Strategy? Take the CHAMPION CHALLENGE on page 302!

Spelling and Technology

Spelling and Technology

Internet Safety

1. _____

2. _____

3. _____

4. _____

Internet Safety

Read the paragraph below. Think about the meanings of the words in dark print.

The Internet isn't always safe! One place to find trouble is on **message boards**. Many strangers go to message boards. Some people **troll** there. That means they post things hoping to trick others into replying. Some people on message boards **forge**, or make up, their names or other facts. Some people also send **spam**, which is unwanted or junk mail. Stay safe on the Net! Remember never to tell anyone your name, address, or phone number.

Learn these terms for Internet safety.

forge	message board	spam	troll

Write the term from the box to complete each sentence. Underline the words that have an /ôr/ sound.

1. Anyone can post information on a _____.

2. Some people _____ for replies on discussion boards.

3. Don't open e-mail that you think is _____.

4. People can easily _____ their names on the Internet.

Content Words

Link to **Science:** Plants

Write the Content Word that matches each definition.

branch	thorn	stem	twig

1. sharp point on a plant
2. small branch
3. large part of a tree that comes out from the trunk
4. slender part of a plant that supports a leaf, fruit, or flower

Link to **Math:** Relationships

Write the Content Word that completes each sentence.

even	plus	odd	minus

5. Two _____ seven equals nine.
6. All _____ numbers end in 1, 3, 5, 7, or 9.
7. All _____ numbers end in 2, 4, 6, 8, or 0.
8. Eleven _____ four equals seven.

Link to **The Spelling Strategy**

Circle the letters that spell the /ôr/ sound in one of the Content Words you wrote.

Content Connection: Science

 Search the Internet to learn more about plants. You might look at http://mbgnet.mobot.org. Choose a plant place, or biome. Write the name of a plant that grows there.

Content Words

Science: Plants

1.

2.

3.

4.

Math: Relationships

5.

6.

7.

8.

Spelling Connections Online
www.zaner-bloser.com

Spelling and Thinking

or

1. _____

2. _____

ur

3. _____

4. _____

5. _____

6. _____

ear

7. _____

8. _____

9. _____

10. _____

11. _____

ir

12. _____

13. _____

14. _____

15. _____

READ the Basic Words 👀 Watch out for easily misspelled words!

1. word	*word*	Be very quiet and do not say a **word**.
👀 **2.** fur	*fur*	Maria brushed her puppy's soft **fur**.
👀 **3.** early	*early*	We get up **early** to go to school.
4. circus	*circus*	Keiko saw clowns at the **circus**.
5. turn	*turn*	We took a left **turn** at the stop sign.
6. skirt	*skirt*	I wore my new **skirt** and sweater.
7. earth	*earth*	The **earth** was too wet for planting.
8. work	*work*	They **work** hard caring for the crops.
9. curl	*curl*	How do I **curl** my hair?
10. learn	*learn*	Dad will **learn** to use my computer.
11. hurt	*hurt*	The boy **hurt** his knee when he fell.
12. dirt	*dirt*	Bill digs in the **dirt** for worms.
13. earn	*earn*	The class will **earn** money.
14. shirt	*shirt*	Juan lost a button on his **shirt**.
👀 **15.** heard	*heard*	Tyler **heard** his mother calling him.

Review
16. birds
17. chirp
18. girls
19. nurse

Challenge
20. firm
21. return
22. thirst
23. turkey

SORT the Basic Words

1–2. Write the words with the /ûr/ sound spelled **or**.

3–6. Write the words with the /ûr/ sound spelled **ur**.

7–11. Write the words with the /ûr/ sound spelled **ear**.

12–15. Write the words with the /ûr/ sound spelled **ir**.

REMEMBER the Spelling Strategy

Remember that the vowel sound in **fur** is spelled in different ways: **ur** in **fur**, **ear** in **earn**, **or** in **word**, and **ir** in **dirt**.

Spelling and Phonics

Word Analysis

Write the Basic Words for these clues.

1–2. These two words rhyme with **fern** but spell the /ûr/ sound **ear**.

3. This word rhymes with **pearl** but spells the /ûr/ sound **ur**.

4. This word rhymes with **jerk** but spells the /ûr/ sound **or**.

5. This word begins with the /ûr/ sound and ends with **th**.

6. This word has two syllables. The first syllable begins with the /s/ sound spelled **c**.

Sounds and Letters

Add the missing letters to write Basic Words.

7. __ __ rly
8. h__r__
9. di__t
10. h__a__d
11. tu__n

  Using the Dictionary

Write the Basic Word for each dictionary respelling.

12. /fûr/
13. /skûrt/
14. /shûrt/
15. /wûrd/

Dictionary Check Be sure to check the respellings in your **Spelling Dictionary**.

Word Analysis
1.
2.
3.
4.
5.
6.
Sounds and Letters
7.
8.
9.
10.
11.
Using the Dictionary
12.
13.
14.
15.

word	fur	early	circus	turn
skirt	earth	work	curl	learn
hurt	dirt	earn	shirt	heard

Name the Categories The words below are smaller parts of something bigger. Write the Basic Word that names that bigger something.

1. consonants, vowels
2. buttons, collar, cuffs
3. zipper, hem, button
4. hills, plains, mountains
5. clowns, jugglers, elephants

Complete the Story Write Basic Words to complete the story.

Do you know what I __6.__? The circus is coming to town! I need to __7.__ some money to buy a ticket. Where can I __8.__? Mr. Ozawa needs help with his garden. Maybe I could help him __9.__ over the soil for planting. I could put the extra __10.__ into flower pots. I would have to start __11.__ in the morning. It will be so cold that I will wish I had a __12.__ coat!

Choose the Word Write the Basic Word that fits each clue.
13. It means "harm."
14. It is something you can do to hair.
15. This is what you do in school.

Name the Categories

1.
2.
3.
4.
5.

Complete the Story

6.
7.
8.
9.
10.
11.
12.

Choose the Word

13.
14.
15.

Spelling and Writing

 Proofread a Poster

First, proofread the poster below for eight misspelled words. Then rewrite the poster. Write the spelling words correctly and make the corrections shown by the proofreading marks.

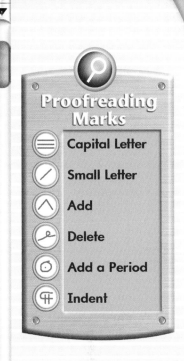

Proofreading Marks

≡	Capital Letter
/	Small Letter
∧	Add
✌	Delete
⊙	Add a Period
⁋	Indent

The Greatest Show on Irth

Have you hurd? The werd is out!

A circous will be held at Jefferson School on saturday, March 2, at Noon.

You can lern more about it and buy your Tickets online at www.bellstent.com. Don't be sorry. Get your tickets urly. You can also urn money if you werk at the show.

More Practice Write and sort the Basic Words.

Write a Poster

Make a poster telling about an event at your school or in your town. Be sure to tell what is happening. Include where and when it will happen. Write why people should come. Use as many spelling words as you can.

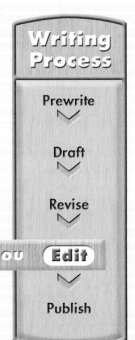

Writing Process

Prewrite
⌄
Draft
⌄
Revise
⌄

> > > > > **Proofread your writing as you** **Edit**
⌄
Publish

When you finish writing your draft, proofread your paper for errors in spelling, grammar, capitalization, and punctuation. Use the **Spelling Dictionary** to check spelling if you are not sure.

◎ Review

Review

Solve the Analogies

1. _____

2. _____

3. _____

4. _____

Replace the Words

5. _____

6. _____

7. _____

8. _____

Onomatopoeia

1. _____

birds	chirp	girls	nurse

Solve the Analogies Write the Review Word to complete each analogy.

1. **Hole** is to **snakes** as **nest** is to _____.

2. **Men** is to **women** as **boys** is to _____.

3. **Cow** is to **moo** as **bird** is to _____.

4. **Restaurant** is to **cook** as **hospital** is to _____.

Replace the Words Write the Review Word that could replace the underlined word or words in each sentence.

5. Each morning, I hear the birds <u>make noise</u> outside my window.

6. Both boys and <u>young ladies</u> can enjoy the same hobbies.

7. The <u>doctor's assistant</u> helped the patient get comfortable.

8. Nate has two <u>parakeets</u> as pets.

Word Study: Onomatopoeia

● **Onomatopoeia** means that a word sounds like what it names. **Baa** and **moo** are examples of onomatopoeia. Write the Review Word that shows onomatopoeia.

◎ Challenge

firm	return	thirst	turkey

Complete the Sentences Write a Challenge Word to complete each sentence.

1. We will _____ from vacation in five days.
2. Viv had some lemonade to relieve her _____.
3. The bed is very _____ but comfortable.
4. A _____ sandwich is a tasty lunch.

Word Groups Write the Challenge Word that completes each group.

5. chicken, ostrich, _____
6. solid, hard, not moving, _____
7. send back, go back, come back, _____
8. hunger, tiredness, _____

Do you think you've mastered the Spelling Strategy? Take the CHAMPION CHALLENGE on page 303!

Challenge

Complete the Sentences

1. _____

2. _____

3. _____

4. _____

Word Groups

5. _____

6. _____

7. _____

8. _____

Spelling and Technology

Spelling and Technology

Web Sites

1.

2.

3.

4.

5.

Web Sites

Web sites are made by different people for different reasons. Always ask yourself who made the Web site and why.

Learn these terms about Web sites.

sponsor: person, business, or group responsible for a Web site

purpose: reason for creating a Web site

.com: part of a Web site address sponsored by a business

.edu: part of a Web site address sponsored by a school

.gov: part of a Web site address sponsored by government

> **sponsor   purpose   .com   .edu   .gov**

Write a term from the box to finish each item. Underline the word with the /ûr/ sound.

1. A Web site with _____ in its address might sell things.

2. The state has a Web site with _____ in its address.

3. Your school's Web site address ends with _____.

4. The school is the _____ of that Web site.

5. Sharing school news is one _____ of the Web site.

Content Words

Link to **Math:** Money

Write the Content Word that completes each sentence.

money	dimes	dollars	nickels

1. One quarter equals five _____.
2. Twenty dimes equals two _____.
3. One dollar equals ten _____.
4. Dollars, dimes, and nickels are kinds of _____.

Link to **Health:** First Aid

Write the Content Word that completes each sentence.

first aid	burn	sting	pain

You can get a __5.__ from fire, heat, or chemicals. You can get a __6.__ from insects. Both of these injuries cause __7.__. If they happen to you, be sure to get __8.__ as soon as possible.

Link to **The Spelling Strategy**

Circle the word that has the /ûr/ sound spelled **ur** in one of the Content Words you wrote.

Content Connection: Math

 Search the Internet to find out more about money. You might look at www.usmint.com/kids. Play a game there. Write its name.

Content Words

Math: Money

1. _____
2. _____
3. _____
4. _____

Health: First Aid

5. _____
6. _____
7. _____
8. _____

Spelling Connections Online
www.zaner-bloser.com

air

1. _____

2. _____

3. _____

4. _____

5. _____

ear

6. _____

7. _____

8. _____

are

9. _____

10. _____

11. _____

12. _____

ere, eir

13. _____

14. _____

15. _____

Spelling and Thinking

READ the Basic Words 👀 Watch out for easily misspelled words!

1. bear	*bear*	The **bear** eats fish and berries.
2. air	*air*	The **air** smells fresh in the forest.
3. fare	*fare*	Do you have change for your bus **fare**?
4. pear	*pear*	Eat the **pear** that is soft and ripe.
5. care	*care*	We will **care** for you if you are sick.
👀 **6.** their	*their*	They put the food in **their** packs.
7. hair	*hair*	You should brush your **hair**.
8. bare	*bare*	The wind felt cold on Ed's **bare** neck.
9. fair	*fair*	I played a **fair** game and did not cheat.
👀 **10.** there	*there*	Please place your marker **there**.
11. pair	*pair*	I got a new **pair** of shoes.
👀 **12.** wear	*wear*	Which hat should I **wear** to the party?
13. chair	*chair*	Kelly sat down in the **chair**.
14. where	*where*	I know **where** to find the lost dog.
15. hare	*hare*	The fox chased the **hare** in the woods.

⊙ Review
16. dear   18. hear
17. deer   19. here

⊙ Challenge
20. beware   22. rare
21. compare   23. stare

SORT the Basic Words

Write the words that spell the /âr/ sound

1–5. air.   **9–12.** are.

6–8. ear.   **13–15.** ere or eir.

REMEMBER the Spelling Strategy

Remember that the vowel sound you hear in **fair** is spelled in different ways: **air** in **fair**, **ear** in **bear**, **are** in **care**, **ere** in **where**, and **eir** in **their**.

Sound and Letter Patterns

Write Basic Words by adding the missing letters.

1. p e __ __   **3.** b __ __ e

2. t h __ __ r   **4.** h __ __ r

Sounds and Spellings

5. Write the Basic Word that sounds like **hair** but means "a rabbit-like animal."

6. Write the Basic Word that sounds like **pear** but means "a set of two."

7. Write the Basic Word that sounds like **there** but means "belonging to them."

8. Write the Basic Word that sounds like **bare** but means "a large, heavy animal."

9–12. Write the two pairs of Basic Words that sound the same but have different spellings and meanings.

 Using the Dictionary

The vowel sound in **pear** is shown as **/âr/** in your **Spelling Dictionary**. Write the Basic Word for each dictionary respelling.

13. /âr/   **14.** /kâr/   **15.** /châr/

◆ ◆ ◆

Dictionary Check Be sure to check the respellings of the words in your **Spelling Dictionary**.

Sound and Letter Patterns

1.
2.
3.
4.

Sounds and Spellings

5.
6.
7.
8.
9.
10.
11.
12.

Using the Dictionary

13.
14.
15.

Complete the Paragraph

1.
2.
3.
4.
5.
6.
7.

Complete the Sentences

8.
9.
10.
11.
12.
13.
14.
15.

bear	air	fare	pear	care
their	hair	bare	fair	there
pair	wear	chair	where	hare

Complete the Paragraph Write the Basic Words that complete the paragraph.

Goldilocks did not have very good manners. She went to the bears' home and ate __1.__ food. She did not __2.__ whose home it was. No matter whose home it was, she should not have been __3.__. Goldilocks sat in each __4.__ in the house. She tried out the bed of each __5.__. One was too hard. One was too soft, but one was just right. She slept in the bed __6.__ she felt most comfortable. It's a wonder she didn't try to __7.__ the bears' clothes!

Complete the Sentences Write a Basic Word to complete each sentence.

8. The umpire wants to keep the game _____.
9. Children under twelve pay half _____.
10. A rabbit is sometimes called a _____.
11. Melanie wears her _____ in a braid.
12. I have a new _____ of shoes.
13. Who would like to eat this sweet _____?
14. The grass tickles my _____ feet.
15. It is important to keep our _____ and water clean.

Spelling and Writing

Proofread a Paragraph

Proofread the paragraph below for eight misspelled words. Then rewrite the paragraph. Write the spelling words correctly and make the corrections shown by the proofreading marks.

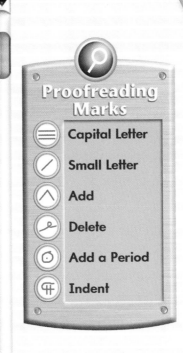

Proofreading Marks

≡	Capital Letter
/	Small Letter
∧	Add
✂	Delete
⊙	Add a Period
⌗	Indent

The Look

⌗ What do kids like to wair? They like to put on a peir of Jeans and a shirt. some like thair jeans baggy. Some like like jeans to fade. Of course, thear are some kids who don't really kare how the jeans look, but they pay a lot of Attention to their hare. No matter whare you live, it's fare to say that no two kids are the same.

More Practice Write and sort the Basic Words.

Write a Paragraph

Write a paragraph about clothing styles, hair styles, or favorite things to do at your school. Be sure to use words that tell what and how. Give interesting details. Use as many spelling words as you can.

Writing Process

Prewrite
∨
Draft
∨
Revise
∨

> Proofread your writing as you **Edit**

∨
Publish

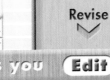

When you finish writing your draft, proofread your paper for errors in spelling, grammar, capitalization, and punctuation. Use the **Spelling Dictionary** to check spelling if you are not sure.

◎ Review

Review

Word Clues

1. _____

2. _____

3. _____

4. _____

Solve the Analogies

5. _____

6. _____

7. _____

8. _____

dear	deer	hear	here

Word Clues Write the Review Word for each clue.

1. It ends with the same three letters as **near**. It begins like **day**.

2. It is spelled with the same letters as **hare,** but it does not have the /âr/ sound.

3. It sounds like your answer to number 2, but it has a different spelling and meaning.

4. It sounds like your answer to number 1, but it has a different spelling and meaning.

Solve the Analogies Write a Review Word to complete each analogy.

5. **Mouth** is to **talk** as **ear** is to _____.

6. **Sea** is to **whale** as **forest** is to _____.

7. **Sad** is to **unhappy** as **loved** is to _____.

8. **Before** is to **after** as **there** is to _____.

Challenge

beware	compare	rare	stare

Word Structure Follow the directions to write a Challenge Word.

1. step – ep + are = _____
2. rate – te + re = _____
3. because – cause + ware = _____
4. come – e + pare = _____

Complete the Sentences Write a Challenge Word to complete each sentence.

5. Tony wanted to _____ prices before he bought a new video game.

6. You shouldn't _____ at people. It isn't nice.

7. The park ranger told the campers to _____ of wild animals.

8. It is _____ to have snow in June!

Challenge

Word Structure

1. _____

2. _____

3. _____

4. _____

Complete the Sentences

5. _____

6. _____

7. _____

8. _____

 Do you think you've mastered the Spelling Strategy? Take the **CHAMPION CHALLENGE** on page 304!

Spelling and Technology

Spelling and Technology

Checking Your Spelling

1. _____

2. _____

3. _____

4. _____

Checking Your Spelling

Aren't spell checkers great? They can find many spelling mistakes. However, they cannot find them all. Sometimes a writer spells a word correctly, but it's the wrong word! For example, do you **sale** a boat or **sail** it? Most computers are just not smart enough to find this kind of mistake.

bare	bear	wear	where

A computer checked the spelling of the following sentences. Find the words the computer missed and write them correctly. Underline words with the /âr/ sound spelled **ear**.

1. When William opened the drawing program, his screen was bear.

2. He decided that he would draw a picture of a bare.

3. After he put a hat and shirt on it, he also drew some pants for it to where.

4. William wanted to add more animals, but he didn't know wear to put them.

Content Words

Link to **Health:** Safety

Write Content Words to complete the paragraph.

| classroom | safety | playground | stairs |

Always follow __1.__ rules at school. In the __2.__, stay in your chair. Never run in the halls or on the __3.__. You can run on the __4.__, but be careful. Don't run into anyone!

Link to **Science:** Insects

Write the Content Word that matches each clue.

| caterpillar | wasp | earthworm | housefly |

5. a common worm with a body divided into parts

6. a fly that you may see at home

7. the worm-like, hairy form of a butterfly's life

8. a flying insect that can sting

Link to **The Spelling Strategy**

Circle the letters that spell the /âr/ sound in one of the Content Words you wrote.

Content Connection: Health

 Search the Internet to find out more about safety. You might look at www.bam.gov. Click on **Your Safety**. Write one safety fact you learn there.

Content Words

Health: Safety

1. _____
2. _____
3. _____
4. _____

Science: Insects

5. _____
6. _____
7. _____
8. _____

Spelling Connections Online
www.zaner-bloser.com

Spelling and Thinking

long a

1. _____
2. _____
3. _____
4. _____
5. _____
6. _____

short e

7. _____
8. _____
9. _____
10. _____
11. _____

long o

12. _____
13. _____

short i

14. _____
15. _____

READ the Basic Words 👀 Watch out for easily misspelled words!

1.	way	*way*	I don't know which **way** to turn.
👀 2.	its	*its*	The dog put **its** head on my lap.
3.	owe	*owe*	I **owe** Jay three dollars for the hat.
4.	sell	*sell*	If you will **sell** that, I will buy it.
5.	great	*great*	What a **great** day we had at the park.
6.	sail	*sail*	We **sail** our boat on the bay.
7.	cell	*cell*	A **cell** is part of all living things.
8.	scent	*scent*	The **scent** of that perfume is strong.
9.	oh	*oh*	It was, **oh,** such a beautiful day.
10.	cent	*cent*	One **cent** does not buy much!
👀 11.	it's	*it's*	I lost my sock, but I know **it's** here.
12.	grate	*grate*	Use this tool to **grate** the cheese.
👀 13.	weigh	*weigh*	Do you **weigh** the baby on that scale?
14.	sale	*sale*	I buy jeans cheap at the **sale**.
15.	sent	*sent*	Meg **sent** me a letter from camp.

◎ **Review**

16. for
17. four
18. meat
19. meet

◎ **Challenge**

20. past
21. passed
22. roll
23. role

SORT the Basic Words

1–6. Write the homophones that have the **long a** sound.

7–11. Write the homophones that have the **short e** sound.

12–13. Write the homophones that have the **long o** sound.

14–15. Write the homophones that have the **short i** sound.

REMEMBER the Spelling Strategy

Remember that **homophones** are words that sound the same but have different spellings and meanings.

Spelling and Phonics

Word Analysis

Write the Basic Words that fit the clues.

1. It spells the /s/ sound with **sc**.
2. It has a **long o** and a **silent h**.
3. It spells the **long a** sound with **ai**.
4–5. They spell the /s/ sound with **c**.
6. It is spelled with the **vowel-consonant-e** pattern. It begins with **gr**.
7. It begins like **sell** and ends like **cent**.
8–9. They rhyme with **bits**.

Word Meanings

Write the Basic Word that replaces each incorrect homophone below.

10. A store near my house will soon have a <u>sail</u>.
11. It will <u>cell</u> model airplanes at half price.
12. They have such <u>grate</u> prices on model airplanes.
13. Please pay back the money that you <u>oh</u> me.

Using the Dictionary

Write two Basic Words for this dictionary respelling.

14–15. /wā/

◆ ◆ ◆

Dictionary Check Be sure to check the respellings of the words in your **Spelling Dictionary**.

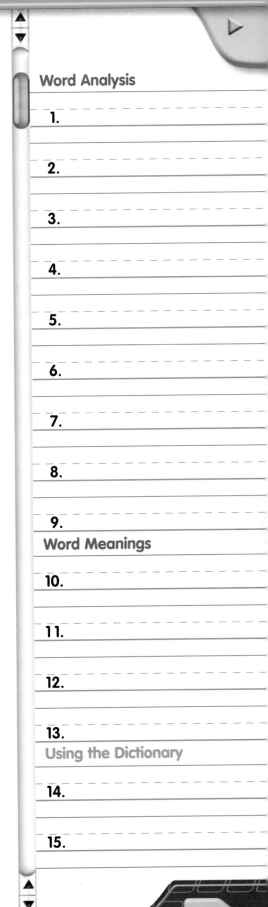

Word Analysis

1. _____
2. _____
3. _____
4. _____
5. _____
6. _____
7. _____
8. _____
9. _____

Word Meanings

10. _____
11. _____
12. _____
13. _____

Using the Dictionary

14. _____
15. _____

Complete the Groups

1.

2.

3.

4.

5.

6.

7.

8.

Complete the Sentences

9.

10.

11.

12.

13.

14.

15.

way	its	owe	sell	great
sail	cell	scent	oh	cent
it's	grate	weigh	sale	sent

Complete the Groups Write the Basic Word that belongs in each group.

1. he's, she's, _____
2. nickel, quarter, dime, _____
3. gee, my, ah, _____
4. fly, drive, ride, _____
5. buy, trade, _____
6. my, her, their, _____
7. chop, shred, _____
8. smell, odor, _____

Complete the Sentences Write the Basic Word that fits each sentence.

9. How much does that large bunch of ripe bananas _____?
10. Plants store water in every tiny _____.
11. I _____ you an apology.
12. Our teacher told us that this is the best _____ to solve the math problem.
13. Our whole class had a _____ time on the trip to the science museum.
14. I _____ an e-mail message to my grandmother in Mexico.
15. My dad always buys his clothes on _____.

Spelling and Writing

Proofread a Paragraph

Proofread the paragraph below for eight misspelled words. Then rewrite the paragraph. Write the spelling words correctly and make the corrections shown by the proofreading marks.

¶ When a person is missing, sometimes a Dog can find the person. It uses it's cents of smell to do this. Someone gives the dog something with the person's sent. Then the dog is cent out to find the person. for many people, it's fun to watch a dog pick up the trail. The wae a dog follows its nose is something to See. How grate it is when the dog can find the person. That is when a dog is worth every csent you paid for it! In fact, you could even say you oh the dog.

More Practice Write and sort the Basic Words.

Write a Paragraph

Choose one animal and write about it. Be sure to write a sentence that tells the main idea. Use examples, facts, or details to explain the point you are making about the animal. Use as many spelling words as you can.

> > > > > **Proofread your writing as you** **Edit**

When you finish writing your draft, proofread your paper for errors in spelling, grammar, capitalization, and punctuation. Use the **Spelling Dictionary** to check spelling if you are not sure.

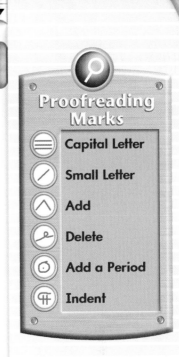

Proofreading Marks

Mark	Meaning
≡	Capital Letter
/	Small Letter
∧	Add
⌿	Delete
⊙	Add a Period
¶	Indent

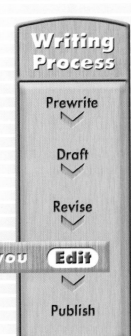

Writing Process

Prewrite
⌄
Draft
⌄
Revise
⌄
Edit
⌄
Publish

◎ Review

Review

Solve the Analogies

1. _____

2. _____

3. _____

4. _____

Complete the Paragraph

5. _____

6. _____

7. _____

8. _____

Idioms

1. _____

for	four	meat	meet

Solve the Analogies Write the Review Word that completes each analogy.

1. **One** is to **two** as **three** is to _____.

2. **Pea** is to **vegetable** as **beef** is to _____.

3. **Wave** is to **greet** as **shake hands** is to _____.

4. **Buy** is to **sell** as **against** is to _____.

Complete the Paragraph Write Review Words to complete the paragraph.

Gene decided to go out with his friends __5.__ a meal. The group would __6.__ at the restaurant at __7.__ o'clock the next day. The restaurant was well-known for its famous __8.__ dishes, so Gene was looking forward to eating there.

Word Study: Idioms

• An **idiom** is a saying that doesn't mean what the words in it say. **Roll up your sleeves** means "get ready to work." Write a Challenge Word to complete this idiom about what you did on a test: _____ **with flying colors**.

Challenge

past	passed	roll	role

Answer the Questions Write the Challenge Word that answers each question.

1. Which word means "time gone by"?
2. Which word means "part in a play"?
3. Which word means "to turn over and over"?
4. Which word means "went by"?

Word Groups Write the Challenge Word that belongs in each group.

5. jump, duck, tumble, _____
6. _____, present, future
7. walked by, went by, _____
8. actor, play, _____

Do you think you've mastered the Spelling Strategy? Take the CHAMPION CHALLENGE on page 305!

Challenge

Answer the Questions

1.

2.

3.

4.

Word Groups

5.

6.

7.

8.

Spelling and Technology

Spelling and Technology

Spell Checkers Can Make Mistakes

1.

2.

3.

4.

Spell Checkers Can Make Mistakes

Spell checkers can't tell which homophone, a word that sounds just like another word, is correct in a sentence. You must therefore be careful when using words such as **two, too,** and **to.**

Some e-mail users have created their own homophones. For example, some users type **u** for **you.** They may also type **ur** for **you are.** These e-mail homophones should never be used in formal writing. A spell checker will not catch most of these e-mail homophones either.

Learn these groups of homophones.

to	too	two	you	you are

Proofread the paragraph below for incorrect homophones. Write the words correctly.

Matt wrote me a note. It was just too sentences long. It said, "I'm having a birthday party. Ur invited." I told him I would come. I asked if Tim was coming to. Matt said that Tim was coming two the party.

Content Words

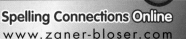

Link to **Language Arts:** Adjectives

Write the Content Word that completes each sentence.

| hungry | chilly | fancy | faraway |

1. Other planets are _____ places.

2. Someone who needs food is _____.

3. Things that are not plain might be called _____.

4. You might wear a sweater on a _____ evening.

Link to **Science:** Medicine

Write the Content Word that matches each definition.

| germs | shot | medicine | vaccine |

5. tiny cells that can cause disease

6. something taken for a disease or injury

7. use of a needle to receive a vaccine or medicine

8. way of protecting against disease

Link to **The Spelling Strategy**

Circle the Content Word you wrote that is a homophone for **chili**.

Content Connection: Science

Search the Internet to find out more about medicine. You might look at **www.bam.gov**. Click on **Diseases**. List the names of two diseases you learn about.

Content Words

Language Arts: Adjectives

1. _____

2. _____

3. _____

4. _____

Science: Medicine

5. _____

6. _____

7. _____

8. _____

Spelling Connections Online
www.zaner-bloser.com

Assessment and Review

ASSESSMENT

Units 19–23

Each Assessment Word in the box fits one of the spelling strategies you have studied over the past five weeks. Read the spelling strategies. Then write each Assessment Word under the unit number it fits.

Unit 19

1–3. The vowel sound you hear in **song** and **lawn** is spelled in different ways: **o** in **song** and **aw** in **lawn**.

Unit 20

4–6. The vowel sound you hear in **form** is spelled in different ways: **or** in **form**, **ore** in **tore**, **oar** in **board**, and **ar** in **warm**.

Unit 21

7–9. The vowel sound in **fur** is spelled in different ways: **ur** in **fur**, **ear** in **earn**, **or** in **word**, and **ir** in **dirt**.

Unit 22

10–12. The vowel sound you hear in **fair** is spelled in different ways: **air** in **fair**, **ear** in **bear**, **are** in **care**, **ere** in **where**, and **eir** in **their**.

Unit 23

13–15. Homophones are words that sound the same but have different spellings and meanings.

bore
sir
bog
waste
dare
horses
purse
paw
steel
stair
claw
snore
blur
aware
steal

REVIEW

Unit 19: Vowel: /ô/

across   draw   belong   straw   soft   lost   song

Write a spelling word for each one of these clues.

1. It has two syllables and rhymes with **boss**.
2. It rhymes with **cost** and ends with a consonant cluster.
3. It rhymes with **wrong** but has two syllables.
4. Change one letter in **sang** to make this word.

Write a spelling word to complete each sentence.

5. Wipe the car with a _____ cloth so you don't scratch it.
6. Go to the chalkboard and _____ a picture of a cat.
7. We made a bed out of _____ in the doghouse.

REVIEW

Unit 20: r-Controlled Vowel: /ôr/

before   forget   warm   morning   story   board   form

Write the spelling word that means the opposite of each word.

8. cool
9. after
10. evening
11. remember

Write a spelling word to complete each sentence.

12. Ms. Bailey told us a _____ about a spider.
13. Dad put a _____ across the muddy walkway.
14. We began to _____ the clay into balls.

Unit 19

1. _____
2. _____
3. _____
4. _____
5. _____
6. _____
7. _____

Unit 20

8. _____
9. _____
10. _____
11. _____
12. _____
13. _____
14. _____

1.

2.

3.

4.

5.

6.

7.

8.

9.

10.

11.

12.

13.

14.

REVIEW

Unit 21: r-Controlled Vowel: /ûr/

circus   heard   early   work   turn   dirt   word

Write the spelling word that completes the sentence.

1. That is a _____ that I have never heard before.

2. Elephants performed in the _____ tent.

3. How _____ can we be ready to leave?

4. I have too much _____ to do to leave tomorrow.

Write a spelling word for each clue.

5. This word rhymes with **burn** and sometimes comes before the word **around**.

6. This word is the past tense of **hear**.

7. Change the first and last letter of **girl** to make this word.

Unit 22: r-Controlled Vowel: /âr/

their   wear   there   where   chair   bear   care

Write the spelling word that completes each sentence.

8. My book is over _____ on that table.

9. Joey and Marsha put _____ books in the other room.

10. Do you know _____ to go next?

11. I don't know what to _____ to that party.

12. The little _____ cub stayed close to its mother.

13. You may sit on this _____.

14. Take great _____ not to break this dish.

Unit 23: Homophones

great	sent	it's	weigh	cent	oh	its

Write the spelling word that fits the clue.

1. big or wonderful

2. one way to find out how heavy something is

3. past tense of **send**

4. another name for a **penny**

5. a word of surprise

Write **it's** or **its** to complete each sentence.

6. I hope _____ not too late to go to the game.

7. The poor little kitten has lost _____ mitten.

WORD SORT

Spelling Study Strategy

Sorting by Vowel Sounds

Here is one way to practice spelling words.

1. Write your spelling words on 3" × 5" cards.

2. Make a stack of words that have the vowel sound you hear in **song** and the **r**-controlled vowel sounds you hear in **warm, fur,** and **fair.**

3. With a partner, take turns reading each other's word cards aloud. Put words with the same vowel sound in the same pile.

4. Read the words in each pile again. Then sort them according to the spelling patterns that spell the vowel sound.

Writer's Workshop

Grammar, Usage, and Mechanics

Verbs That Tell About the Past

Past-tense verbs show that the action happened in the past. Many past-tense verbs end in **-ed**.

> Yesterday we **worked** in the yard.

> The children **played** in the sand.

Some verbs form their past tense in other ways.

> We **give** presents on birthdays.

> Last year, I **gave** her a book.

● Practice ACTIVITY

A. Write the past-tense verb in each sentence.

  1. Emma listened to her brother's report.

  2. Last night my father walked the dog.

  3. I finally opened that package!

  4. The painter finished the watercolor.

  5. The horse jumped over the fence.

B. The underlined verbs below are from your spelling lists in Units 19–23. If a verb is in the past tense, write the word. If it is not in the past tense, write the verb's past-tense form.

  6. Those gloves <u>belong</u> to Sal.

  7. They <u>work</u> at the food store.

  8. Yesterday I <u>heard</u> a robin.

  9. Last Monday my teacher <u>sent</u> a note home.

  10. The children <u>form</u> clay into bowls.

● Practice Activity

A.

1.

2.

3.

4.

5.

B.

6.

7.

8.

9.

10.

Writing a Character Sketch

● Prewriting

Who is your hero? What makes this person special? As you think about this person, write down why he or she is your hero. You can find books at the library about special people. An adult can help you look for heroes on Internet sites such as IMA Hero (www.imahero.com).

● Drafting

Use your ideas to write a character sketch. Include several describing words to tell about the character. Use as many spelling words as possible. If you don't know how to spell a word, make your best guess.

● Revising

When you have finished your first draft, read your sketch from beginning to end. Have you included all of your ideas? Now write your final draft.

● Editing

Use the editing checklist to proofread your character sketch. Be sure to use proofreading marks when you make corrections.

● Publishing

Make a copy of your character sketch. Draw a portrait of your character to share with your readers.

Editing Checklist

Spelling

○ I circled words that contain the spelling strategies I learned in Units 19–23.

○ I checked the circled words in my Spelling Dictionary.

○ I also checked for other spelling errors.

Capital Letters

○ Important words in the title

○ Beginning of all sentences

○ Proper nouns

Punctuation

○ Each sentence ends with the correct punctuation.

○ Commas, apostrophes, and quotation marks are used correctly.

Grammar, Usage, and Mechanics

○ Each past-tense verb tells about actions that already happened.

Double Consonants

short u, short a

1. _____

2. _____

3. _____

4. _____

5. _____

short e, short o

6. _____

7. _____

8. _____

9. _____

10. _____

11. _____

short i

12. _____

13. _____

14. _____

15. _____

READ the Basic Words 👀 Watch out for easily misspelled words!

👀 **1.** supper	*supper*	We often have soup for **supper**.
👀 **2.** happen	*happen*	What will **happen** at the game?
3. pepper	*pepper*	I put **pepper** on my potatoes.
4. kitten	*kitten*	The **kitten** stayed near its mother.
5. sudden	*sudden*	We heard a **sudden** clap of thunder.
6. letter	*letter*	Mail the **letter** at the post office.
👀 **7.** dinner	*dinner*	We ate rice and beans for **dinner**.
8. cotton	*cotton*	These pants are made from **cotton**.
9. lesson	*lesson*	My piano **lesson** lasts one hour.
10. mitten	*mitten*	I lost one **mitten** in the snow.
11. bottom	*bottom*	The **bottom** of a glass is flat.
12. summer	*summer*	We go to the beach in the **summer**.
13. better	*better*	Colin will feel **better** after a rest.
14. ladder	*ladder*	Climb the **ladder** to reach the window.
15. ribbon	*ribbon*	The bow is made from red **ribbon**.

◎ Review

16. apple   18. puzzle

17. cannot   19. yellow

◎ Challenge

20. bubble   22. rattle

21. collar   23. zipper

SORT the Basic Words

1–5. Write the words with a **short u** or **short a** sound.

6–11. Write the words with a **short e** or **short o** sound.

12–15. Write the words with a **short i** sound.

REMEMBER the Spelling Strategy

Remember that two-syllable words with a short vowel sound in the first syllable are often spelled with double consonants: **dinner, better**.

Spelling and Phonics

Sound and Letter Patterns

Write the Basic Word that matches each description.

1. It spells the /**k**/ sound with **c**.

2. It has three of the same consonants.

3. It doubles the consonant **b**.

4. It spells the /**k**/ sound with **k**.

Word Structure

Two-syllable words with double consonants in the middle are usually divided between the two consonants. Write these Basic Words. Draw a line between the two syllables.

5. bottom

6. better

7. dinner

8. happen

9. mitten

 Using the Dictionary

10–15. Write these six Basic Words in a-b-c order.

letter	summer	supper
lesson	ladder	sudden

Dictionary Check Be sure to check the a-b-c order of the words in your **Spelling Dictionary**.

Sound and Letter Patterns

1.

2.

3.

4.

Word Structure

5.

6.

7.

8.

9.

Using the Dictionary

10.

11.

12.

13.

14.

15.

Spelling and Reading

supper	happen	pepper	kitten	sudden
letter	dinner	cotton	lesson	mitten
bottom	summer	better	ladder	ribbon

Complete the Groups

Complete the Groups Write the Basic Word that belongs in each group.

1. silk, wool, _____
2. chili powder, salt, _____
3. scarf, hat, _____
4. occur, take place, _____
5. escalator, steps, _____
6. lunch, brunch, dinner, _____

Complete the Story Write the Basic Words to complete the story.

I'll never forget my eighth birthday. It was a very hot __7.__ day. After my swimming __8.__, my mother took me home. I looked in our mailbox and found a birthday card and a __9.__ from my grandparents. Then I went inside. All of a __10.__, my friends yelled, "Happy birthday!" I was so surprised!

We all played games on the __11.__ table. Finally, it was time to open the presents. Mom said I should open the box with holes that was tied with yellow __12.__. Inside was a soft, furry __13.__. It looked so tiny sitting in the __14.__ of that box. I've never gotten a __15.__ present in my whole life!

Complete the Groups

1.

2.

3.

4.

5.

6.

Complete the Story

7.

8.

9.

10.

11.

12.

13.

14.

15.

Spelling and Writing

Proofread a Letter

Proofread the letter below for eight misspelled words. Then rewrite the letter. Write the spelling words correctly and make the corrections shown by the proofreading marks.

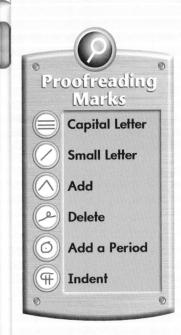

Proofreading Marks

☰	Capital Letter
/	Small Letter
∧	Add
✐	Delete
⊙	Add a Period
⌗	Indent

> Dear kenesha,
>
> My mom just said I could have a sleepover on friday. I hoped this would happin. It is kind of suden, but can you come? You can have diner here. My mom will make the peper steak that you like! After super, we can play with my kiten. please answer this leter soon! It might be our last chance this summur.
>
> Your pal
>
> Alison

More Practice Write and sort the Basic Words.

Write a Letter

Invite a friend to do something with you. Be sure to use commas after your opening and closing. Indent your paragraphs, your closing, and your signature. Persuade your friend with interesting ideas or details. Use as many spelling words as you can.

Writing Process

Prewrite
⌄
Draft
⌄
Revise
⌄
Edit
⌄
Publish

> > > > Proofread your writing as you **Edit**

When you finish writing your draft, proofread your paper for errors in spelling, grammar, capitalization, and punctuation. Use the **Spelling Dictionary** to check spelling if you are not sure.

◎ Review

Review

Complete the Groups

1. _____

2. _____

3. _____

4. _____

Complete the Sentences

5. _____

6. _____

7. _____

8. _____

Coined Words

1. _____

---

apple	cannot	puzzle	yellow

Complete the Groups Write the Review Word that completes each group.

1. red, blue, _____
2. maze, riddle, _____
3. plum, peach, _____
4. do not, would not, _____

Complete the Sentences Write a Review Word to complete each sentence.

5. Since I don't know how to swim, I _____ go to the pool.
6. Her favorite color is blue, but I prefer _____.
7. Eating an _____ a day helps to keep the doctor away.
8. Jack usually works a jigsaw_____ with his grandfather on the weekends.

Word Study: Coined Words

- A **coined word** is made up to name something new. Write the Challenge Word that was coined to name a special fastener on pants or jackets.

Challenge

bubble   collar   rattle   zipper

Solve the Analogies Write the Challenge Word that completes each analogy.

1. **Leaves** is to **rustle** as **windows** is to_____.
2. **Water** is to **drop** as **air** is to _____.
3. **Shirt** is to **buttons** as **pants** is to _____.
4. **Wrist** is to **cuff** as **neck** is to _____.

Answer the Questions Write the Challenge Word that answers each question.

5. What is one way to close a jacket or pants?
6. What is around the neck of a shirt?
7. When you wash your hands, what does the soap make?
8. What might a snake's tail do?

 Do you think you've mastered the Spelling Strategy? Take the CHAMPION CHALLENGE on page 306!

Spelling and Technology

Spelling and Technology

Which E-mail Is Safe to Answer?

1. _____

2. _____

3. _____

4. _____

Which E-mail Is Safe to Answer?

If you want to get e-mail, you need an e-mail address. Here is an example of an address:

soccergirl@newnetwork.com

Some e-mail will be from friends. Other e-mail will be junk mail, or spam. Do not reply to e-mail from people you do not know. If an unknown sender attaches anything to an e-mail, do not open it. It may contain something that will harm your computer.

Learn these words about answering—or not answering—your e-mail.

| address | attach | junk | reply |

Write a word from the box for each clue. Underline the two-syllable words that have a double consonant.

1. fisher909@newnetwork.com

2. connect to

3. rhymes with **skunk**

4. answer

Content Words

Link to **Social Studies:** Government

Write Content Words to complete the paragraph.

| United States | president | elect | ballot |

Some countries are ruled by kings or queens. Some are ruled by other kinds of leaders. In our country, the __1.__, we have a __2.__. The people __3.__ the president to office by casting a __4.__.

Link to **Science:** Machines

Write Content Words to complete the paragraph.

| raise | machine | lever | pulley |

A simple __5.__ has very few moving parts. One of these is like a seesaw. It is called a __6.__. You push one side down to __7.__ the other side. Another is a wheel and axle used with a rope. That is called a __8.__.

Link to **The Spelling Strategy**

Circle the double consonant letters in two of the Content Words you wrote.

Content Connection: Social Studies

Search the Internet to find out more about our government. You might look at this site: **www.whitehousekids.gov**. Be prepared to give the class a report on the facts you learn.

Content Words

Social Studies: Government

1. ____
2. ____
3. ____
4. ____

Science: Machines

5. ____
6. ____
7. ____
8. ____

Spelling Connections Online
www.zaner-bloser.com

Spelling and Thinking

READ the Basic Words 👀 Watch out for easily misspelled words!

👀 **1.**	carry	*carry*	Please help me **carry** this box.
2.	bunny	*bunny*	The **bunny** has big ears.
3.	happy	*happy*	The clown made the children **happy**.
4.	muddy	*muddy*	I will take off my **muddy** shoes.
5.	berry	*berry*	What kind of **berry** is on that bush?
6.	furry	*furry*	A hamster is a small **furry** animal.
7.	puppy	*puppy*	The **puppy** is just six weeks old.
8.	sorry	*sorry*	She felt **sorry** for the hurt bird.
9.	merry	*merry*	Everyone at the party was **merry**.
10.	jelly	*jelly*	I eat peanut butter with **jelly**.
👀 **11.**	hurry	*hurry*	We **hurry** to catch the bus.
👀 **12.**	pretty	*pretty*	Erica looks **pretty** in that dress.
13.	cherry	*cherry*	This **cherry** is big, red, and ripe.
14.	worry	*worry*	Did Pam **worry** about her lost dog?
15.	funny	*funny*	The joke Matt told was **funny**.

Review
16. fluffy
17. glossy
18. hobby
19. penny

Challenge
20. ferry
21. silly
22. unhappy
23. witty

SORT the Basic Words

1–8. Write the words with a **double r**.

9–10. Write the words with a **double n**.

11–12. Write the words with a **double p**.

13–15. Write the words with a **double d, l, or t**.

REMEMBER the Spelling Strategy

Remember that a final **long e** sound in words like **happy** usually follows a double consonant and is spelled **y**.

---

double r

1.
2.
3.
4.
5.
6.
7.
8.

double n

9.
10.

double p

11.
12.

double d, l, or t

13.
14.
15.

Spelling and Phonics

Word Structure

1. Change one letter in **poppy** to make a Basic Word.
2. Replace the second syllable in **sorrow** to make a Basic Word.
3. Replace the first syllable in **tidy** to make a Basic Word.
4. Change one letter in **jolly** to make a Basic Word.

Sound and Letter Patterns

Write Basic Words by adding the missing letters.

5. hap ___ ___
6. bu ___ ___ y
7. be ___ r ___
8. f ___ n ___ y
9. ch ___ r ___ y

 Using the Dictionary

Write the Basic Word for each dictionary respelling.

10. /mĕr′ ē/
11. /fûr′ ē/
12. /wûr′ ē/
13. /kăr′ ē/
14. /hŭr′ ē/
15. /prĭt′ ē/

Word Structure

1.

2.

3.

4.

Sound and Letter Patterns

5.

6.

7.

8.

9.

Using the Dictionary

10.

11.

12.

13.

14.

15.

carry	bunny	happy	muddy	berry
furry	puppy	sorry	merry	jelly
hurry	pretty	cherry	worry	funny

Replace the Words Write the Basic Word that could best replace each underlined word or words.

1. Do you like grape <u>jam</u> on your toast?
2. That <u>baby dog</u> is so playful.
3. "She'll Be Comin' Round the Mountain" is a <u>jolly</u> tune we sing in school.
4. We must be <u>quick</u>, or we will miss the train and lose a day of vacation.
5. I just saw a <u>rabbit</u> eating the lettuce and carrots in our garden.

Complete the Sentences Write the Basic Word to complete each sentence.

6. That was a _____ joke you told.
7. It is too _____ to play in the yard.
8. I saw three clowns with _____ faces.
9. Can you help me _____ this heavy package to the post office today?
10. Dad will _____ if we are late for supper.
11. A kitten is soft and _____.
12. I am _____ that I bumped your leg.
13. Look at the _____ flowers.
14. That _____ is so big and blue.
15. A _____ tree has beautiful pink and white blossoms in the spring.

Replace the Words

1.
2.
3.
4.
5.

Complete the Sentences

6.
7.
8.
9.
10.
11.
12.
13.
14.
15.

Spelling and Writing

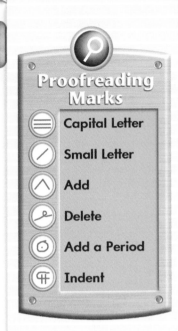

Proofread a Thank-You Letter

Proofread the letter below for eight misspelled words. Then rewrite the letter. Write the spelling words correctly and make the corrections shown by the proofreading marks.

> Dear Grandma∧
>
>   Thank you ~~you~~ for the pritty dress. I hope saturday comes in a hurre because I want to wear it. I also liked the card with the bunney on it that you sent.
>
> ⌗For my birthday I also got a new pack to cary my ~~B~~ooks. Best of all, Dad got me a furrey pupy⊙
>
>   It was a very happy day for me. I am sory you could not be here.
>
>   Love,
>   Jemma

More Practice Write and sort the Basic Words.

Proofreading Marks

≡	Capital Letter
/	Small Letter
∧	Add
✐	Delete
⊙	Add a Period
⌗	Indent

Write a Thank-You Letter

Write a letter to thank someone for a present. Be sure to use commas after your opening and closing. Indent your paragraphs and your closing. Say something kind about the gift. Use as many spelling words as you can.

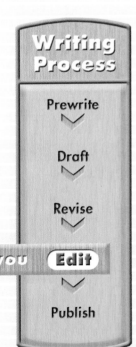

Writing Process

Prewrite
⌄
Draft
⌄
Revise
⌄
Edit
⌄
Publish

> ❯ ❯ ❯ ❯ ❯   **Proofread your writing as you** Edit

When you finish writing your draft, proofread your paper for errors in spelling, grammar, capitalization, and punctuation. Use the **Spelling Dictionary** to check spelling if you are not sure.

◎ Review

Review

Word Clues

1. _____

2. _____

3. _____

4. _____

Complete the Sentences

5. _____

6. _____

7. _____

8. _____

fluffy	glossy	hobby	penny

Word Clues Write the Review Word that fits each clue.

1. It means "smooth and shiny."

2. An example of it is building model airplanes.

3. It belongs in the same group with the words **dime** and **nickel**.

4. This word could describe fur, feathers, or a blanket.

Complete the Sentences Write a Review Word to complete each sentence.

5. The _____ kitten took a nap in the sunshine.

6. A gumball only costs one _____.

7. Will's favorite _____ is collecting stamps.

8. She cleaned the car until the finish was _____.

 # Challenge

ferry	silly	unhappy	witty

Answer the Questions Write a Challenge Word to answer each question.

1. Which word tells about a person who is clever at making jokes?
2. Which word describes a happy, giggling feeling?
3. Which word names a type of large boat?
4. Which word describes someone who is wearing a frown?

Replace the Words Write the Challenge Word that could replace the underlined word in each sentence.

5. The clown in the play acted very <u>foolish</u>.
6. Deena likes to sing when she is <u>sad</u>.
7. There is a <u>boat</u> to the other side of the river.
8. Sam is very <u>clever</u> and friendly.

Challenge

Answer the Questions

1. _____

2. _____

3. _____

4. _____

Replace the Words

5. _____

6. _____

7. _____

8. _____

 Do you think you've mastered the Spelling Strategy? Take the **CHAMPION CHALLENGE** on page 307!

Spelling and Technology

Spelling and Technology

Storing Your Work

1. _____

2. _____

3. _____

4. _____

Storing Your Work

Computers save and store work in different ways. In this lesson you will learn four places where you can put your work for safekeeping.

DVD: a disk used to store video or films

floppy: a removable small disk used in early computers to store work

hard copy: a printed copy of your work

hard drive: part of a computer's hardware that stores all your computer's electronic information and programs

DVD   floppy   hard copy   hard drive

Write the word from the box that best completes each sentence. Underline the word that is spelled with a double consonant and has a final **long e** sound.

1. The computer's _____ keeps all the information about the computer and software.

2. The printed copy of my report is the _____.

3. My dad used a _____ to store work, but I never used one.

4. Our films are stored on this _____.

Content Words

Link to **Health:** Safety

Write Content Words to complete the paragraph.

crosswalk	signal	sidewalk	stoplight

Remember these rules for riding a bicycle in traffic. Always __1.__ before you turn. Stay off the __2.__ . Obey any __3.__ you come to. Walk your bike across the __4.__ .

Link to **Science:** Ocean Life

Write the Content Word that matches each definition.

jellyfish	snake	sea horse	turtle

5. land animal with a long body and no legs

6. sea animal with a head like a horse and a tail

7. animal that can live on land or water and whose body is covered by a large shell

8. sea animal that can sting

Link to **The Spelling Strategy**

Circle the Content Word you wrote in which a double consonant is followed by the **long e** sound spelled **y**.

Content Connection: Health

 Search the Internet to find out more about safety. You might look at www.nhtsa.dot.gov/kids. Write a safety fact or make a bulletin board display of something you learn.

Content Words

Health: Safety

1.

2.

3.

4.

Science: Ocean Life

5.

6.

7.

8.

Spelling Connections Online
www.zaner-bloser.com

Adding -ing

consonant and vowel

1. _____

2. _____

3. _____

4. _____

5. _____

6. _____

7. _____

8. _____

9. _____

consonant digraph or consonant cluster

10. _____

11. _____

12. _____

13. _____

14. _____

15. _____

Spelling and Thinking

READ the Basic Words 👀 Watch out for easily misspelled words!

👀 **1.** coming	*coming*	Is Zach **coming** to your party?
2. skating	*skating*	We went ice **skating** at the rink.
3. taking	*taking*	Ron is **taking** Spot for a walk.
4. giving	*giving*	Mr. Kay is **giving** me a ride home.
👀 **5.** choosing	*choosing*	We are **choosing** a team leader.
6. smiling	*smiling*	The boys are **smiling** at the clown.
7. baking	*baking*	I like the smell of bread **baking**.
8. sliding	*sliding*	Mud is **sliding** onto the road.
9. changing	*changing*	Is the car **changing** lanes?
10. waving	*waving*	The flag is **waving** in the breeze.
11. leaving	*leaving*	Is Ned **leaving** your house?
12. making	*making*	I am **making** a salad for dinner.
13. hoping	*hoping*	We are **hoping** you feel better soon.
14. trading	*trading*	Is that your stack of **trading** cards?
👀 **15.** having	*having*	I am **having** a sleepover tonight.

🔘 Review
16. grade   18. live
17. drive   19. save

🔘 Challenge
20. greeting   22. painting
21. handwriting 23. weaving

SORT the Basic Words

1–9. Write the spelling words that begin with a consonant followed by a vowel.

10–15. Write the spelling words that begin with a consonant digraph or consonant cluster.

REMEMBER the Spelling Strategy

Remember that when you add **-ing** to a word that ends in **silent e,** drop the **e** and add the ending: **take, taking.**

Spelling and Phonics

Word Analysis

Write the Basic Word that fits each clue.

1. It spells the **long e** sound with **ea**.

2. It spells the **short u** sound with **o**.

3. It has a **short a** sound and looks like **waving**.

4. Change one letter in **living**.

5. It has the **ng** digraph twice.

Rhyming Words

Write the Basic Word that completes each sentence and rhymes with the underlined word.

6. The judges are <u>rating</u> each skater's _____.

7. I am <u>raking</u> leaves, and Jan is _____ them away.

8. Fred is <u>making</u> cookies, and Jill is _____ bread.

9. We are _____ to the crew <u>paving</u> the street.

10. The babies keep _____ noise and <u>waking</u> me up.

Using the Dictionary

Dictionaries usually list only the base form of a word ending in **-ing**. Write the Basic Word that would be found in the entry for each of these base words.

11. choose

12. trade

13. smile

14. slide

15. hope

Word Analysis

1.

2.

3.

4.

5.

Rhyming Words

6.

7.

8.

9.

10.

Using the Dictionary

11.

12.

13.

14.

15.

coming	skating	taking	giving	choosing
smiling	baking	sliding	changing	waving
leaving	making	hoping	trading	having

Solve the Analogies

1.
2.
3.
4.
5.
6.

Complete the Sentences

7.
8.
9.
10.
11.
12.
13.
14.
15.

Solve the Analogies Write a Basic Word to complete each analogy.

1. **Destroying** is to **breaking** as **creating** is to _____.
2. **Leaving** is to **arriving** as **going** is to _____.
3. **Meat** is to **cooking** as **bread** is to _____.
4. **Track** is to **running** as **rink** is to _____.
5. **Sad** is to **frowning** as **happy** is to _____.
6. **Ball** is to **rolling** as **sled** is to _____.

Complete the Sentences Write the Basic Word that fits each sentence.

7. I am _____ my new soccer ball for Ann's new basketball.
8. Do you have trouble _____ from a menu?
9. Carlos said he plans on _____ the flat tire on my bike tomorrow.
10. Those old newspapers and magazines are _____ up too much space.
11. Sandy was _____ to get a bicycle for her birthday.
12. I will be _____ early for school tomorrow.
13. We are _____ hamburgers, potatoes, and fresh vegetables for dinner.
14. Gifts are for _____.
15. The children are looking out the window and _____ good-bye to their favorite teacher.

Proofread a Paragraph

First, proofread the paragraph below for eight misspelled words. Then rewrite the paragraph. Write the spelling words correctly and make the corrections shown by the proofreading marks.

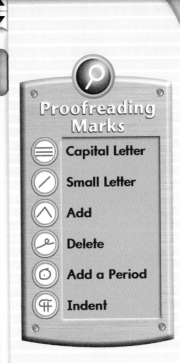
Proofreading Marks

≡	Capital Letter
/	Small Letter
∧	Add
✎	Delete
⊙	Add a Period
¶	Indent

¶ The scouts were haveing a meeting after school. Everyone was waiting outside, hopeing that mary would be comming soon⊙She was bringing a new member. Suddenly the scouts started makking a lot of noise and wavving at a car. It was Mary. Soon everyone was smileing and givving the new member a warm welcome. it looked like the new member was happy for choozing to join the Scouts.

More Practice Write and sort the Basic Words.

Write a Paragraph

Write about a time when you waited for someone to arrive or for something to happen. Be sure to tell who was there, when it happened, and what happened. Use as many spelling words as you can.

Writing Process

Prewrite
∨
Draft
∨
Revise
∨
Edit
∨
Publish

Proofread your writing as you

When you finish writing your draft, proofread your paper for errors in spelling, grammar, capitalization, and punctuation. Use the **Spelling Dictionary** to check spelling if you are not sure.

◎ Review

Review

Word Structure

1.

2.

3.

4.

Complete the Paragraph

5.

6.

7.

8.

| grade | drive | live | save |

Word Structure Combine each Review Word with **-ing** to make a new word.

1. grade + ing = _____

2. drive + ing = _____

3. live + ing = _____

4. save + ing = _____

Complete the Paragraph Combine each Review Word with **-ing** to complete the paragraph.

Mr. and Mrs. Franklin are teachers at the same school. For years, they have been __5.__ in a house only a few miles away. People often see them riding their bikes instead of __6.__ to school. They ride their bikes because they are __7.__ money. Cycling saves time, too. Now the Franklins have more time for __8.__ papers!

◎ Challenge

greeting   handwriting   painting   weaving

Word Clues Write the Challenge Word that fits each of these clues.

1. This word is made up of two words.
2. **Watercolor** is an example of this word.
3. **Hello** is an example of this word.
4. **Making a rug** is an example of this word.

Complete the Sentences Write a Challenge Word to complete each sentence.

5. The women are _____ cloth to sell to tourists who visit the area.
6. The famous _____ was stolen from the art museum.
7. Sue put a comma after the _____ in each of the letters she wrote.
8. His _____ is so bad that I can't read it!

 Do you think you've mastered the Spelling Strategy? Take the **CHAMPION CHALLENGE** on page 308!

Challenge

Word Clues

1.

2.

3.

4.

Complete the Sentences

5.

6.

7.

8.

Spelling and Technology

Spelling and Technology

Computer Uses

1. _____

2. _____

3. _____

4. _____

Computer Uses

You can do all sorts of things on a computer. You can write paragraphs and reports. You can write stories and letters. You can address envelopes and make labels. Computers are great for gaming, too. You can play video games, board games, and many other kinds of games.

| gaming | labels | reports | stories |

A. Write the word that matches each clue. Underline the word that drops a **silent e** before adding **-ing**.

1. Change one letter in **naming**.

2. I start like **storm** and end like **puppies**.

3. Find the word **port** in me.

4. I rhyme with **tables**.

B. For some fun and easy-to-use online games, check out Funschool at www. kidsdomain.com/games. Ask an adult to help you play a puzzle or board game. Write the name of the game and tell why you think others should play this game.

Content Words

Link to **Language Arts:** Vacations

Write the Content Word that completes each sentence.

camp	trail	cabin	explore

1. We will hike on a _____ in the Rocky Mountains.
2. At the end of the day, we will set up a _____.
3. The next day we will _____ the high country.
4. At the end of the hike, we will rent a _____ in the park.

Link to **Social Studies:** Manufacturing

Write the Content Word that matches each definition.

factory	goods	mill	trade

5. a building where grain is ground into flour
6. buying and selling
7. a building where furniture is made
8. things that workers make

Link to **The Spelling Strategy**

Circle the two Content Words you wrote that would drop their final **e** before adding the ending **-ing**.

Content Connection: Language Arts

Search the Internet to find out more about vacations. Look at www.travelforkids.com. Write the name of a place you would like to visit. Explain why you chose this place.

Content Words

Language Arts: Vacations

1. _____
2. _____
3. _____
4. _____

Social Studies: Manufacturing

5. _____
6. _____
7. _____
8. _____

Spelling Connections Online
www.zaner-bloser.com

Spelling and Thinking

-ed

1.

2.

3.

4.

5.

6.

7.

-ing

8.

9.

10.

11.

12.

13.

14.

15.

READ the Basic Words 👀 Watch out for easily misspelled words!

👀 **1.** stopped	*stopped*	The car **stopped** at the stop sign.
2. digging	*digging*	The dog is **digging** a hole.
3. rubbed	*rubbed*	I **rubbed** the cat's back.
4. sitting	*sitting*	Who was **sitting** in my chair?
5. planned	*planned*	We **planned** Mom's birthday party.
👀 **6.** wrapping	*wrapping*	We are **wrapping** the gift.
7. sledding	*sledding*	Brett went **sledding** on that hill.
8. dropped	*dropped*	Pat **dropped** the bat on my toe.
9. scrubbing	*scrubbing*	Pete is **scrubbing** the pot clean.
10. hopped	*hopped*	The rabbit **hopped** away.
👀 **11.** putting	*putting*	I am **putting** my shoes on now.
12. tripped	*tripped*	Ari **tripped** over the dog's bone.
13. swimming	*swimming*	We went **swimming** in the pool.
14. spotted	*spotted*	Ty **spotted** an eagle on the cliff.
15. running	*running*	Who is **running** in today's race?

◎ Review

16. bat   18. nod
17. chop   19. stop

◎ Challenge

20. grabbed   22. knitting
21. jogging   23. strolled

SORT the Basic Words

Write the spelling words that

   1–7. double the consonant and add **-ed**.

   8–15. double the consonant and add **-ing**.

REMEMBER the Spelling Strategy

Remember that when you add **-ed** or **-ing** to a word that ends with one vowel and one consonant, double the consonant and add the ending: **stop, stopped**.

Spelling and Phonics

Beginning and Ending Sounds

Write the Basic Words for these clues.

1–3. Write the Basic Words that rhyme with **mopped**.

4–5. Write the Basic Words that begin with consonant clusters with **l**.

Word Structure

6. Write the Basic Word that ends with **-ed** and has two syllables.

7. Add one letter to **ripped** to make this word.

8. Take away two letters from **scrubbed** to make this word.

9–10. Change the first syllables of **hugging** and **stopping** to make these words.

11. Change two letters in **trimming** to make this word.

 Using the Dictionary

Write the Basic Word that you would find under each of these dictionary entry words.

12. run   **13.** scrub   **14.** put   **15.** sit

◆ ◆ ◆

Dictionary Check Be sure to check your answers in your **Spelling Dictionary**.

Beginning and Ending Sounds

1.

2.

3.

4.

5.

Word Structure

6.

7.

8.

9.

10.

11.

Using the Dictionary

12.

13.

14.

15.

Edit the Categories

1.

2.

3.

4.

5.

6.

7.

Complete the Sentences

8.

9.

10.

11.

12.

13.

14.

15.

stopped	digging	rubbed	sitting	planned
wrapping	sledding	dropped	scrubbing	hopped
putting	tripped	swimming	spotted	running

Edit the Categories Write the Basic Word that does not belong in each group.

1. walking, jogging, running, sitting
2. swimming, putting, setting, placing
3. sledding, scrubbing, skating, swimming
4. hopped, jumped, tripped, bounced
5. planned, hoped, stopped, dreamed
6. skated, walked, dropped, jogged
7. hopping, putting, jumping, bouncing

Complete the Sentences Write a Basic Word to complete each sentence.

8. Carol _____ her hands together near the campfire to warm them.
9. The dog was _____ a hole in the ground to bury its bone.
10. Roberto likes to go _____ on these steep hills after a snowstorm.
11. A frog _____ in the mud by the pond.
12. Angela _____ to build a doghouse.
13. The cowboy rode a _____ pony in the Fourth of July parade.
14. Kaitlin is _____ after her dog again.
15. We have finished _____ the gifts and making the cookies for the party.

Spelling and Writing

Proofread a Paragraph

First, proofread the paragraph below for eight misspelled words. Then rewrite the paragraph. Write the spelling words correctly and make the corrections shown by the proofreading marks.

⌐ We had a great time at the zoo ⊙ We saw sea Lions swiming in their tank. We heard the monkeys screaming as they they jumped and droped from trees. We saw a spoted snake wrappin itself around a tree trunk. A prairie Dog even hoped across our path. Then a chipmunk went runing by. That stoped us in our tracks! We couldn't have plannd a better trip to the zoo.

More Practice Write and sort the Basic Words.

Write a Paragraph

Tell about a place you have visited. Make it come to life by giving details about what you saw there. Add any other details you observed with your senses, such as things you heard or smelled. Use as many spelling words as you can.

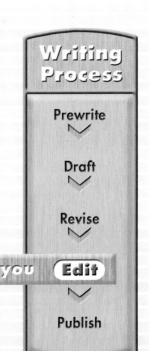

Proofreading Marks

≡	Capital Letter
/	Small Letter
∧	Add
ℒ	Delete
⊙	Add a Period
⌐	Indent

Writing Process

Prewrite
∨
Draft
∨
Revise
∨

Proofread your writing as you **Edit**
∨
Publish

When you finish writing your draft, proofread your paper for errors in spelling, grammar, capitalization, and punctuation. Use the **Spelling Dictionary** to check spelling if you are not sure.

◉ Review

Review

Word Structure

1. _____

2. _____

3. _____

4. _____

Complete the Sentences

5. _____

6. _____

7. _____

8. _____

More Than One Meaning

1. _____

bat	chop	nod	stop

Word Structure Combine each Review Word with **-ing** to make a new word.

1. nod + ing = _____   **3.** chop + ing = _____

2. bat + ing = _____   **4.** stop + ing = _____

Complete the Sentences Add **-ed** to a Review Word to complete each sentence.

5. He _____ in agreement.

6. The kitten _____ the ball of yarn.

7. Dan _____ firewood for the campfire.

8. The cars _____ at the red light.

Word Study: More Than One Meaning

Many words have more than one meaning. Write the one Review Word that has all these meanings:

- a flying mammal
- a stick for hitting a ball
- to hit a ball

Challenge

grabbed   jogging   knitting   strolled

Replace the Words Write the Challenge Word that best replaces the underlined word or words.

1. Robyn's favorite sport is <u>running</u>.

2. Tom likes <u>making things with yarn and needles</u>.

3. The Ramirez family <u>walked slowly</u> down the avenue.

4. Zoe <u>quickly reached for and held on to</u> the dog's collar before the dog could run away.

Word Groups Write the Challenge Word that belongs in each group.

5. sewing, stitching, _____

6. walked, wandered, _____

7. running, sprinting, _____

8. took, caught, _____

 Do you think you've mastered the Spelling Strategy? Take the CHAMPION CHALLENGE on page 309!

Challenge

Replace the Words

1.

2.

3.

4.

Word Groups

5.

6.

7.

8.

Spelling and Technology

Online Chatting and Blogging

The Internet can bring people together. People chat on messenger services and in chat rooms. Many people blog. That means they keep Web logs. These are journals that other people can read. Some people add photos of their family and friends.

Here are some terms about talking online.

blog	blogging	chat	chatting

Four words are not spelled correctly in these paragraphs. Write the words correctly. Underline the words that doubled the final consonant before adding **-ing**.

Lily and Rose like to chate online. They send messages to each other and to other friends, too. They go on chating until one of them signs off.

Lily's mom plans to start a Web log, or blawg, online. She wants to record their experience with their new dog, Max. Lily thinks bloging about their dog will be fun. She can't wait to share it with Rose.

Content Words

Link to   **Social Studies:** Business

Write the Content Word that matches each definition.

logging	mining	shipping	fishing

1. catching fish
2. cutting trees and turning them into logs
3. sending goods by ship, truck, train, or air
4. taking minerals from the earth

Link to   **Language Arts:** Synonyms

Write the Content Word that is a synonym for each word below.

cool	tote	alike	sew

5. same
6. stitch
7. carry
8. chilly

Link to   **The Spelling Strategy**

Circle the double consonant letters in two of the Content Words you wrote.

Content Connection: Social Studies

 Search the Internet to find out more about running a business. Work with a partner to discuss a business you would like to start. Report your choice to the class.

Content Words

Social Studies: Business

1. _____
2. _____
3. _____
4. _____

Language Arts: Synonyms

5. _____
6. _____
7. _____
8. _____

Spelling and Thinking

READ the Basic Words 👀 Watch out for easily misspelled words!

1.	he's	*he's*	Tell Bob **he's** next at bat.
2.	what's	*what's*	I do not know **what's** happening.
3.	don't	*don't*	I **don't** have Ken's e-mail address.
4.	I'm	*I'm*	He is Nick, and **I'm** Ben.
5.	that's	*that's*	Tell me **that's** your best work.
👀 **6.**	doesn't	*doesn't*	A lion **doesn't** have stripes.
7.	there's	*there's*	Where **there's** smoke, there is fire.
8.	she's	*she's*	Tammy says **she's** coming to the party.
9.	isn't	*isn't*	That joke **isn't** very funny.
10.	I'll	*I'll*	On my next birthday, **I'll** be ten.
👀 **11.**	won't	*won't*	Grandma **won't** get here until Monday.
12.	here's	*here's*	There is your pen, and **here's** mine.
13.	didn't	*didn't*	Who **didn't** get any dessert?
👀 **14.**	who's	*who's*	Do you know **who's** knocking?
15.	can't	*can't*	I **can't** see a thing in the dark.

Review
16. he 18. they
17. she 19. will

Challenge
20. hasn't 22. let's
21. I'd 23. you're

SORT the Basic Words

1–2. Write the contractions that contain **I**.

3–9. Write the contractions that shorten **is**.

10–15. Write the contractions that shorten **not**.

REMEMBER the Spelling Strategy

Remember that a **contraction** shortens two words into one word: **I am** becomes **I'm**. The apostrophe (') in a contraction takes the place of letters or sounds that are left out.

contain I

1.
2.

shorten is

3.
4.
5.
6.
7.
8.
9.

shorten not

10.
11.
12.
13.
14.
15.

Spelling and Phonics

Word Structure

Follow the directions to write a Basic Word. Be sure to add an apostrophe in the correct place.

1. who + is – i = _____
2. that + is – i = _____
3. did + not – o = _____
4. what + is – i = _____
5. there + is – i = _____
6. do + not – o = _____

Word Replacements

Write the Basic Words that can replace the underlined words.

7. Mrs. Rocco thinks that <u>she is</u> the winner.
8. I <u>cannot</u> find the pencil I dropped.
9. Maya <u>does not</u> know the answer to the question.
10. This <u>is not</u> the same place I remember.
11. I think <u>I am</u> next in line.
12. Jared <u>will not</u> tell your secret.

Using the Dictionary

Write the Basic Word for each dictionary respelling.

13. /hēz/   14. /īl/   15. /hîrz/

Dictionary Check Be sure to check each respelling in your **Spelling Dictionary**.

Word Structure

1. _____
2. _____
3. _____
4. _____
5. _____
6. _____

Word Replacements

7. _____
8. _____
9. _____
10. _____
11. _____
12. _____

Using the Dictionary

13. _____
14. _____
15. _____

Complete the Sentences

1.
2.
3.
4.
5.
6.
7.
8.
9.

Solve the Analogies

10.
11.
12.
13.
14.
15.

he's	what's	don't	I'm	that's
doesn't	there's	she's	isn't	I'll
won't	here's	didn't	who's	can't

Complete the Sentences Write the Basic Word that completes each sentence. Use a contraction of the words in parentheses.

1. Today _____ going to help Sarah. (I am)
2. Sarah said _____ finally going to clean up the attic. (she is)
3. I know _____ a lot of work. (that is)
4. She _____ do it alone. (cannot)
5. Besides, I would like to find out _____ up there. (what is)
6. I think _____ a trunk somewhere up there from her grandparents. (there is)
7. Maybe _____ get Terry to help us, too. (I will)
8. If _____ free, I think he will help us. (he is)
9. Terry _____ like to say "no" to his friends when they ask a favor. (does not)

Solve the Analogies Write the Basic Word that completes each analogy.

10. **Yes** is to **no** as **did** is to _____.
11. **What** is to **what's** as **who** is to _____.
12. **Far** is to **near** as **there's** is to _____.
13. **Does** is to **doesn't** as **do** is to _____.
14. **Try** is to **quit** as **will** is to _____.
15. **Find** is to **lose** as **is** is to _____.

Spelling and Writing

Proofread a Postcard

Proofread the postcard for eight misspelled words. Then rewrite it. Write the spelling words correctly and make the corrections shown by the proofreading marks.

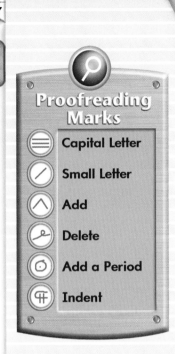
Proofreading Marks

≡	Capital Letter
/	Small Letter
∧	Add
✄	Delete
⊙	Add a Period
¶	Indent

dear Mark,

¶ Im having so much fun. Thats our hotel on the other side of this card⊙Ther'es a pool and a place to play games. I met a boy whose from Ohio, too. Hees here with his family on vacation. You cen't see the ocean, but it is ~is~ warm. The waves are small but fun. The beach isnt crowded either. Ill see you soon⊙

     Your friend,

     sean

More Practice Write and sort the Basic Words.

Write a Postcard

Write a postcard about a place you have visited. Give details that help your reader imagine the place. Use commas after your opening and closing. Indent your paragraphs, your closing, and your signature. Use as many spelling words as you can.

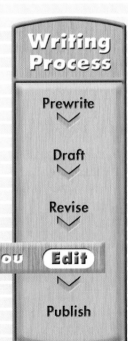
Writing Process

Prewrite
∨
Draft
∨
Revise
∨

> > > > > **Proofread your writing as you** **Edit**
∨
Publish

When you finish writing your draft, proofread your paper for errors in spelling, grammar, capitalization, and punctuation. Use the **Spelling Dictionary** to check spelling if you are not sure.

◎ Review

Review

Complete the Sentences

_____ 1. _____

_____ 2. _____

_____ 3. _____

_____ 4. _____

Complete the Paragraph

_____ 5. _____

_____ 6. _____

_____ 7. _____

_____ 8. _____

Writer's Tip

_____ 1. _____

he	she	they	will

Complete the Sentences Write a Review Word to complete each sentence.

1. **She'll** is a contraction of the words _____ and **will**.

2. **He'll** is a contraction of the words _____ and **will**.

3. **They'll** is a contraction of the words _____ and **will**.

4. **Won't** is a contraction of the words _____ and **not**.

Complete the Paragraph Change the Review Words into contractions to complete the paragraph.

Lola is in third grade. __5.__ be eight years old on Wednesday. Benny is in fourth grade. __6.__ be nine years old in two months. __7.__ walk to school together this year. But next year, they __8.__ walk to school. They will take the bus!

Word Study: Writer's Tip

● Good writers need to use words correctly when they write. **Your** means that something belongs to you. Write the Challenge Word that means "you are."

Challenge

| hasn't | I'd | let's | you're |

Word Clues Write the Challenge Word for each clue.

1. It means "I would" or "I had."
2. It means the opposite of **has**.
3. It is the contraction for the words **let us**.
4. It belongs in a group of words with **they're** and **we're**.

Complete the Sentences Write a Challenge Word to complete each sentence.

5. _____ go to the park together after school to play catch.
6. _____ like to go fishing, but I don't have a fishing pole.
7. He _____ practiced the piano in two weeks because he broke his finger.
8. If _____ in a hurry, you should take a taxi to the airport.

Challenge

Word Clues

1.
2.
3.
4.

Complete the Sentences

5.
6.
7.
8.

 Do you think you've mastered the Spelling Strategy? Take the CHAMPION CHALLENGE on page 310!

Spelling and Technology

Spelling and Technology

Spell Checkers: Contractions

1. _____

2. _____

3. _____

4. _____

5. _____

6. _____

Spell Checkers: Contractions

Contractions sometimes look very much like other words. Therefore spell checkers do not always catch errors in contractions. You will need to proofread carefully to be sure you have spelled contractions correctly.

Study the differences between each pair of words.

she'll	we're	who's
shell	were	whose

Read these paragraphs. Write the missing words from the box. Be sure to use capital letters correctly.

 A strange thing happened on the hike. Maria found a __1.__ on the mountain. All of us __2.__ so surprised! We asked, "How could it have gotten here? __3.__ pocket did it fall out of?"

 What will Maria do with the shell? __4.__ probably just leave it where she found it. Tim, __5.__ our guide, says that it looks beautiful on the tree moss. The rest of us agree. __6.__ happy to leave it behind.

Content Words

Link to **Math:** Operations

Write Content Words to complete the paragraph.

hundreds	rename	borrow	regroup

To subtract 39 from 51, you must __1.__ one ten and __2.__ or __3.__ it as ten ones. When you subtract numbers with three digits, such as 299 from 321, you have to borrow from the tens and also from the __4.__ .

Link to **Social Studies:** Geography

Write the Content Word that matches each definition.

border	foothill	shoreline	hillside

5. side of a hill

6. line that marks where a body of water begins or ends

7. low hill near the bottom of a mountain

8. line that divides one area from another

Link to **The Spelling Strategy**

Circle the double consonant letters in three of the Content Words you wrote.

Content Connection: Math

 Search the Internet to find out more about math operations. You might look at **www.kidsnumbers.com**. Click on **Subtraction**. Write the name of a game and then play it.

Content Words

Math: Operations

1. _____

2. _____

3. _____

4. _____

Social Studies: Geography

5. _____

6. _____

7. _____

8. _____

Spelling Connections Online
www.zaner-bloser.com

Assessment and Review

Unit 25

1.

2.

3.

Unit 26

4.

5.

6.

Unit 27

7.

8.

9.

Unit 28

10.

11.

12.

Unit 29

13.

14.

15.

ASSESSMENT

Units 25-29

Each Assessment Word in the box fits one of the spelling strategies you have studied over the past five weeks. Write each Assessment Word under the unit number it fits.

Unit 25

1-3. Two-syllable words with a short vowel sound in the first syllable are often spelled with double consonants: **dinner, better**.

Unit 26

4-6. The final **long e** sound in words like **happy** usually follows a double consonant and is spelled **y**.

Unit 27

7-9. When you add **-ing** to a word that ends in **silent e,** drop the **e** and add the ending: **take, taking**.

Unit 28

10-12. When you add **-ed** or **-ing** to a word that ends with one vowel and one consonant, double the consonant and add the ending: **stop, stopped**.

Unit 29

13-15. A **contraction** shortens two words into one word: **I am** becomes **I'm**. The apostrophe (') in a contraction takes the place of letters or sounds that are left out.

getting
you've
driving
mommy
butter
puppet
daddy
aren't
chasing
hopping
gallop
dizzy
using
stepped
hadn't

REVIEW

Unit 25: Double Consonants

happen	sudden	letter	summer
cotton	lesson	better	

Write the spelling word that completes the sentence.

1. The brakes squealed as the car came to a _____ stop.
2. I studied my science _____ carefully.
3. My teacher says I am doing _____.
4. How could that accident _____?
5. It gets very hot in the _____.
6. My new shirt is made of _____.
7. There was a long _____ from my grandmother in today's mail.

REVIEW

Unit 26: Double Consonants + y

funny	pretty	happy	sorry
hurry	carry	puppy	

Write the spelling word that means the opposite of each word or words.

8. ugly
9. sad
10. grown dog
11. glad

Write the spelling word that rhymes with each word.

12. scurry
13. marry
14. honey

Unit 25

1.
2.
3.
4.
5.
6.
7.

Unit 26

8.
9.
10.
11.
12.
13.
14.

1.

2.

3.

4.

5.

6.

7.

8.

9.

10.

11.

12.

13.

14.

REVIEW

Unit 27: Adding -ing

| baking | having | coming | leaving |
| taking | giving | changing | |

Write the spelling word that completes each sentence.

1. Dad was _____ cookies for our party.
2. Will you be _____ to the party with me?
3. No, I am _____ for the party now.
4. What are you _____ with you?
5. Our picture was taken just as we were _____ Mother the present.
6. We have been _____ a good time.
7. Sit close to me because we are supposed to start _____ places soon.

REVIEW

Unit 28: Adding -ed and -ing

| dropped | stopped | running | swimming |
| planned | putting | sitting | |

Find the misspelled word in each sentence. Write it correctly.

8. He droped the ball.
9. It was stoppped in time.
10. No runing is allowed at the pool.
11. He was sittin on the porch.
12. Meg planed to go with me.
13. Swiming is my favorite sport.
14. He was puttng away the art supplies.

Unit 29: Contractions

can't   that's   didn't   won't
I'm   don't   he's

Write the spelling word that is a contraction for each word or pair of words below.

1. he is
2. that is
3. will not
4. did not

5. cannot
6. do not
7. I am

GAME

Spelling Study Strategy

Word Swap

Practicing spelling words can be fun if you make it into a game.

1. Swap spelling lists with a partner.

2. Ask your partner to read the first word on your list. Write the word on a piece of scrap paper.

3. Ask your partner to check your spelling. If you spelled the word correctly, your partner should say the next word on your list. If you did not spell the word correctly, ask your partner to spell the word out loud for you. Write the correct spelling.

4. Keep going until you have practiced five words. Then trade jobs. Continue until you and your partner have practiced all the words on your lists.

1.
2.
3.
4.
5.
6.
7.

Writer's Workshop

Grammar, Usage, and Mechanics

Adjectives

An **adjective** describes, or tells about, a noun. Adjectives make sentences more interesting.

> A **huge** lizard hid behind the **open** door.

> The **hungry** girls quickly ate the **delicious** pizza.

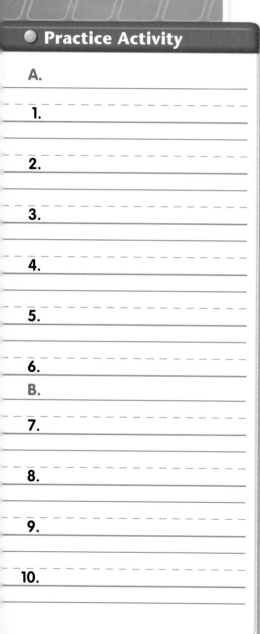

Practice Activity

A.

1.

2.

3.

4.

5.

6.

B.

7.

8.

9.

10.

Practice ACTIVITY

A. Write the adjective that describes the underlined noun in each sentence.

1. My older <u>brother</u> met me after school.
2. The Florios got a blue <u>van</u>.
3. The sound came from the dark <u>basement</u>.
4. You will need a sharp <u>pencil</u> for this.
5. Be careful with the hot <u>soup</u>!
6. Everyone wants to meet the new <u>teacher</u>.

B. Write an adjective from the spelling lists in Units 25–29 that can complete each sentence.

7. Alan told a very _____ joke!
8. A _____ rainstorm caught us by surprise.
9. Your new dress is so _____!
10. A _____ baby giggles and smiles.

The Writing Process PERSUASIVE

Writing a Persuasive Paragraph

Prewriting

There are many types of pets: cats, dogs, and snakes. Which animal makes the best pet? There are books about pets at the library. You can also find information on Internet sites such as Care For Animals (www.avma.org/careforanimals). As you think about a pet, list the reasons you think that pet is the best to have.

Drafting

Use your reasons to write a persuasive paragraph. Begin with a topic sentence. Follow your ideas as you write supporting sentences. Use as many spelling words as possible.

Revising

When you have finished your first draft, read your paragraph from beginning to end. Check to see if you have included all of your reasons. Now write your final draft.

Editing ✓

Use the editing checklist to proofread your paragraph. Be sure to use proofreading marks when you make corrections.

Publishing

Make a copy of your persuasive paragraph. Add a picture of the best pet and share it with your readers.

✓ Editing Checklist

Spelling

- ○ I circled words that contain the spelling strategies I learned in Units 25–29.
- ○ I checked the circled words in my Spelling Dictionary.
- ○ I also checked for other spelling errors.

Capital Letters

- ○ Important words in the title
- ○ Beginning of all sentences
- ○ Proper nouns

Punctuation

- ○ Each sentence ends with the correct punctuation.
- ○ Commas, apostrophes, and quotation marks are used correctly.

Grammar, Usage, and Mechanics

- ○ Adjectives are used correctly to make sentences more interesting.

Spelling and Thinking

READ the Basic Words 👀 Watch out for easily misspelled words!

1. flags	*flags*	That ship is flying two **flags**.
2. inches	*inches*	There are twelve **inches** in a foot.
👀 3. dresses	*dresses*	Pam's **dresses** are all too short.
4. pies	*pies*	Two **pies** are baking in the oven.
5. bushes	*bushes*	The ball is lost in the **bushes**.
6. classes	*classes*	My dad takes **classes** in French.
7. apples	*apples*	Some **apples** fell from the tree.
👀 8. colors	*colors*	What **colors** are in the painting?
9. drums	*drums*	Marge plays the **drums** in the band.
10. branches	*branches*	Some tree **branches** need cutting.
11. things	*things*	I put my **things** in my pack.
👀 12. buses	*buses*	The school **buses** bring us home.
13. benches	*benches*	People sit on **benches** in the park.
14. tracks	*tracks*	We followed the deer's **tracks**.
15. brushes	*brushes*	Those **brushes** are for oil painting.

◎ Review

16. boats   18. snacks
17. foxes   19. wishes

◎ Challenge

20. friends   22. sandwiches
21. patches   23. slippers

SORT the Basic Words

1–7. Write the spelling words that form the plural by adding **-s**.

8–15. Write the spelling words that form the plural by adding **-es**.

REMEMBER the Spelling Strategy

Remember that you can add **-s** or **-es** to many words to make them plural.

add -s

1.

2.

3.

4.

5.

6.

7.

add -es

8.

9.

10.

11.

12.

13.

14.

15.

Spelling and Phonics

Word Analysis

Write the Basic Word that fits each clue.

1. It begins with the **short a** sound.

2. It has the letter **o** in both syllables.

3–4. Their base words end with **ss**.

5. It begins with the **short i** sound.

6. Its base word ends with a single **s**.

Rhyming Words

Write the Basic Word that completes each sentence and rhymes with the underlined word.

7. He <u>tries</u>, but John cannot make apple _____.

8. Lisa <u>hums</u> a tune while Jeremy plays the _____.

9. The skier <u>brags</u>, "I'm the first to pass the _____."

10. My aunt <u>brings</u> lots of funny _____.

11. They loaded their <u>packs</u>, and followed the bear's _____.

12. If Matt <u>pushes</u>, he will move the _____.

Using the Dictionary

Write the Basic Words that are on the page with these guide words.

13–14. bloom • brick   **15.** beep • blood

◆ ◆ ◆

Dictionary Check Be sure to check the guide words in your **Spelling Dictionary**.

Word Analysis

1.

2.

3.

4.

5.

6.

Rhyming Words

7.

8.

9.

10.

11.

12.

Using the Dictionary

13.

14.

15.

Complete the Sentences

1. _____
2. _____
3. _____
4. _____
5. _____
6. _____
7. _____
8. _____

Complete the Groups

9. _____
10. _____
11. _____
12. _____
13. _____
14. _____
15. _____

flags	inches	dresses	pies	bushes
classes	apples	colors	drums	branches
things	buses	benches	tracks	brushes

Complete the Sentences Write the Basic Word that completes each sentence.

1. We will need several different sizes of _____ to paint this wall.
2. Orange and red are warm _____.
3. There are many _____ happening at school this week besides classes.
4. A train is coming down the _____.
5. Two _____ are flying on the tall poles in front of our school.
6. Those rose _____ have grown a lot since we planted them last year.
7. There are new _____ on the field for each team's players.
8. Nell is taking ballet _____.

Complete the Groups Write the Basic Word that belongs in each group.

9. flutes, pianos, _____
10. miles, yards, feet, _____
11. bananas, peaches, pears, _____
12. cookies, cakes, _____
13. cars, trucks, _____
14. skirts, pants, _____
15. trunks, leaves, _____

Spelling and Writing

Proofread an E-Mail Message

Proofread the e-mail message for eight misspelled words. Then rewrite it. Write the spelling words correctly and make the corrections shown by the proofreading marks.

To: Lauren2010@edirect.com

From: Rferrara@fastserve.com

Subject: Picking Apples

Dear lauren,

After my brother finishes his clases he will take us to pick appels. Can you come? He wants to see the fall colores of the Leaves on the branchs. I want to follow the rabbit trackes through the bushs. There are are many thinges we can make with the apples. You can eat peies with us later.

Ava

More Practice Write and sort the Basic Words.

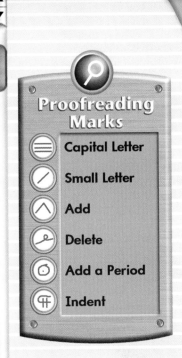

Proofreading Marks

≡ Capital Letter

/ Small Letter

∧ Add

⌀ Delete

⊙ Add a Period

¶ Indent

 **EXPOSITORY**

Write an E-Mail Message

Write an e-mail message inviting someone to go somewhere with you. Tell where you will go and what you will do. Use as many spelling words as you can.

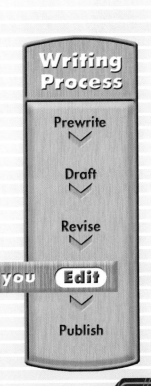

Writing Process

Prewrite

∨

Draft

∨

Revise

∨

Edit

∨

Publish

 **Proofread your writing as you**

When you finish writing your draft, proofread your paper for errors in spelling, grammar, capitalization, and punctuation. Use the **Spelling Dictionary** to check spelling if you are not sure.

Review

Review

Word Analysis

1.

2.

3.

4.

Complete the Paragraph

5.

6.

7.

8.

Eponyms

1.

boats	foxes	snacks	wishes

Word Analysis Write the Review Word that fits each clue.

1. It begins like **foot**.
2. It rhymes with **dishes**.
3. It spells the **long o** sound **oa**.
4. It rhymes with **tracks**.

Complete the Paragraph Write the Review Words to complete the paragraph.

One of Mark's __5.__ for his birthday was to go to the zoo. So his mother packed some __6.__ for the family to eat, and they went. They saw lions, zebras, deer, __7.__, and many other animals. Then they got into __8.__ and sailed through the zoo on a small river. It was a great birthday for Mark!

Word Study: Eponyms

An **eponym** is a word that comes from someone's name. The **leotard** was named after Jules **Leotard**, a trapeze artist. Write the Challenge Word that came from the name **Earl of Sandwich**.

Challenge

| friends | patches | sandwiches | slippers |

Answer the Questions Write a Challenge Word to answer each question.

1. What might you use to cover holes in a pair of pants?
2. What might you make for lunch?
3. What might you wear on your feet inside your home?
4. What might you have if you are kind?

Complete the Sentences Write a Challenge Word to complete each sentence.

5. Her favorite _____ are pink and fuzzy.
6. Ryan is meeting his _____ at three o'clock.
7. The hikers ate some _____ when they stopped to rest.
8. Grandmother used the _____ to make a quilt.

Challenge

Answer the Questions

1. _____
2. _____
3. _____
4. _____

Complete the Sentences

5. _____
6. _____
7. _____
8. _____

Do you think you've mastered the Spelling Strategy? Take the CHAMPION CHALLENGE on page 311!

Spelling and Technology

Spelling and Technology

Skimming a Web Page

1. _____

2. _____

3. _____

4. _____

Skimming a Web Page

You type in a Web address for news or maps. A page pops up. What do you do next? You can skim the page for the information you want. Here's how:

News: Read the headlines. Read the first paragraph. Read headings, too. Then look at photos and read their captions.

Maps: Look at the title of the map. Study the key to find out more about the map.

These words name parts of online text.

headlines	maps	news	photos

Write the word from the box that completes each sentence. Underline the word that ends with **s** but is not plural.

1. Many people find _____ on the Web for driving.

2. You can read the latest _____ stories on the Web, too.

3. Often, _____ on Web pages are set in large type.

4. You can also find _____ of famous people on the Web.

Content Words

Link to **Language Arts:** Fairy Tales

Write Content Words to complete the paragraph.

castle	princess	prince	kingdom

Once upon a time in a faraway land, a __1.__ and a __2.__ lived in a huge __3.__ on a hill. From their tower, they could see the whole __4.__.

Link to **Math:** Geometry

Write the Content Word that completes each sentence.

endpoints	lines	segments	sides

5. You can draw straight _____ with a ruler.

6. Line _____ are parts of lines.

7. A line segment has two _____.

8. A rectangle has four _____.

Link to **The Spelling Strategy**

Circle the letters that form the plural in four of the Content Words you wrote.

Content Connection: Language Arts

Search the Internet to find out more about fairy tales. Try www.grimmfairytales.com. Listen to a fairy tale. Write its name.

Content Words

Language Arts: Fairy Tales

1. _____

2. _____

3. _____

4. _____

Math: Geometry

5. _____

6. _____

7. _____

8. _____

Spelling and Thinking

one or more

1. _____

one

2. _____
3. _____
4. _____
5. _____
6. _____
7. _____
8. _____

more than one

9. _____
10. _____
11. _____
12. _____
13. _____
14. _____
15. _____

READ the Basic Words 👀 Watch out for easily misspelled words!

1.	goose	*goose*	We cooked a **goose** for dinner.
2.	woman	*woman*	The **woman** held her son's hand.
👀 3.	calf	*calf*	The **calf** stays near its mother.
4.	fish	*fish*	I saw **fish** swimming in the lake.
5.	mouse	*mouse*	The **mouse** lives in the hayfield.
6.	leaf	*leaf*	A **leaf** takes in light for a plant.
👀 7.	children	*children*	The **children** are six years old.
8.	geese	*geese*	The **geese** fly together in flocks.
9.	calves	*calves*	Many **calves** are in the barn.
10.	leaves	*leaves*	The **leaves** fell from the elm tree.
11.	half	*half*	We split the orange in **half**.
12.	child	*child*	The **child** is looking for her father.
👀 13.	women	*women*	These **women** are studying law.
14.	mice	*mice*	If **mice** come inside, get a cat.
15.	halves	*halves*	Two **halves** make a whole.

Review
16. foot   18. tooth
17. feet   19. teeth

Challenge
20. reindeer   22. lava
21. air mail   23. spinach

SORT the Basic Words

1. Write the word that can name both "one" or "more than one."

2–8. Write the words that name "one."

9–15. Write the words that name "more than one."

REMEMBER the Spelling Strategy

Remember that you must change several letters in some words to make the plural form.

Spelling and Phonics

Sound and Letter Patterns

Follow the directions to write Basic Words.

1. leaves – ves + f = _____

2. women – en + an = _____

3. catch – tch + lf = _____

4. hallway – way – l + f = _____

5. mountain – ntain + se = _____

Word Structure

6–8. Write the Basic Words that are formed by changing **f** to **v** and adding **-es**.

9. Change one letter in **loose** to make this word.

10. Change one letter in **fist** to make this word.

11. Change two letters in **goose** to make this word.

12. Change the final consonant cluster in **chirp** to make this word.

Using the Dictionary

The dictionary lists plural forms of words that do not form the plural by adding **-s** or **-es**. Write the Basic Word that you would find in the dictionary entry for each of these words.

13. child　　　**14.** mouse　　　**15.** woman

◆ ◆ ◆

Dictionary Check Use the **Spelling Dictionary** to check your answers.

Sound and Letter Patterns

1. _____

2. _____

3. _____

4. _____

5. _____

Word Structure

6. _____

7. _____

8. _____

9. _____

10. _____

11. _____

12. _____

Using the Dictionary

13. _____

14. _____

15. _____

goose	woman	calf	fish	mouse
leaf	children	geese	calves	leaves
half	child	women	mice	halves

Complete the Groups

1.
2.
3.
4.
5.

Name the Categories

6.
7.
8.

Complete the Story

9.
10.
11.
12.
13.
14.
15.

Complete the Groups Write the Basic Word that belongs in each group.

1. bulls, cows, _____
2. quarters, thirds, _____
3. infant, baby, _____
4. stem, twig, _____
5. hamster, gerbil, _____

Name the Categories Write the Basic Word that names the category into which these examples fit.

6. guppies, sharks, cod
7. Town Mouse, Mickey Mouse, Mighty Mouse
8. Mrs. Green, Ms. Ramos, Lady Jane

Complete the Story Write Basic Words to complete the story.

Once upon a time, there was a family that lived near the forest. They sold spices and tea __9.__. When fall came, all the __10.__ needed new shoes. The family had only __11.__ of the money they needed. They decided to sell their only __12.__, a young bull, to raise the rest of the money.

On the way to the market, the man and the __13.__ saw a __14.__ flapping its wings and honking wildly. They saw that the bird was hurt. They bandaged its leg.

As the goose flew off to join the other __15.__, he called down to them, "You will be rewarded for your kindness."

Spelling and Writing

Proofread a Story Beginning

Proofread the story beginning below for eight misspelled words. Then rewrite the story beginning. Write the spelling words correctly and make the corrections shown by the proofreading marks.

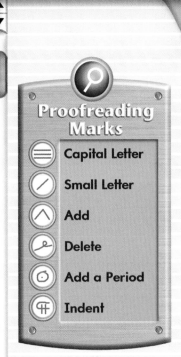

Proofreading Marks

≡ Capital Letter
/ Small Letter
∧ Add
✎ Delete
⊙ Add a Period
¶ Indent

¶ *A long time ago, on a small farm down a Quiet road, there lived a mowse named Louisa and her chilldren. They lived under a small pile of hay and leafs. Haf of the time, louisa and the other myce had little to eat. They were poor, but they had a good Life. Their only neighbors were two loud but friendly geeses, some calfs, and some fishes.*

More Practice Write and sort the Basic Words.

Write a Story Beginning

Begin a story of your own. Remember that good story beginnings include the characters and setting. Be sure to tell the names of the people or animals. Write where and when your story takes place. Use as many spelling words as you can.

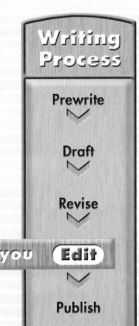

Writing Process

Prewrite
⌄
Draft
⌄
Revise
⌄
Edit
⌄
Publish

> > > > > Proofread your writing as you **Edit**

When you finish writing your draft, proofread your paper for errors in spelling, grammar, capitalization, and punctuation. Use the **Spelling Dictionary** to check spelling if you are not sure.

◎ Review

Review

Solve the Analogies

1.

2.

3.

4.

Complete the Sentences

5.

6.

7.

8.

Related Words

1.

| foot | feet | tooth | teeth |

Solve the Analogies Write the Review Word that completes each analogy.

1. **Gloves** is to **hands** as **shoes** is to _____.

2. A **yard** is to a **mile** as an **inch** is to a _____.

3. A **hand** is to a **fingernail** as a **mouth** is to a _____.

4. **Taste** is to **tongue** as **chew** is to _____.

Complete the Sentences Write a Review Word to complete each sentence.

5. Don't forget to brush your _____ before bed.

6. That hotdog was a _____ long!

7. Jacob lost his first baby _____ last week.

8. Someone who is clumsy is said to have "two left _____."

Word Study: Related Words

● Related words have the same word or word part in them. For example, **toothbrush** and **toothpaste** are related words. Write the one Review Word that relates these words: ____**ball,** ____**hills,** ____**step.**

Challenge

| reindeer | air mail | lava | spinach |

Word Clues Write the Challenge Word that fits each clue.

1. This word is the same whether you are talking about a whole herd or just one.
2. This word names a vegetable.
3. This word names a way of sending letters.
4. This word names a kind of liquid rock.

Complete the Groups Write the Challenge Word that belongs in each group.

5. rock, volcano, _____
6. vegetable, leaves, _____
7. letter, plane, _____
8. animal, cold climate, _____

 Do you think you've mastered the Spelling Strategy? Take the CHAMPION CHALLENGE on page 312!

Challenge

Word Clues

1.
2.
3.
4.

Complete the Groups

5.
6.
7.
8.

Spelling and Technology

Search With Singular and Plural Forms

1. _____

2. _____

3. _____

4. _____

Spelling and Technology

Search With Singular and Plural Forms

You can search the Net using the singular or plural form of a word. Either way, be sure you spell the keywords correctly. If you don't, the search engine might not find what you want. Here are some plural words you might use in a search. Note that not all plurals are formed by just adding **s** or **es**.

Learn these plural forms.

butterflies	**dogs**	**moose**	**wolves**

Write a plural word from the box for each clue. Underline the words that change several letters to make the plural form.

1. The plural spelling is the same as the singular spelling.

2. It ends with a /**z**/ sound spelled **s**.

3. An **f** changed to a **v** in this plural word.

4. A **y** changed to an **i** in this plural word.

Content Words

Link to **Language Arts:** Nouns and Verbs

Write the Content Word that completes each sentence.

cries	talks	tries	walks

1. The baby is crying. His _____ are loud.
2. I walk to school with Carrie. We enjoy our _____.
3. Jason and I talk often. We have long _____, too.
4. The coach gave Paula three _____ to toss the ball into the basket.

Link to **Science:** Human Body

Write the Content Words to complete the paragraph.

cells	organ	nerves	blood

Your heart is an __5.__ that pumps blood. The __6.__ carries oxygen to all parts of your body. Your __7.__ carry messages to and from your brain. Every part of your body is made up of tiny __8.__.

Link to **The Spelling Strategy**

Circle the two words in which one or more letters change to make the plural form.

Content Connection: Language Arts

Search the Internet to find out more about nouns and verbs. Try www.funbrain.com/grammar. Click on **Beginner**. Play the game. Write a list of nouns and verbs from the game.

Content Words

Language Arts: Nouns and Verbs

1. _____
_____
2. _____
_____
3. _____
_____
4. _____

Science: Human Body

5. _____
_____
6. _____
_____
7. _____
_____
8. _____

Spelling Connections Online
www.zaner-bloser.com

Spelling and Thinking

READ the Basic Words 👀 Watch out for easily misspelled words!

1. larger	*larger*	This shoe is **larger** than that one.
2. sadder	*sadder*	Ed is **sadder** than I am.
👀 **3.** widest	*widest*	I have more room on the **widest** track.
4. sharper	*sharper*	I need to make this pencil **sharper**.
5. closest	*closest*	Leah sits **closest** to the door.
6. hotter	*hotter*	Upstairs is **hotter** than downstairs.
👀 **7.** saddest	*saddest*	The **saddest** child cried and cried.
8. redder	*redder*	The more he ran, the **redder** he got.
9. reddest	*reddest*	Tara has the **reddest** cheeks of all.
10. wider	*wider*	Trucks can drive on this **wider** road.
👀 **11.** later	*later*	I will get there **later** than Sue will.
12. largest	*largest*	The whale is the **largest** animal.
13. closer	*closer*	Can you ride **closer** to the fence?
14. hottest	*hottest*	Which frying pan is the **hottest**?
15. latest	*latest*	We listen to the **latest** news on TV.

Review
16. longer   18. whiter
17. longest   19. whitest

Challenge
20. safer   22. thinner
21. safest   23. thinnest

SORT the Basic Words

1–8. Write the spelling words that end with **-er**.

9–15. Write the spelling words that end with **-est**.

REMEMBER the Spelling Strategy

Remember to drop the **silent e** at the end of a word when you add the suffixes **-er** and **-est**: **wide, wider, widest**. If a word ends in a vowel and consonant, double the consonant when you add **-er** and **-est**: **hot, hotter, hottest**.

-er
1.
2.
3.
4.
5.
6.
7.
8.
-est
9.
10.
11.
12.
13.
14.
15.

Spelling and Phonics

Word Structure

Follow the directions to write a Basic Word.

1. late – e + er = _____ **4.** hot + t + est = _____

2. red + d + er = _____ **5.** close – e + er = _____

3. large – e + est = _____ **6.** late – e + est = _____

Beginning and Ending Sounds

Write the Basic Word that fits each clue.

7. It begins like **shop**.

8. It begins like **clap** and ends like **best**.

9. It begins like **was** and ends like **after**.

10. It rhymes with **madder**.

11. It begins like **won** and ends like **test**.

12. It rhymes with **gladdest**.

13. It begins like **rock** and ends like **best**.

 Using the Dictionary

Each item below lists an entry word and one Basic Word you would find in that entry. Write another Basic Word you would find in the same entry.

14. hot, hottest   **15.** large, largest

◆ ◆ ◆

Dictionary Check Be sure to check your answers in your **Spelling Dictionary**.

Word Structure

1. _____

2. _____

3. _____

4. _____

5. _____

6. _____

Beginning and Ending Sounds

7. _____

8. _____

9. _____

10. _____

11. _____

12. _____

13. _____

Using the Dictionary

14. _____

15. _____

Spelling and Reading

larger	sadder	widest	sharper	closest
hotter	saddest	redder	reddest	wider
later	largest	closer	hottest	latest

Add to the Groups Write the Basic Word that completes each group of words.

1. sad, _____, saddest
2. wide, wider, _____
3. sharp, _____, sharpest
4. red, redder, _____

Complete the Sentences Write the **-er** or **-est** form of the underlined word that completes each sentence.

5. His <u>red</u> shirt is _____ than mine.
6. That <u>sad</u> clown has the _____ face I have ever seen.
7. Miguel's <u>hot</u> chili is the _____ chili in town.
8. I am <u>late</u> because the bus was _____ than usual.
9. The _____ pig of all is that <u>large</u> one over there.
10. This <u>wide</u> path is _____ than the one behind my house.

Complete the Paragraph Write Basic Words from the box to complete the paragraph.

We went to the mall on a hot day. In fact, we couldn't have picked a **11.** day. It was also a busy day. The **12.** we got to the mall, the more traffic we saw. The **13.** we could park our car was in the **14.** of the two lots. By the time we walked to the stores, it was 5:00. The **15.** the stores are open is 6:00.

closest
latest
closer
hotter
larger

Add to the Groups

1.
2.
3.
4.

Complete the Sentences

5.
6.
7.
8.
9.
10.

Complete the Paragraph

11.
12.
13.
14.
15.

Spelling and Writing

Proofread an Ad

First, proofread the ad below for eight misspelled words. Then rewrite the ad. Write the spelling words correctly and make the corrections shown by the proofreading marks.

> ### Cool clothes for Kids
>
> We have the lattest and the hotest styles. We have a largger selection than other stores. You won't find a wyder choice anywhere. We have all sizes, from largesst to smallest. You can can look sharpper, and you can pay less Latur in the year, our prices go even lower. If you are paying high prices, take a closser look at Cool Clothes for kids.

More Practice Write and sort the Basic Words.

Write an Ad

PERSUASIVE

Write an ad for something you want to sell. Be sure to give details about the item for sale. Persuade your reader to buy what you are selling. Use as many spelling words as you can.

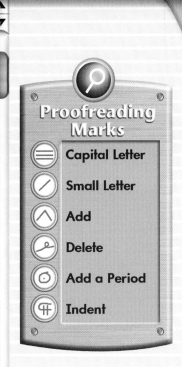

Proofreading Marks

≡	Capital Letter
/	Small Letter
∧	Add
⌐	Delete
⊙	Add a Period
¶	Indent

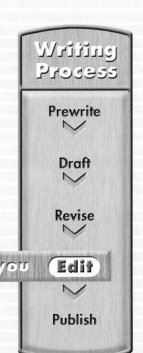

Writing Process

Prewrite
∨
Draft
∨
Revise
∨
Edit
∨
Publish

> > > > > Proofread your writing as you **Edit**

When you finish writing your draft, proofread your paper for errors in spelling, grammar, capitalization, and punctuation. Use the **Spelling Dictionary** to check spelling if you are not sure.

◎ Review

Review

Complete the Sentences

1.

2.

3.

4.

Complete the Paragraph

5.

6.

7.

8.

Hidden Words

1.

| longer | longest | whiter | whitest |

Complete the Sentences Write a form of the word in parentheses to complete each sentence. Your answer will be a Review Word.

1. The _____ day of the year is in the month of June. (long)
2. My shirt was _____ than Jim's. (white)
3. Lisa's hair is _____ than Colleen's. (long)
4. William has the _____ teeth I have ever seen. (white)

Complete the Paragraph Write the Review Words to complete the paragraph.

My grandmother's hair is very white! It is __5.__ than my grandfather's hair. In fact, she has the __6.__ hair I've ever seen. Her hair is also very long. She has the __7.__ hair of anyone in our family. Her hair is certainly __8.__ than mine!

Word Study: Hidden Words

● **Closed** is hiding the word **lose**. Write the Challenge Word that is hiding the word **nest**.

Challenge

| safer | safest | thinner | thinnest |

Word Clues Write a Challenge Word for each clue.

1. It means "more safe."
2. It means the opposite of **thickest**.
3. It means "most safe."
4. It means the opposite of **thicker**.

Complete the Sentences Write a Challenge Word to complete each sentence.

5. It is _____ to be inside during a thunderstorm than to be outside.
6. The tall, skinny man at the circus was the _____ man we had ever seen.
7. My father wants to be _____, so he started an exercise program.
8. That car is the _____ car that you can buy.

Challenge

Word Clues

1.
2.
3.
4.

Complete the Sentences

5.
6.
7.
8.

 Do you think you've mastered the Spelling Strategy? Take the CHAMPION CHALLENGE on page 313!

Spelling and Technology

Spelling and Technology

Computer Tools

1.

2.

3.

4.

Computer Tools

A computer is just a machine. You must put information into it. To do this, you need an input tool such as a mouse or a **joystick**. A joystick is a lever that is often used to play games. A **scanner** is another kind of input tool. It lets you put text or graphics directly into your computer. A **printer** is an output tool. It puts information from the computer on paper.

Sometimes you need a computer program called a driver. It can be used for input or output. A **driver** lets you operate a scanner, mouse, printer, or another tool.

| driver | joystick | printer | scanner |

Write the word from the box that matches each clue.

1. My lever controls a pointer on a screen.
2. I put information on paper.
3. I put a page from a book on your screen.
4. I am a computer program.

Content Words

Link to **Social Studies:** Camouflage

Write the Content Word that means the opposite of the underlined word or words.

hidden	gain	enemy	closed

1. The road to the bridge was <u>opened</u>.
2. Each side tried to <u>lose</u> ground.
3. They fought against their <u>friend</u>.
4. The trucks were <u>in clear view</u>.

Link to **Math:** Measurement

Write the Content Word that best completes each sentence.

metric	liter	meter	gram

5. A meter is a unit of length in the _____ system.
6. A _____ equals 100 centimeters.
7. A _____ is used to measure liquids.
8. A _____ is used to measure weight.

Link to **The Spelling Strategy**

Circle the Content Word you wrote that has a base word to which you could add the suffixes **-er** and **-est**.

Content Connection: Math

Search the Internet to find out more about the metric system. Name three countries that do not use the metric system.

Content Words

Social Studies: Camouflage

1. _____

2. _____

3. _____

4. _____

Math: Measurement

5. _____

6. _____

7. _____

8. _____

Spelling Connections Online
www.zaner-bloser.com

Suffix: -ly

Spelling and Thinking

READ the Basic Words 👀 Watch out for easily misspelled words!

1. slowly	*slowly*	Cars move **slowly** in a traffic jam.
2. mainly	*mainly*	Often we walk, but **mainly** we run.
3. badly	*badly*	I **badly** need new sneakers.
👀 4. hourly	*hourly*	The clock chimes **hourly**.
5. suddenly	*suddenly*	Rain fell **suddenly,** without warning.
6. lately	*lately*	Our team has been winning **lately**.
7. partly	*partly*	The **partly** open door let in air.
👀 8. closely	*closely*	We listened **closely** to his speech.
👀 9. really	*really*	Will I be a bit late or **really** late?
10. lastly	*lastly*	We ate stew and **lastly** had dessert.
11. plainly	*plainly*	I could see the boat **plainly**.
12. loudly	*loudly*	Cows moo **loudly** at milking time.
13. shortly	*shortly*	Mom will help us **shortly**.
14. monthly	*monthly*	Many people are paid **monthly**.
15. softly	*softly*	I talk **softly,** so the baby can sleep.

◎ Review	
16. cleanly	18. neatly
17. gladly	19. timely

◎ Challenge	
20. carelessly	22. keenly
21. carefully	23. unfriendly

SORT the Basic Words

1–3. Write the spelling words that begin with **a** through **i**.

4–10. Write the spelling words that begin with **j** through **q**.

11–15. Write the spelling words that begin with **r** through **z**.

REMEMBER the Spelling Strategy

Remember that you can add the suffix **-ly** to some words to make new words.

a–i

1.
2.
3.

j–q

4.
5.
6.
7.
8.
9.
10.

r–z

11.
12.
13.
14.
15.

Spelling and Phonics

Sound and Letter Patterns

Write Basic Words by adding the missing letters.

1. h ___ ___ rly
2. s ___ dd ___ nl ___
3. bad ___ ___
4. m ___ ___ nly
5. ___ ___ stly
6. cl ___ s ___ l ___

Word Structure

Replace the underlined syllables to make Basic Words.

7. plai<u>ner</u>
8. slow<u>est</u>
9. short<u>cut</u>
10. soft<u>en</u>
11. loud<u>er</u>

 Using the Dictionary

Write the Basic Word that matches each dictionary definition.

12. in part
13. once each month
14. in fact; actually
15. in recent time

◆ ◆ ◆

Dictionary Check Be sure to check your spelling in your **Spelling Dictionary**.

Sound and Letter Patterns

1.
2.
3.
4.
5.
6.

Word Structure

7.
8.
9.
10.
11.

Using the Dictionary

12.
13.
14.
15.

Spelling and Reading

slowly	mainly	badly	hourly	suddenly
lately	partly	closely	really	lastly
plainly	loudly	shortly	monthly	softly

Replace the Words Write the Basic Word that best replaces the underlined word or words.

1. Most cats swim <u>poorly</u>.
2. Have you been to the movies <u>recently</u>?
3. Aesop <u>mostly</u> wrote stories about animals to teach a lesson.
4. I clean my room <u>once a month</u>.
5. Tomatoes are <u>actually</u> fruits, not vegetables.
6. We turned off the lights, closed our eyes, and <u>finally</u> went to sleep.
7. We could <u>clearly</u> see the stars and the full moon in the dark sky.
8. The thunderstorm hit the area <u>quickly and without warning</u>.
9. The train will arrive <u>soon</u>.

Answer the Questions Write the Basic Word that best answers each question.

10. How does a snail crawl?
11. How does a noisy rooster crow?
12. How does a gentle breeze blow?
13. How often does a tower clock usually chime?
14. How was the half-painted house painted?
15. How can you look at things through a microscope?

1.

2.

3.

4.

5.

6.

7.

8.

9.

Answer the Questions

10.

11.

12.

13.

14.

15.

Spelling and Writing

Proofread a Book Report

Proofread the book report below for eight misspelled words. Then rewrite the report. Write the spelling words correctly and make the corrections shown by the proofreading marks.

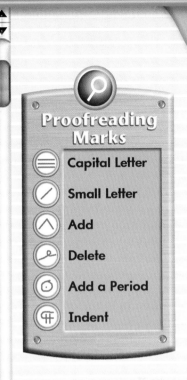

Proofreading Marks

- ≡ Capital Letter
- / Small Letter
- ∧ Add
- ✎ Delete
- ⊙ Add a Period
- ¶ Indent

¶ *The best book I have read lateley is <u>The Magic School bus Inside a Hurricane</u> by Joanna cole. The magic school bus changes sudenly into a hot-air balloon. It rises slowley but surely into a storm⊙The children look closly at how a hurricane forms. Then the bus becomes an airplane, and the children realy have an exciting Time. This book is planely not all true, but it is fun to read. I liked the book parrtly because of the pictures. But I mainley enjoyed it because I learned about hurricanes.*

More Practice Write and sort the Basic Words.

EXPOSITORY

Write a Book Report

Think about a book you liked. Tell about it. Be sure to give the title and author of the book. Tell some details about the book and why someone else might like it. Use as many spelling words as you can.

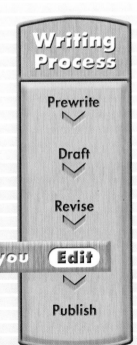

Writing Process

Prewrite
⌄
Draft
⌄
Revise
⌄
Edit
⌄
Publish

> > > > > Proofread your writing as you **Edit**

When you finish writing your draft, proofread your paper for errors in spelling, grammar, capitalization, and punctuation. Use the **Spelling Dictionary** to check spelling if you are not sure.

Review

Review

Word Structure

1. _____

2. _____

3. _____

4. _____

Complete the Sentences

5. _____

6. _____

7. _____

8. _____

cleanly	gladly	neatly	timely

Word Structure Write the Review Word that completes the word math.

1. glad + ly = _____

2. neat + ly = _____

3. time + ly = _____

4. clean + ly = _____

Complete the Sentences Write a Review Word to complete each sentence.

5. Because she was quite tired and bored, she _____ left the party.

6. His _____ arrival allowed us to eat dinner at 6:00.

7. Carla cut the pie _____, so that every piece looked perfect.

8. I folded my clothes _____ before I put them in the drawer.

Challenge

carelessly   carefully   keenly   unfriendly

Word Clues Write the Challenge Word that fits each clue.

1. This word has the two suffixes **-ful** and **-ly** added to it.

2. This word begins with **un-** and has the suffix **-ly**.

3. This word has the two suffixes **-less** and **-ly** added to it.

4. This word has the suffix **-ly** but does not begin with **un-**.

Complete the Sentences Write a Challenge Word to complete each sentence.

5. Mark _____ packed the glasses so that they wouldn't break.

6. The four-year-old watched the funny program _____.

7. Our new neighbor is _____. He won't even say hello!

8. Joanna _____ threw the candy wrapper onto the ground.

 Do you think you've mastered the Spelling Strategy? Take the CHAMPION CHALLENGE on page 314!

Challenge

Word Clues

1. _____

2. _____

3. _____

4. _____

Complete the Sentences

5. _____

6. _____

7. _____

8. _____

Spelling and Technology

Making a Web Page

1. _____

2. _____

3. _____

4. _____

Spelling and Technology

Making a Web Page

How do people make Web pages? They use a computer code language. This code tells the browser what to show on the screen, such as words, pictures, or links to other pages.

Study the meaning of these words. Each one has something to do with making Web pages.

HTML: a programming language for all Web documents

user friendly: easy to use

text block: part of a Web page made up of a group of words

headings: words printed in larger or heavier type that tell what text blocks are about

headings   HTML   text block   user friendly

Write the term from the box that best completes each sentence. Circle the word with the suffix **-ly**.

1. Emma used a code called _____ to make a Web page.

2. Each group of related words on the screen appears in one _____.

3. All of Emma's text blocks have _____.

4. Emma made a simple, clear page that is _____.

Content Words

Link to **Social Studies:** Building

Write the Content Word that matches each definition.

| electric | cement | resources | dam |

1. powered by electricity
2. a wall built across a river
3. sources of wealth to a country and to people
4. something that can be mixed with water and then poured to hold other solids together

Link to **Health:** Feelings

Write the Content Words to complete the paragraph.

| healthy | feelings | understand | angry |

A friend is someone who can __5.__ your __6.__ . Friends do not get __7.__ over little differences. Understanding can help to create a __8.__ friendship.

Link to **The Spelling Strategy**

Circle the two Content Words you wrote to which you could add an **-ly** suffix with one spelling change.

Content Connection: Social Studies

Search the Internet to find out more about building. You might look at **www.simscience.org**. Click on **Cracking Dams** and **Beginning**. Write one fact you learn about dams.

Content Words

Social Studies: Building

1. _____
2. _____
3. _____
4. _____

Health: Feelings

5. _____
6. _____
7. _____
8. _____

Spelling Connections Online
www.zaner-bloser.com

Spelling and Thinking

one syllable in first word

1. _____
2. _____
3. _____
4. _____
5. _____
6. _____
7. _____
8. _____
9. _____
10. _____
11. _____

two syllables in first word

12. _____
13. _____
14. _____
15. _____

READ the Basic Words 👀 Watch out for easily misspelled words!

1. herself   *herself*   Li made a cake by **herself**.
2. nobody   *nobody*   There's **nobody** home now.
3. airplane   *airplane*   The **airplane** flies overhead.
4. grandfather   *grandfather*   Our **grandfather** visited us.
👀 5. someone   *someone*   Did you see **someone** run by?
6. rainbow   *rainbow*   We saw a colorful **rainbow**.
7. anything   *anything*   Is there **anything** in the box?
8. grandmother   *grandmother*   My **grandmother** lives here.
👀 9. everything   *everything*   I put **everything** away.
10. afternoon   *afternoon*   I eat lunch in the **afternoon**.
11. sunshine   *sunshine*   The **sunshine** feels warm.
12. himself   *himself*   He drew that **himself**.
13. anybody   *anybody*   Has **anybody** seen my cat?
👀 14. something   *something*   Tell me **something** about him.
15. without   *without*   Don't go out **without** a hat.

Review
16. baseball   18. notebook
17. downtown   19. shoelace

Challenge
20. basketball   22. newspaper
21. everyday   23. seat belt

SORT the Basic Words

1–11. Write the spelling words in which the first word of the compound word has one syllable.

12–15. Write the spelling words in which the first word of the compound word has two syllables.

REMEMBER the Spelling Strategy

Remember that a **compound word** is formed from two or more words: **rainbow, sunshine**.

Word Analysis

Two words in each sentence can make a Basic Word. Write the word.

1. Pepperoni pizza is one thing some people love to eat.

2. Julie traded some marbles for one baseball.

3. A book is a thing any library will have.

4. The human body has no tail.

5. Pat went out the door with Aaron.

6. Are there any colorful fish in this body of water?

7. The plane flew high in the air.

8. We left home at noon after we ate.

Word Structure

9–10. Write the Basic Words that begin with **grand**.

11–12. Write the Basic Words that begin with a pronoun and end with the same word.

13. Write the Basic Word that begins with **every**.

 Using the Dictionary

Write the Basic Words that you would find between each pair of guide words.

14. proud • right   15. straw • switch

Dictionary Check Be sure to check the guide in your **Spelling Dictionary**.

Word Analysis

1. _____

2. _____

3. _____

4. _____

5. _____

6. _____

7. _____

8. _____

Word Structure

9. _____

10. _____

11. _____

12. _____

13. _____

Using the Dictionary

14. _____

15. _____

Complete the Sentences

1.

2.

3.

4.

5.

6.

7.

8.

9.

10.

Solve the Analogies

11.

12.

13.

14.

15.

herself	nobody	airplane
grandfather	someone	rainbow
anything	grandmother	everything
afternoon	sunshine	himself
anybody	something	without

Complete the Sentences Part of a Basic Word is missing from one word in each sentence. Add the missing part and write the Basic Word.

1. I would give any_____ to visit England.

2. The _____plane was an hour late.

3. My _____father will be sixty-five years old tomorrow.

4. Judy's grand_____ was the first woman doctor in our town.

5. Pam decided to make the dress _____self.

6. Jack looks at _____self in the mirror.

7. The sun_____ always follows the rain.

8. Can you work this _____noon?

9. A rain_____ hung in the clouds for several minutes.

10. Some people lost _____thing in the fire.

Solve the Analogies Write a Basic Word to complete each analogy.

11. All is to **everybody** as **none** is to _____.

12. Every is to **everyone** as **some** is to _____.

13. Everyone is to **everybody** as **anyone** is to _____.

14. Present is to **absent** as **with** is to _____.

15. Whole is to **part** as **everything** is to _____.

Spelling and Writing

Proofread a Letter

Proofread the letter for eight misspelled words. Then rewrite it. Write the spelling words correctly and make the corrections shown by the proofreading marks.

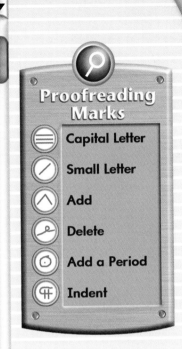
Dear Luella,

℗ *If anebody had told me evrything I would do at the fair, i would not have believed it. First my grindfather and I took an airplain ride. I have never done anythinng so fun before! In the aftirnoon, we saw prize-winning pies and animals. We couldn't leave withowt playing a few games. Grandpa enjoyed himslf, too! You can come ~~with~~ with us next year!*

love,

Jess

More Practice Write and sort the Basic Words.

Write a Letter

Write a letter to a friend. Tell about somewhere you went or something you did. Be sure to include details about some different events or parts of what happened. Tell the events in the order they happened. Use as many spelling words as you can.

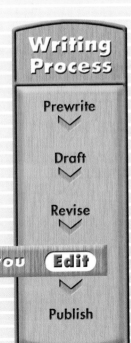

Writing Process

Prewrite
⌄
Draft
⌄
Revise
⌄

Edit
⌄
Publish

〉 〉 〉 〉 〉 **Proofread your writing as you** **Edit**

When you finish writing your draft, proofread your paper for errors in spelling, grammar, capitalization, and punctuation. Use the **Spelling Dictionary** to check spelling if you are not sure.

Review

Review

Answer the Questions

1.

2.

3.

4.

Solve the Analogies

5.

6.

7.

8.

Coined Words

1.

| baseball | downtown | notebook | shoelace |

Answer the Questions Write the Review Word that answers each question.

1. Where can you sometimes find stores and offices?

2. What can you use to keep a sneaker closed tightly over your foot?

3. What game can you play with a bat and ball?

4. Where can you put papers you want to save?

Solve the Analogies Write a Review Word to complete each analogy.

5. **Zip** is to **zipper** as **tie** is to _____.

6. **Home** is to **suburb** as **business** is to _____.

7. **Quarter** is to **football** as **inning** is to _____.

8. **Article** is to **magazine** as **paper** is to _____.

Word Study: Coined Words

• Write the Challenge Word that was coined, or made up, to name a game played with a ball and a basket.

◎ Challenge

basketball   everyday   newspaper   seat belt

Word Structure Write the Challenge Word that fits each clue.

1. This compound word is two separate words.
2. This compound word rhymes with **play**.
3. Two syllables in this compound word begin with the letter **p**.
4. Two syllables in this compound word begin with the letter **b**.

Word Groups Write the Challenge Word that belongs in each group.

5. magazine, journal, _____
6. steering wheel, windshield, _____
7. usual, ordinary, _____
8. soccer, football, _____

Challenge

Word Structure

1. _____
2. _____
3. _____
4. _____

Word Groups

5. _____
6. _____
7. _____
8. _____

Do you think you've mastered the Spelling Strategy? Take the CHAMPION CHALLENGE on page 315!

Spelling and Technology

Spelling and Technology

Shortcuts on a Keyboard

1.

2.

3.

4.

Shortcuts on a Keyboard

There is usually more than one way to do things on a computer. The quicker, easier ways are called shortcuts. Here are some words and a code you should know.

Shortcut	When to Use It
tab	If you are filling in a form—instead of moving your cursor, hit tab.
return	When you are using a search box—instead of clicking on go, hit return.
CTRL+C	When you want to copy something—instead of using the copy command in the menu, hit CTRL+C.

Write words from the box to complete this paragraph. Underline the compound word.

CTRL+C	return	shortcuts	tab

There are lots of __1.__ you can use on your computer. The __2.__ key is a shortcut for selecting the "go" box when you search. The __3.__ key is a shortcut for moving from cell to cell on a chart or from box to box on a form. The shortcut key for copy is __4.__.

Content Words

Link to **Language Arts:** Setting

Write the Content Words that complete the paragraph.

foghorn	folktale	moonlight	footprint

Some words tell about setting. For example, a __1.__ could begin by telling about someone walking in the __2.__. As the person walks along, a __3.__ might sound. Later, the person might disappear. The only clue might be a __4.__.

Link to **Health:** Hygiene

Write the Content Word that completes each sentence.

toothpaste	drugstore	haircut	checkup

5. Mom buys cold medicine at the _____.

6. I go to the doctor for a _____.

7. Mona uses both dental floss and _____.

8. Drew got a _____ at the barber shop.

Link to **The Spelling Strategy**

Circle the Content Words you wrote that are compound words.

Content Connection: Language Arts

 Use an online dictionary to look up the word **setting**. You might go to www.wordcentral.com. Write the meaning of **setting** when writing or talking about a story.

Content Words

Language Arts: Setting

1. _____

2. _____

3. _____

4. _____

Health: Hygiene

5. _____

6. _____

7. _____

8. _____

Spelling Connections Online
www.zaner-bloser.com

Assessment and Review

Unit 31

1.

2.

3.

Unit 32

4.

5.

6.

Unit 33

7.

8.

9.

Unit 34

10.

11.

12.

Unit 35

13.

14.

15.

ASSESSMENT

Units 31–35

Each Assessment Word in the box fits one of the spelling strategies you have studied over the past five weeks. Read the spelling strategies. Then write each Assessment Word under the unit number it fits.

Unit 31

1–3. You can add **-s** or **-es** to many words to make them plural.

Unit 32

4–6. You must change several letters in some words to make the plural form.

Unit 33

7–9. Drop the **silent e** at the end of a word when you add the suffixes **-er** and **-est: wide, wider, widest**. If a word ends in a vowel and consonant, double the consonant when you add **-er** and **-est: hot, hotter, hottest**.

Unit 34

10–12. You can add the suffix **-ly** to some words to make new words.

Unit 35

13–15. A **compound word** is formed from two or more words: **rainbow, sunshine**.

animals
bigger
safely
shelves
sunlight
states
older
mostly
wives
rowboat
sunglasses
friendly
speeches
nicest
loaves

Unit 31: Plurals: -s, -es

branches   colors   classes   things
tracks   dresses   buses

Write the spelling word that completes each group of words.

1. one dress; many _____
2. my class; all the _____ in the school
3. a small branch; several _____ on the tree
4. this bus; those big yellow _____
5. the color red; all the _____ of the rainbow
6. one thing; three _____
7. that broken track; those railroad _____

Unit 32: Irregular Plurals

children   leaves   half   woman
fish   mouse   child

Write the spelling word that completes the sentence.

8. Our cat caught a _____ yesterday.
9. You may have _____ my sandwich.
10. Each third grader will help one young _____.
11. All the _____ in the play were from the kindergarten.
12. Do you like to rake _____ in the fall?
13. I caught only one _____ at the lake.
14. There is a part in the play for a man and a part for a _____.

Unit 31

1.
2.
3.
4.
5.
6.
7.

Unit 32

8.
9.
10.
11.
12.
13.
14.

1.

2.

3.

4.

5.

6.

7.

8.

9.

10.

11.

12.

13.

14.

REVIEW
Unit 33: Suffixes: -er, -est

| closer | largest | hottest | sadder |
| widest | sharper | later | |

Write the spelling word that belongs in each group.

1. late, _____, latest
2. sharp, _____, sharpest
3. sad, _____, saddest
4. wide, wider, _____

5. hot, hotter, _____
6. close, _____, closest
7. large, larger, _____

REVIEW
Unit 34: Suffix: -ly

| hourly | really | monthly | shortly |
| slowly | suddenly | lastly | |

Write the spelling words that complete the paragraph.

Once a month our class goes to the zoo. I count the days very carefully. It seems that time __8.__ goes by __9.__. Monday is the day for our class's __10.__ zoo visit. We will do a lot on Monday. At two o'clock we will begin the __11.__ feedings of the animals. __12.__ after each feeding, we will watch them play in their cages. Before we know it, the day will be over. __13.__, we will ride the zoo train back to the gate. Then __14.__ we will find ourselves back at school. I always look forward to our trips to the zoo.

REVIEW

Unit 35: Compound Words

afternoon   nobody   everything   without

herself   grandfather   anything

1–7. Match a word in Column A with a word in Column B to write a spelling word.

Column A	Column B
any	out
after	body
her	father
every	self
grand	thing
with	noon
no	thing

WORD SORT

Spelling Study Strategy

Sorting by Endings

A good way to practice spelling is to place words into groups according to a spelling pattern.

1. Make five columns on a large piece of paper or on the chalkboard.

2. Write one of the following words at the top of each column: **things**, **classes**, **closer**, **closest**, **slowly**. Include the underlines.

3. Have a partner choose a spelling word from Units 31 through 35 and say it aloud.

4. Write the spelling word under the word with the same ending.

Writer's Workshop

Practice Activity

A.

1.

2.

3.

4.

5.

B.

6.

7.

8.

9.

10.

Grammar, Usage, and Mechanics

Pronouns

A **pronoun** takes the place of one or more nouns.
A pronoun can be singular or plural.

> My friends met Rosa. **They** liked **her**.

> Roberto saw Tom and **me**. **He** saw **us**.

These pronouns are singular: **I, me, you, he, she, him, her, it**.

These pronouns are plural: **we, us, you, they, them**.

Practice ACTIVITY

A. Write the pronoun in each sentence.

1. Do you want another glass of milk?

2. Alan liked the picture that I drew.

3. Can we go to the library?

4. Father gave the boxes to them yesterday.

5. A friend sent me a picture of a kitten.

B. Write a word from your spelling lists in Units 31–35 that can take the place of each underlined pronoun.

6. Grandmother and <u>he</u> live nearby.

7. A man and <u>she</u> bought the car.

8. <u>They</u> like this playground.

9. The cat and <u>it</u> play hide-and-seek.

10. A mother and <u>he</u> went to the zoo.

The Writing Process EXPOSITORY

Writing Directions

Prewriting

How do you get to the library or to another place in your community? You can find city maps at the library, or you can ask your teacher to help you find city maps on the Internet. As you think about how to get to a certain place, write down the directions from start to finish.

Drafting

Use your directions to write a rough draft. Follow your steps as you write sentences. Use as many spelling words as possible. If you don't know how to spell a word, make your best guess.

Revising

When you have finished your draft, read your directions from beginning to end. Check to see if you have included all of the directions a person would need. Now, write your final draft.

Editing

Use the editing checklist to proofread your directions. Be sure to use proofreading marks when you make corrections.

Publishing

Make a copy of your directions. Draw a map and share it with your readers.

Editing Checklist

Spelling

- I circled words that contain the spelling strategies I learned in Units 31–35.
- I checked the circled words in my Spelling Dictionary.
- I also checked for other spelling errors.

Capital Letters

- Important words in street names and addresses
- Beginning of all sentences
- Proper nouns

Punctuation

- Each sentence ends with the correct punctuation.
- Commas, apostrophes, and quotation marks are used correctly.

Grammar, Usage, and Mechanics

- Singular and plural pronouns are used correctly.

CHAMPION  CHALLENGE

| packet | magnet | grasp | slim | whiskers |

A. Look at the picture and read the small word that names the picture. Then find the small word in a Champion Challenge Word. Write the Champion Challenge Word.

1. net   **2.** pack   **3.** whisk   **4.** asp

B. Write a Champion Challenge Word to complete each sentence. You will write one word twice.

1. The seeds came in a brown _____.

2. There is a _____ chance that we will win.

3. My cat has long white _____.

4. I can use a _____ to pick up the pins.

5. My friend is tall and _____.

6. The pilot will _____ the steering wheel with his hands.

C. Write at least two sentences to answer each question.

1. What can you pick up with a magnet?

2. What could you put in a packet?

3. Who or what can have whiskers?

4. What might you grasp?

A.
1.
2.
3.
4.
B.
1.
2.
3.
4.
5.
6.

CHAMPION  CHALLENGE

| lemon | welcome | necklace | empty | pocket |

A. 1–2. Write the two Champion Challenge Words that contain the letters **c, k,** and **e.**

3–5. Write the three Champion Challenge Words that contain the letters **e** and **m.**

B. Write a Champion Challenge Word for each clue.

1. a small bag sewn into clothing

2. a juicy, yellow, sour fruit

3. an ornament worn around the neck

4. the opposite of **full**

5. to greet with pleasure

C. Think of words or phrases to finish each incomplete sentence. Write your complete sentences. Underline the Champion Challenge Words.

1. A lemon tastes _____, but it _____.

2. I will welcome _____, for my _____.

3. _____ is now empty, so I can _____.

4. The necklace was made of _____, and it _____.

5. The deep pocket was large enough to hold _____ that were _____.

A.

1.

2.

3.

4.

5.

B.

1.

2.

3.

4.

5.

CHAMPION  CHALLENGE

| trunk | bushel | bucket | ugly | sponge |

A. Some words in the sentences below are missing vowel letters. Write the words correctly.

1–2. Wash the b __ ck __ t with a sp __ ng __.

3. You can put a b __ sh __ l of apples in it.

4–5. Do you think the tr __ nk of the tree is __ gly?

B. Write a Champion Challenge Word to complete each sentence.

1. Caboose is to **train** as _____ is to **car**.

2. Carton is to **eggs** as _____ is to **water**.

3. Gallon is to **milk** as _____ is to **apples**.

4. Straw is to **broom** as _____ is to **mop**.

5. Beautiful is to **princess** as _____ is to **witch**.

C. Write two sentences to answer each question. In the first sentence, just answer the question. For your second sentence, change the underlined word. Use the word in ( ) and answer the new question.

Example: I <u>can't</u> put a giraffe in a large trunk. I can put my favorite toys, books, and photograph album in a large trunk.

1. What <u>can't</u> you put in a large trunk? (can)

2. What <u>wouldn't</u> you clean with a sponge? (would)

3. What <u>isn't</u> put in a bucket? (is)

A. _____

1. _____

2. _____

3. _____

4. _____

5. _____

B. _____

1. _____

2. _____

3. _____

4. _____

5. _____

CHAMPION CHALLENGE

scout	trout	outfit	broil	ointment

A. Put **oi** or **ou** with the scrambled letters. Unscramble the letters to make Champion Challenge Words. Write the words.

1. tift + ou = _____

2. mettnn + oi = _____

3. rtt + ou = _____

4. lbr + oi = _____

5. tcs + ou = _____

B. Write a Champion Challenge Word that can replace the underlined word in each sentence.

1. She wore a new <u>suit</u> to the wedding.

2. The nurse put <u>lotion</u> on the cut.

3. We sent him to <u>search</u> for a new trail.

4. Mom will <u>cook</u> the meat in the oven.

5. My family had <u>fish</u> for dinner.

C. You are with some friends at a camp for a weekend. The bugs are terrible, but the fishing and other lake activities are great. Write about your weekend. Use as many Champion Challenge Words as possible.

A.

1.

2.

3.

4.

5.

B.

1.

2.

3.

4.

5.

CHAMPION  CHALLENGE

| stew | scoop | kangaroo | mushroom | toadstool |

A. _____

1. _____

2. _____

3. _____

4. _____

5. _____

B. _____

1. _____

2. _____

3. _____

4. _____

5. _____

A. Think of the missing letters that will finish each Champion Challenge Word. Then write the complete words.

1. __ __ oo __

2. __ __ __ __ __ __ oo __

3. __ __ __ __ __ oo __

4. __ __ __ __ __ __ oo

5. Write the Champion Challenge Word that does not fit in the **oo** pattern.

B. Write the Champion Challenge Word that goes with each picture. Two different words could go with one picture.

1.   2–3.   4.   5.

C. A cook is about to reveal his recipe for a world-famous stew. You are a reporter. Write a news article about the cook and the famous stew. Use some Champion Challenge Words.

CHAMPION  CHALLENGE

ripen	siren	grace	erase	shone

A. Read the sentences. Find a little word hidden in each sentence that is also hidden in a Champion Challenge Word. Write the Champion Challenge Word.

1. A certain time in history is called an era. (The word **era** is in the word **erase**. The answer is **erase**.)

2. I ask you, sir, did you hear the loud warning?

3. Will you race me to that tree?

4. There is only one empty seat.

5. Be careful not to rip your dress on that fence.

B. Write the missing Champion Challenge Word that belongs in each sentence.

1. A cat's movement has natural _____.

2. My teacher may ask me to _____ the chalkboard.

3. The fire truck sounded its _____.

4. Grapes must _____ on the vine.

5. Last night our flashlight _____ in the darkness.

C. You are interviewing an orange! Think of some questions you may ask it. Think of the answers it might give. Use the Champion Challenge Words where possible. Write your questions as well as the answers to your questions.

A.

1.

2.

3.

4.

5.

B.

1.

2.

3.

4.

5.

CHAMPION  CHALLENGE

drain	sprain	tailor	stray	delay

A. Read the rhyming words. Pick one or more Champion Challenge Words to add to each group. Write the words.

1. paler, trailer, sailor, _____

2–3. plane, grain, train, _____, _____

4–5. obey, okay, spray, _____, _____

B. Write a Champion Challenge Word that can be used in place of each clue.

1. injure   **4.** postpone

2. pipe   **5.** wander

3. one who makes and mends clothes

C. The Champion Challenge Words suggest the five ideas below. Pick one idea and write an explanation. Tell how something happened. (Write the steps in the correct order.)

- what happened to your ankle when you were playing football
- the sink got clogged up
- you were late for school
- your cat got lost
- you (a tailor) made wonderful clothes for a wedding

A.

1. _____

_____

2. _____

_____

3. _____

_____

4. _____

_____

5. _____

_____

B.

1. _____

_____

2. _____

_____

3. _____

_____

4. _____

_____

5. _____

_____

CHAMPION  CHALLENGE

| peanut | scream | peacock | greet | sleeping |

A. Each Champion Challenge Word below is missing letters. Think of the missing letters. Then write the complete words.

1. __ ea __ __ __ __
2. __ __ __ ea __
3. __ __ ee __

4. __ __ ee __ __ __ __
5. __ ea __ __ __

B. Three words belong together in each group. Write the one word that does not belong.

1. lemon, peach, pear, peanut
2. talk, scream, say, speak
3. peacock, tuna, shrimp, shark
4. sleeping, playing, running, jumping
5. hands, feet, greet, arms

C. Write a sentence telling about each picture. Use a Champion Challenge Word in each sentence.

1.

2.

3.

4.

5.

A.

1.

2.

3.

4.

5.

B.

1.

2.

3.

4.

5.

CHAMPION  CHALLENGE

| nightmare | highlight | grind | rewind | wildcat |

A. Use one part of each word below to form a Champion Challenge Word. Write the Champion Challenge Words.

1. flashlight

2. alley cat

3. nightingale

4. refreshments

B. Write a Champion Challenge Word to answer each question.

1. What might you see in forests or mountains?

2. What might the best part of something be called?

3. What might you do to wheat to make flour? You _____ it.

4. What might you have on a bad night?

5. What must you do to your videotape after you watch a movie? You _____ it.

C. You have just awakened from a bad dream. Use some of the Champion Challenge Words to write about your bad dream.

A.

1.

2.

3.

4.

B.

1.

2.

3.

4.

5.

CHAMPION CHALLENGE

| potato | tomato | toast | loaf | swallow |

A. Write the Champion Challenge Word that each word below suggests to you.

1. gulp
2. juice
3. baked
4. meat
5. breakfast

B. Write the Champion Challenge Word that matches each definition.

1. to brown by heat
2. commonly grown reddish fruit
3. pass from mouth to throat to stomach
4. vegetable grown underground
5. food baked in one large piece

C. It's four o'clock. You and your older friend want to make a surprise meal for your family. You have two hours. Make a timetable. Write what you will do in those two hours. Use some of the Champion Challenge Words.

A.

1.
2.
3.
4.
5.

B.

1.
2.
3.
4.
5.

CHAMPION CHALLENGE

| chance | hatch | seashore | shipwreck | depth |

A.
_____
1. _____
_____
2. _____
_____
3. _____
_____
4. _____
_____
5. _____

B.
_____
1. _____
_____
2. _____
_____
3. _____
_____
4. _____
_____
5. _____

A. Some letters got into the wrong places in these Champion Challenge Words. Write each word correctly.

   1. sheasore

   2. wripsheck

   3. ancech

   4. tchha

   5. thdep

B. Each sentence has a missing Champion Challenge Word. Write the missing word.

   1. My class hopes the eggs will _____ soon.

   2. We saw many shells along the _____.

   3. The whale can dive to a great _____.

   4. You can see the terrible _____ on the rocks.

   5. I never take a _____ and cross the street when the light is red.

C. Write a story about a mysterious old ship you found on a nearby coast. Use as many Champion Challenge Words as you can in your story.

CHAMPION  CHALLENGE

cedar	cider	pounce	plunge	nudge

A. Read the clues below. Write the Champion Challenge Word that best fits each clue.

1. jump into, rush into

2. juice made from apples

3. reddish wood

4. a little push with the elbow

5. suddenly swoop or jump

B. 1–5. Proofread the sentence. Find five spelling mistakes. Rewrite each misspelled word correctly.

A tyger was redy too pounse on the dear.

C. Write a short story about a little apple that accidentally got onto the wrong tree. It was a cedar tree, not an apple tree. You may use some of the ideas given below. Put them in your own words. You might pretend you were the apple!

The apple was afraid to go back to its own tree.

A boy down below wanted the apple for a snack.

A.

1.

2.

3.

4.

5.

B.

1.

2.

3.

4.

5.

CHAMPION

CHALLENGE

shade	panther	twitch	crouch	hunger

A. Write the Champion Challenge Word that goes with each pair.

1. tiger, cheetah   **4.** shelter, dark

2. stoop, squat   **5.** thirst, crave

3. tremble, jerk

B. Add **-s** or **-es** to a Champion Challenge Word to complete each sentence. Write each new word you made.

1. My puppy _____ while he waits for me to throw the ball.

2. A big maple tree _____ our back lawn.

3. The rabbit _____ its nose as it searches for food.

4. Jim reads a great deal because he _____ for knowledge.

5. The three _____ chased the antelopes.

C. Write a fable about a gentle panther that is eating fruits and vegetables as he sits at a table in the shade. Which little animal is nearby? What is it doing? How does it feel? What will the gentle panther do? Use some or all of the Champion Challenge Words in your fable.

A.

1.

2.

3.

4.

5.

B.

1.

2.

3.

4.

5.

CHAMPION  CHALLENGE

| award | banana | several | odor | gorilla |

A. Write the Champion Challenge Words that have these vowel patterns.

1. __ o __ i __ __ a
2. __ a __ a __ a
3. a __ a __ __
4. __ e __ e __ a __
5. o __ o __

B. What am I? Write your answer for each clue.

1. I am an animal in the monkey family.
2. I am more than two.
3. I am a prize.
4. I am a yellow fruit.
5. I am a strong smell.

C. Write a story about one of the pictures. Tell what happened. Use the Champion Challenge Words where possible.

A.
1.
2.
3.
4.
5.

B.
1.
2.
3.
4.
5.

CHAMPION  CHALLENGE

| poor | sugar | secret | yourself | o'clock |

A. In this code each letter stands for the letter that comes before it in the alphabet. Write the Champion Challenge Word for each code word.

Example: bdu = act

1. tvhbs
2. qpps
3. p'dmpdl

4. zpvstfmg
5. tfdsfu

B. Write the Champion Challenge Word that fits each definition.

1. not good enough
2. pronoun referring to you
3. a sweet substance
4. of or according to the clock
5. something kept from other people

C. You just joined a special club. Using the Champion Challenge Words, write a story about the first meeting you attend.

A.

1.

2.

3.

4.

5.

B.

1.

2.

3.

4.

5.

CHAMPION  CHALLENGE

| jigsaw | yawning | drawer | mossy | defrost |

A. What are these Champion Challenge Words? Add and subtract letters to find out. Then write the words.

1. den – n + from – m + last – la = _____
2. day – da + lawn – l + sing – s = _____
3. almost – al – t + easy – ea = _____
4. and – an + raw + her – h = _____
5. j + pig – p + sat – t + w = _____

B. Write a Champion Challenge Word to complete each sentence.

1. The rocks along the stream were _____.
2. Dad used his _____ to cut out the design.
3. I put my clean clothes in my dresser _____.
4. I knew my sister was tired because she was _____.
5. Mom had to _____ the car's windshield.

C. Imagine that you had a very strange dream. Use some of the Champion Challenge Words to write about your dream.

A. _____
1. _____
2. _____
3. _____
4. _____
5. _____
B. _____
1. _____
2. _____
3. _____
4. _____
5. _____

CHAMPION  CHALLENGE

glory	hoarse	boredom	warn	warp

A. Unscramble these Champion Challenge Words. Write the words correctly.

1. r o l g y
4. r a w p

2. r a w n
5. s o a r e h

3. d o o r m e b

B. Write the Champion Challenge Word that fits each definition.

1. low or rough in sound or voice
2. to bend or buckle from dampness
3. a weary feeling because something is not interesting
4. to tell of coming danger
5. great honor or praise

C. Choose one of these questions and write two or more sentences to answer it.

1. What might make a person hoarse?
2. What might a person have done to receive praise or glory?
3. When might you have to warn others?
4. Which things can warp?

Left margin answer lines:

A.
1.
2.
3.
4.
5.

B.
1.
2.
3.
4.
5.

CHAMPION  CHALLENGE

curve	worm	pearl	twirl	whirl

A. Use every second letter to decode these Champion Challenge Words. Start with the second letter. Write the words you find.

Example: abtiprotihedmaly = birthday

1. ptrwaitrel
2. swootrame
3. twaheipralt
4. speekadrill
5. schubraveer

B. What Champion Challenge Word does each picture make you think of?

1.   2.  3.

4.  5.

C. You own a very talented worm. It can do many tricks. Tell about your pet worm. Write a short story using Champion Challenge Words.

A. _____

1. _____

2. _____

3. _____

4. _____

5. _____

B. _____

1. _____

2. _____

3. _____

4. _____

5. _____

CHAMPION CHALLENGE

| armchair | barefoot | farewell | fairy tale | somewhere |

A. _____

1. _____

2. _____

3. _____

4. _____

5. _____

6. _____

B. _____

1. _____

2. _____

3. _____

4. _____

A. These "words" are not quite right. Correct these misspelled homophones. Write the Champion Challenge Words. You'll write one word twice.

1. bearfoot   3. fairy tail   5. armchare

2. somewear   4. fairwell   6. ferry tale

B. What word do these pictures suggest? Say the picture words. Then write a Champion Challenge Word that sounds the same.

1.

2.

3.

4.

C. Make a hidden word puzzle on a grid that has ten squares across and down. Use any spelling words you have studied this school year. Give it to a friend to find the words. Here is an example of how to begin.

a	i	d			
g	c				
e	e				

CHAMPION  CHALLENGE

| foul | fowl | yoke | yolk | heal |

A. Write each Champion Challenge Word. Use the code below.

a =   e =   f =   h =   k =

l =   o =   u =   w =   y =

1.

2.

3.

4.

5.

B. Write the homophone that belongs in each sentence.

1. He hit a (foul, fowl) ball.
2. A turkey is one type of (foul, fowl).
3. The oxen wore a (yoke, yolk) across their necks.
4. The yellow part of an egg is the (yoke, yolk).
5. My skinned knee will (he'll, heal) soon.

C. In your own words, write definitions for two Champion Challenge Words. Explain what they mean. Then use the words you defined in sentences.

A.

1.

2.

3.

4.

5.

B.

1.

2.

3.

4.

5.

CHAMPION  CHALLENGE

| carrot | barrel | platter | shutter | hiccup |

A. Use the small words below to make Champion Challenge Words. Write the Champion Challenge Words. You'll write one word twice.

1. cup   **4.** bar

2. shut   **5.** at

3. rot   **6.** up

B. Which Champion Challenge Word fits? Write the missing word.

1. Plum is to **fruit** as _____ is to **vegetable**.

2. Bowl is to **soup** as _____ is to **Thanksgiving turkey**.

3. Basket is to **apples** as _____ is to **water**.

4. Curtain is to **shower** as _____ is to **window**.

C. Write five sentences. Use a Champion Challenge Word or a form of it in each sentence and underline it. Try to use words that start with the same letter as the Champion Challenge Word.

Example: Harry Hippo happens to have the hiccups.

A.

1.

2.

3.

4.

5.

6.

B.

1.

2.

3.

4.

CHAMPION  CHALLENGE

| holly | lobby | shaggy | fuzzy | woolly |

A. Which Champion Challenge Word has these double consonants? Write each word.

1. __ __ ll __
2. __ __ bb __
3. __ __ __ ll __
4. __ __ zz __
5. __ __ __ gg __

B. Match the Champion Challenge Words with these meanings. Write the words.

1. blurred
2. a hall or waiting room in a hotel
3. consisting of wool
4. a shrub or tree that has evergreen leaves
5. having long, thick, rough hair

C. You are a desk clerk in a large hotel when a strange animal wanders in. Describe the hotel, the animal, and what happens. Use as many Champion Challenge Words as you can.

A. _____
1. _____
2. _____
3. _____
4. _____
5. _____
B. _____
1. _____
2. _____
3. _____
4. _____
5. _____

CHAMPION  CHALLENGE

| facing | saving | becoming | curving | loving |

A.

1.

2.

3.

4.

5.

B.

1.

2.

3.

4.

5.

A. Form Champion Challenge Words by dropping the final **e** and adding **-ing**. Write the words.

   1. become – e + ing = _____

   2. curve – e + ing = _____

   3. face – e + ing = _____

   4. love – e + ing = _____

   5. save – e + ing = _____

B. Read the first sentence. Finish the second sentence in each set with a Champion Challenge Word.

   1. I am looking in your direction. I am _____ you.

   2. I am putting money away. I am _____ it.

   3. I care a lot about others. I am a _____ person.

   4. I am not walking on a straight path. I am _____ through the park.

   5. I am a tadpole. I am _____ a frog.

C. Write more than one answer to each question. Use the underlined Champion Challenge Word in each answer.

   1. What could you be <u>facing</u>?

   2. Why might you be <u>saving</u> something?

   3. What are you <u>becoming</u>?

   4. How do you show your friends that you are <u>loving</u>?

CHAMPION  CHALLENGE

| shopping | spinning | planning | hugged | wrapped |

A. Write the **-ed** form for each of these base words.

  1. hug

  2. wrap

B. Write the **-ing** form for each base word.

  1. shop

  2. plan

  3. spin

C. Write the correct **-ed** or **-ing** form for each underlined word.

  1. I am going <u>shop</u> with my parents tonight.

  2. He <u>hug</u> his new brown puppy.

  3. Our family is <u>plan</u> a trip this summer.

  4. The birthday gift was <u>wrap</u> neatly.

  5. Rumpelstiltskin was <u>spin</u> straw into gold.

D. Pretend you went to a birthday party last week. Tell what you did before the party. Then tell about the party. Use as many Champion Challenge Words as you can.

A.

1.

2.

B.

1.

2.

3.

C.

1.

2.

3.

4.

5.

CHAMPION  CHALLENGE

couldn't	they're	they've	weren't	we're

A. Write the contraction that is a short form for each word pair.

1. we are   **4.** they have

2. were not   **5.** they are

3. could not

B. 1–5. Five contractions are missing from the story. Read the story. Write the correct contractions.

Alice and Adrienne were born on the same day. In fact, __1.__ twins. Since kindergarten, __2.__ attended our school. Alice hoped to be in our homeroom this year, but it __3.__ be arranged. Adrienne is in our room, and __4.__ happy about that. We like Alice, too, so we __5.__ pleased that she is in another class. Maybe next year we will have Alice with us, and we will not have Adrienne!

C. Your class is having difficulty finding a way to raise money for a class trip. Using your Champion Challenge Words, write a paragraph describing the problem. Then tell how you solved the problem.

A.

1.

2.

3.

4.

5.

B.

1.

2.

3.

4.

5.

CHAMPION  CHALLENGE

| hoofs | roofs | scarfs | switches | walruses |

A. Finish each sentence. Write plural forms.

1–2. The two words whose plurals are formed with **-es** are _____ and _____.

3–5. The three words whose plurals are formed with just **-s** are _____, _____, and _____.

B. Write Champion Challenge Words to identify the pictures.

1.

4.

2.

5.

3.

C. Mr. Walrus was sitting quietly at home watching TV when a sudden noise outside disturbed him. Use the Champion Challenge Words to write a short story about what happened.

A.

1.

2.

3.

4.

5.

B.

1.

2.

3.

4.

5.

CHAMPION  CHALLENGE

| tuna | oxen | elf | elves | popcorn |

A. What are these Champion Challenge Words? Write them.

1. boxer – b – r + n = _____
2. eat – at + lift – i – t = _____
3. spot – s – t + p + corner – er = _____
4. stun – s – n + nap – p = _____
5. motel – mot + paves – pa = _____

B. Write a Champion Challenge Word to answer each question.

1. Which strong beasts can pull heavy loads?
2. What might you put in a deep bowl for a TV snack?
3. What is often put in salads or sandwiches?
4. Which make-believe being is said to have magical powers?
5. Who are supposed to be Santa's helpers?

C. What might little elves be doing? Where might they go? Could they help someone? How? Write a story about what the little creatures decide to do.

A.

1.

2.

3.

4.

5.

B.

1.

2.

3.

4.

5.

CHAMPION  CHALLENGE

| braver | bravest | flatter | flattest | smoothest |

A. Finish the chart. Write the base word. Then write the missing form. Put the words that mean "more than" in the middle column. If a word means "most," put it in the last column.

1–2. brave ____ ____

3–4. flat ____ ____

5. smooth   smoother ____

B. Write the correct Champion Challenge Word for each blank.

1–2. The first knight is brave, the second knight is ____, and our king is ____ of all.

3. Silk is the ____ material because it is smoother than wool, cotton, and other material.

4–5. Jim's stone is flat, Tim's stone is ____, and Kim's stone is the ____ of all.

C. Using the Champion Challenge Words, write sentences telling about a knight's adventures.

A.

1.

2.

3.

4.

5.

B.

1.

2.

3.

4.

5.

CHAMPION CHALLENGE

| greatly | secretly | brightly | happily | easily |

A.
1.
2.
3.
4.
5.
B.
1.
2.
3.
4.
5.

A. Unscramble these base words. Then write the Champion Challenge Word that is related to the base word.

1. paphy
2. streec
3. trage
4. tribhg
5. eyas

B. Write a Champion Challenge Word to answer each question.

1. How do parents plan surprises and wrap gifts?
2. How do people greet friends at an airport?
3. How do many stars shine?
4. If your class went to the circus and you had to stay home with a bad cold, how much would you miss the trip?
5. How did you figure out these answers?

C. Write five sentences that describe something or someone. Use a Champion Challenge Word in each sentence.

CHAMPION  CHALLENGE

everywhere	anyone	paintbrush	washcloth	bathroom

A. Use one part of each compound word below to form a Champion Challenge Word. Write the words.

1. hairbrush   **3.** anyplace   **5.** nowhere
2. birdbath   **4.** tablecloth

B. Write the Champion Challenge Word that goes with each pair.

1. kitchen, bedroom

2. paint, old rags

3. soap, towel

4. any person, anybody

5. in every place, all around

C. Choose group 1, 2, or 3 in Activity B above. Write a name for the group of words you choose. List the names of other things that could be in that group. Then write a sentence that tells how someone might use that group of things.

A.
1.
2.
3.
4.
5.

B.
1.
2.
3.
4.
5.

Spelling
and the
Writing Process

Writing anything—a friendly letter, a paper for school—usually follows a process. The writing process has five steps. It might look like this if you tried to draw a picture of it:

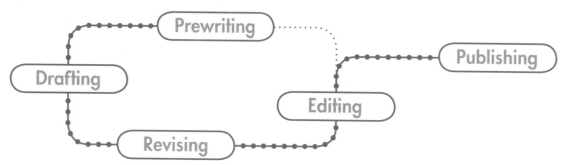

Part of the writing process forms a loop. That is because not every writing task is the same. It is also because writers often jump back and forth between the steps as they change their minds and think of new ideas.

Here is a description of each step:

Prewriting This is thinking and planning ahead to help you write.

Drafting This means writing your paper for the first time. You usually just try to get your ideas down on paper. You should spell correctly those words that you do know. Attempt to spell those that you don't. You can fix them later.

Revising This means fixing your final draft. Here is where you rewrite, change, and add words.

Editing This is where you feel you have said all you want to say. Now you proofread your paper for spelling errors and errors in grammar and punctuation.

Publishing This is making a copy of your writing and sharing it with your readers. Put your writing in a form that your readers will enjoy.

Spelling
and
Writing Ideas

Being a good speller can help make you a more confident writer. Writing often can make you a better writer. Here are some ideas to get you started.

Ideas for DESCRIPTIVE Writing

You might...

- describe something small and something big.
- describe something from the point of view of a zoo animal. Ask an adult to help you look on the Internet at this site: http://nationalzoo.si.edu/Animals.

Ideas for NARRATIVE Writing

You might...

- write a story about your first visit to someplace new. Ask an adult to help you look on the Internet at this site: www.geographia.com.
- write a story with your best friend as the main character.

Ideas for PERSUASIVE Writing

You might...

- try to persuade your teacher to change a class rule.
- try to persuade your classmates to read a book you like. Ask your teacher to help you look at this Internet site: www.bookhooks.com.

Ideas for EXPOSITORY Writing

You might...

- find out how your local government works and write a report. Ask an adult to help you look at this Internet site: http://bensguide.gpo.gov/3-5.
- interview an animal caregiver and write a report about the job.
- inform your classmates how to create a craft project.

Manuscript Handwriting Models

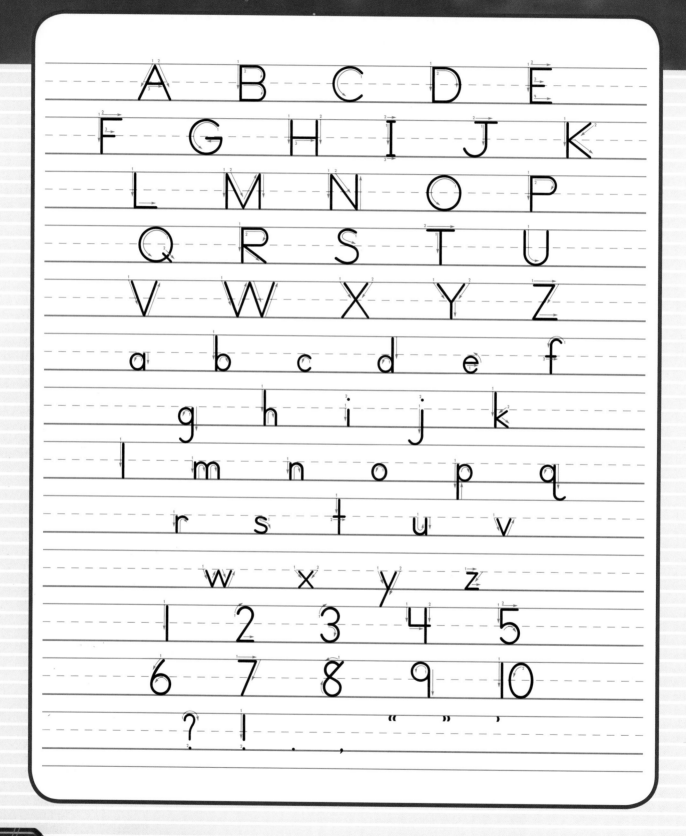

Cursive Handwriting Models

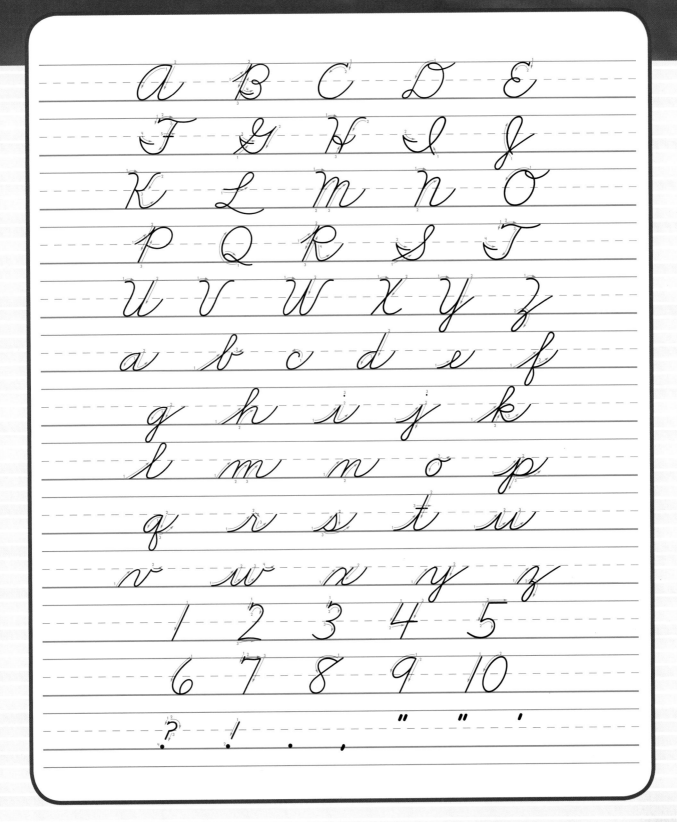

High Frequency Writing Words

A

a
about
afraid
after
again
air
all
almost
also
always
am
America
an
and
animal
animals
another
any
anything
are
around
as
ask
asked
at
ate
away

B

baby
back
bad
ball
balloons
baseball
basketball

be
bear
beautiful
because
become
bed
been
before
being
believe
best
better
big
bike
black
boat
book
books
both
boy
boys
bring
broke
brother
build
bus
but
buy
by

C

call
called
came
can
candy
can't

car
care
cars
cat
catch
caught
change
charge
children
Christmas
circus
city
class
clean
clothes
come
comes
coming
could
couldn't
country
cut

D

Dad
day
days
decided
did
didn't
died
different
dinner
do
does
doesn't
dog

dogs
doing
done
don't
door
down
dream

E

each
earth
eat
eighth
else
end
enough
even
every
everybody
everyone
everything
except
eyes

F

family
fast
father
favorite
feel
feet
fell
few
field
fight
finally
find
fire

first
fish
five
fix
food
football
for
found
four
free
Friday
friend
friends
from
front
fun
funny
future

G

game
games
gas
gave
get
gets
getting
girl
girls
give
go
God
goes
going
good
got
grade

grader
great
ground
grow

H

had
hair
half
happened
happy
hard
has
have
having
he
head
heard
help
her
here
he's
high
hill
him
his
hit
home
homework
hope
horse
horses
hot
hour
house
how
hurt

I

I
I'd
if
I'm
important
in
into
is
it
its
it's

J

job
jump
just

K

keep
kept
kids
killed
kind
knew
know

L

lady
land
last
later
learn
leave
left
let
let's
life

like
liked
likes
little
live
lived
lives
long
look
looked
looking
lost
lot
lots
love
lunch

M

mad
made
make
making
man
many
math
may
maybe
me
mean
men
might
miss
Mom
money
more
morning
most

mother
mouse
move
Mr.
Mrs.
much
music
must
my
myself

N

name
named
need
never
new
next
nice
night
no
not
nothing
now

O

of
off
oh
OK
old
on
once
one
only
or
other
our

out
outside
over
own

P

parents
park
party
people
person
pick
place
planet
play
played
playing
police
president
pretty
probably
problem
put

R

ran
read
ready
real
really
reason
red
responsibilities
rest
ride
riding
right
room

rules
run
running

S

said
same
saw
say
scared
school
schools
sea
second
see
seen
set
seventh
she
ship
shot
should
show
sick
since
sister
sit
sleep
small
snow
so
some
someone
something

sometimes
soon
space
sport
sports
start
started
states
stay
still
stop
stopped
store
story
street
stuff
such
sudden
suddenly
summer
sure
swimming

T

take
talk
talking
teach
teacher
teachers
team
tell
than
Thanksgiving

that
that's
the
their
them
then
there
these
they
they're
thing
things
think
this
thought
three
through
throw
time
times
to
today
together
told
too
took
top
tree
trees
tried
trip
trouble
try

trying
turn
turned
TV
two

U

united
until
up
upon
us
use
used

V

very

W

walk
walked
walking
want
wanted
war
was
wasn't
watch
water
way
we
week
weeks
well

went
were
what
when
where
which
while
white
who
whole
why
will
win
winter
wish
with
without
woke
won
won't
work
world
would
wouldn't

Y

yard
year
years
yes
you
your
you're

USING THE Dictionary

Guide Words

The **guide words** at the top of each dictionary page can help you find the word you want quickly. The first guide word tells you the first word on that page. The second guide word tells you the last word on that page. The entries on the page fall in alphabetical order between these two guide words.

Entries

Words you want to check in the dictionary are called **entries**. Entries provide a lot of information besides the correct spelling. Look at the sample entry below.

- Practice using guide words in a dictionary. Think of words to spell. Then use the guide words to find each word's entry. Do this again and again until you can use guide words easily.

- Some spellings are listed with the base word. To find **angrier,** you would look up **angry**. To find **planned,** you would look up **plan**. To find **classes,** you would look up **class**.

- If you do not know how to spell a word, guess the spelling before looking it up. Try to find the first three letters of the word. (If you use just the first letter, you will probably take too long.)

- If you can't find a word, think of how else it might be spelled. For example, if a word starts with the **/k/ sound,** the spelling might begin with **k, c,** or even **ch**.

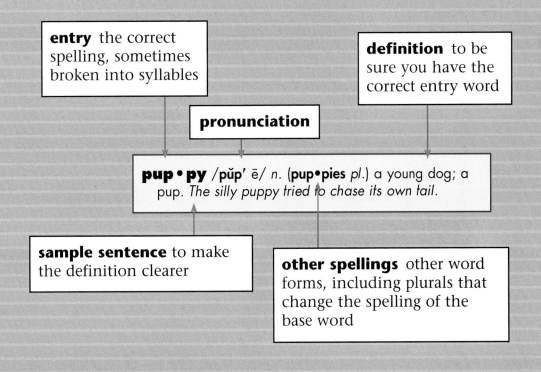

entry the correct spelling, sometimes broken into syllables

pronunciation

definition to be sure you have the correct entry word

pup•py /pŭp′ ē/ n. (**pup•pies** pl.) a young dog; a pup. *The silly puppy tried to chase its own tail.*

sample sentence to make the definition clearer

other spellings other word forms, including plurals that change the spelling of the base word

a • bout¹ /ə bout'/ *prep.* of; having to do with; concerning. *Let me tell you something about baseball.*

a • bout² /ə bout'/ *adv.* somewhere near. *She guessed it was about seven o'clock.*

a • bove¹ /ə bŭv'/ *adv.* in a higher place. *The plane was flying far above.*

a • bove² /ə bŭv'/ *prep.* higher than; over. *The plane went above the clouds.*

a • cross¹ /ə krôs'/ or /ə krŏs'/ *adv.* from side to side. *The room is twenty feet across.*

a • cross² /ə krôs'/ or /ə krŏs'/ *prep.* to the other side of. *The bridge goes across the river.*

act¹ /ăkt/ *n.* a division of a play. *Most plays today have three acts.*

act² /ăkt/ *v.* to perform. *Many girls would like to act in the movies.*

a • do • be¹ /ə dō' bē/ *n.* brick made of baked clay and straw. *Many pueblos are built of adobe.*

a • do • be² /ə dō' bē/ *adj.* made of adobe. *We saw many adobe houses in New Mexico.*

adobe

a • fraid /ə frād'/ *adj.* frightened; filled with fear. *Some people are afraid of falling from high places.*

af • ter /ăf' tər/ *prep.* **a.** behind. *Don't forget that you come after me in the parade!* **b.** following; later in time than. *After lunch let's go on with the game.*

af • ter • noon /ăf' tər nōōn'/ *n.* the part of the day that follows noon and lasts until evening. *Little children often take naps in the afternoon.*

a • gain /ə gĕn'/ *adv.* once more. *When no one answered the door, the mailman rang the bell again.*

age /āj/ *n.* number of years old. *The baby's age is now two years.*

a • gree /ə grē'/ *v.* to have the same opinion. *We all agree that Mr. Jansen would make a good mayor.*

aid¹ /ād/ *v.* to help. *The doctor aided him promptly.*

aid² /ād/ *n.* **a.** assistance. *Send aid at once to the men lost in the cave.* **b. first aid** quick help for the injured. *Girl Scouts learn first aid.*

air /âr/ *n.* **a.** the mixture of gases surrounding the earth. *All people breathe air.* **b.** the space above the earth. *Birds and airplanes fly in the air.*

air mail /âr' māl'/ *n.* mail carried by airplanes. *The air mail is placed in special bags.*

air • plane /âr' plān'/ *n.* a machine for flying that has a motor, wings, and a tail. *The airplane will land in ten minutes.*

a • larm /ə lärm'/ *n.* a warning signal that danger is near. *The alarm went off moments after the fire started.*

a • like¹ /ə līk'/ *adj.* similar; without a difference. *The twin sisters look alike.*

a • like² /ə līk'/ *adv.* in the same way. *You can't treat all children alike.*

a • live /ə līv'/ *adj.* living; not dead. *People sometimes forget that trees are alive.*

al•most /ôl′ mōst′/ or /ôl **mōst**′/ *adv.* nearly; just about. *That bus is almost on time; it is only two minutes late.*

a•loud /ə loud′/ *adv.* with a speaking voice. *Please read this book aloud to the class.*

al•ways /ôl′ wāz/ or /ôl′ wēz/ *adv.* all the time; constantly. *At the North Pole, it is always cold.*

an•gry /ăng′ grē/ *adj.* (**an•gri•er, an•gri•est; an•gri•ly** *adv.*) feeling or showing anger; filled with anger. *He became angry when he spilled ink on his homework.*

an•i•mal /ăn′ ə məl/ *n.* a living being that is not a plant. *Dogs, worms, elephants, and snakes are all animals.*

an•oth•er /ə nŭth′ ər/ *adj.* **a.** one more. *Let me read another story.* **b.** any other; a different. *I am going to another part of the country.*

an•y /ĕn′ ē/ *adj.* **a.** one out of a group. *Read any book you like.* **b.** some. *Would you like any orange juice?*

an•y•bod•y /ĕn′ ē bŏd′ ē/ or /ĕn′ ē bŭd′ ē/ *pron.* any person. *Did you see anybody that I know at the meeting?*

an•y•one /ĕn′ ē wŭn′/ or /ĕn′ ē wən′/ *pron.* anybody; any person. *Does anyone know how to get to the library?*

an•y•thing /ĕn′ ē thĭng′/ *pron.* any thing; something. *We couldn't find anything for Grandma's birthday.*

ap•ple /ăp′ əl/ *n.* a fruit for eating, usually round, that grows on a tree. *Green apples are often used in pies.*

arm•chair /ärm′ châr′/ *n.* a chair with sides that support a person's arms or elbows. *Dad likes to sit in his armchair when he reads.*

a•round¹ /ə round′/ *prep.* **a.** in a circular path about. *We rode around the block on our bikes.* **b.** on every side of. *There was nothing but water around us.*

a•round² /ə round′/ *adv.* in a circular path. *The merry-go-round went around.*

Pronunciation Key

ă	pat	ŏ	pot	th	thin
ā	pay	ō	toe	*th*	this
âr	care	ô	paw, for	hw	which
ä	father	oi	noise	zh	vision
ĕ	pet	ou	out	ə	about,
ē	be	ŏŏ	took		item,
ĭ	pit	ōō	boot		pencil,
ī	pie	ŭ	cut		gallop,
îr	pier	ûr	urge		circus

a•sleep¹ /ə slēp′/ *adj.* not awake; sleeping. *The dog is asleep after a long walk.*

a•sleep² /ə slēp′/ *adv.* into a state of sleep. *He fell asleep during the movie.*

a•wake /ə wāk′/ *adj.* alert; not asleep. *She was already awake when the alarm clock rang.*

a•ward /ə wôrd′/ *n.* a prize. *The winner accepted the award.*

a•way /ə wā′/ *adv.* **a.** from a place; to a different place. *Our dog ran away last week.* **b.** aside; out of the way. *He put the dishes away after supper.*

bad•ly /băd′ lē/ *adv.* poorly; in a bad manner. *He plays the piano well but sings badly.*

bake /bāk/ *v.* (**bakes, baked, bak•ing**) to cook without applying fire directly; to cook in an oven. *We bake bread every week.*

bal•loon /bə lōōn′/ *n.* a brightly colored rubber bag that can be filled with air or gas and used as a toy. *Can you blow up this balloon?*

ba•nan•a /bə năn′ ə/ *n.* a tropical, yellow fruit with a slight curve and a peel. *The monkey ate the banana.*

band /bănd/ *n.* **a.** a number of persons who play musical instruments together. *She plays the drums in a band.* **b.** any flat strip of material used for holding something together. *Put a rubber band around each newspaper.*

bang[1] /băng/ *n.* a sudden, sharp noise. *We heard the bang of the car door.*

bang[2] /băng/ *v.* to strike with noisy blows. *Will you please stop banging those pots and pans?*

bar /bär/ *n.* **a.** a long, evenly shaped piece of something solid. *I went to the store for a bar of soap.* **b.** a solid rectangle used to show an amount on a graph. *Color the longest bar on the graph red.*

bare /bâr/ *adj.* **a.** not wearing clothes; not covered. *Should you be walking outside in your bare feet?* **b.** without a covering. *The floor is bare because the rug is being cleaned.*

bare•foot /bâr' fŏŏt'/ *adv.* and *adj.* without shoes or socks. *The barefoot boy played in the sand.*

bar•rel /băr' əl/ *n.* a bulging container with a flat top and bottom. *Oil comes in a barrel.*

base•ball /bās' bôl/ *n.* a game played with a bat and a ball by two teams of nine players each. *Debbie wants to play baseball.*

bas•ket•ball /bās' kĭt bôl'/ *n.* **a.** a game in which points are scored by throwing a ball through a basket. *Basketball is usually played indoors.* **b.** the ball used in this game. *Our basketball had lost all its air.*

bat[1] /băt/ *n.* a heavy stick used to hit a ball. *Mike showed me how to hold the bat.*

bat[2] /băt/ *v.* to hit something, as a ball, with a heavy stick or other object. *Throw me the ball, and I will bat it.*

bath•room /băth' rŏŏm'/ *n.* a room usually with a toilet, sink, bathtub, and shower. *We are replacing the tub in our bathroom.*

bay /bā/ *n.* a part of a large body of water that extends into the land; a gulf. *Several small boats came into the bay to escape the storm.*

be /bē/ *v.* (**am, are, is; was, were; been; be•ing**) used as a helping verb in addition to having the following meanings: **a.** to have the identity of; to equal. *Carlos is my cousin.* **b.** to have a particular quality, appearance, or character. *The sand was hot.* **c.** to happen; to take place. *The finals are at two o'clock.*

beach /bēch/ *n.* (**beach•es** *pl.*) the shore of a lake, sea, etc., usually of sand or small stones, that is washed by waves. *During the summer we go to the beach.*

bean /bēn/ *n.* a seed or pod that can be eaten as a vegetable. *We ate green beans for lunch.*

bear /bâr/ *n.* a large, heavy animal with long, coarse fur, short legs, and a very short tail. *The bear stood on its hind legs.*

beat[1] /bēt/ *v.* (**beats, beat•en** or **beat, beat•ing**) **a.** to hit again and again. *Beat the drum loudly.* **b.** to throb. *Her heart was beating fast.* **c.** to defeat. *Linda beat Don in the election.*

beat[2] /bēt/ *n.* a throbbing sound. *Listen to the beat of the drum.*

bea•ver /bē' vər/ *n.* a furry animal with strong, sharp teeth, a broad, flat tail, and webbed hind feet. *Beavers are noted for building dams.*

be•cause /bĭ kôz'/ *conj.* for the reason that. *I study because I want to learn.*

be•come /bĭ kŭm'/ *v.* (**be•comes, be•came, be•come, be•com•ing**) to develop into; to come or grow to be. *A caterpillar may become a butterfly or a moth.*

be•com•ing /bĭ kŭm' ĭng/ *v.* (**be•comes, be•came, be•come, be•com•ing**) turning into. *The caterpillar is becoming a butterfly in the cocoon.*

bee /bē/ *n.* a small insect that gathers pollen from plants and lives in a colony. *Bees make honey and wax.*

beep¹ /bēp/ *n.* a short, high-pitched sound. *The horn gave a loud beep.*

beep² /bēp/ *v.* to make such a sound. *My watch beeps once every hour.*

bees•wax /bēz′ wăks′/ *n.* the wax made by bees. *Beeswax is used for making candles.*

bee•tle /bēt′ l/ *n.* an insect that has four wings, two of which form a hard, shiny covering. *A ladybug is a small beetle that eats insects that harm garden plants.*

be•fore¹ /bǐ fôr′/ *prep.* at an earlier time than. *I had to be home before six o'clock.*

be•fore² /bǐ fôr′/ *adv.* previously; at an earlier time. *Have you heard this story before?*

be•fore³ /bǐ fôr′/ *conj.* earlier than the time when; previous to the time that. *Before you cross the street, look both ways.*

be•long /bǐ lông′/ or /bǐ lŏng′/ *v.* **a.** to have a proper place. *Pots and pans belong in the kitchen.* **b.** **belong to** to be the property of someone. *The bike belongs to Anita.*

be•low¹ /bǐ lō′/ *adv.* beneath; in a lower place. *Far below, we could see the bottom of the pit.*

be•low² /bǐ lō′/ *prep.* in a lower place than; to a lower place than. *Kansas is below Nebraska on the map.*

bench /bĕnch/ *n.* (**bench•es** *pl.*) a long, low, wooden or stone seat that sometimes has a back. *George fell asleep on a bench in the park.*

ber•ry /bĕr′ ē/ *n.* (**ber•ries** *pl.*) **a.** a small, juicy fruit with soft flesh and many seeds. *We had berries and ice cream for dessert.* **b.** the dry seed of certain plants. *The seed used in making coffee is a berry.*

bet•ter /bĕt′ ər/ *adj.* higher in quality; more excellent; finer. *Does anyone have a better plan?*

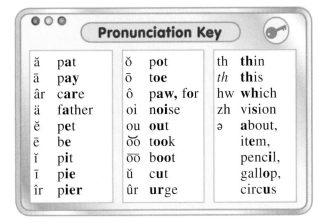

Pronunciation Key

ă	pat	ŏ	pot	th	thin
ā	pay	ō	toe	*th*	this
âr	care	ô	paw, for	hw	which
ä	father	oi	noise	zh	vision
ĕ	pet	ou	out	ə	about,
ē	be	ŏŏ	took		item,
ĭ	pit	ōō	boot		pencil,
ī	pie	ŭ	cut		gallop,
îr	pier	ûr	urge		circus

be•tween /bǐ twēn′/ *prep.* in the space that separates two things. *There were four people between me and the door.*

be•ware /bǐ wâr′/ *v.* to be cautious of. *Beware of the undertow when you swim in the ocean.*

birch /bûrch/ *n.* (**birch•es** *pl.*) **a.** a tree with smooth bark and hard wood. *Birches grow in North America and Europe.* **b.** the wood of this tree. *Much furniture is made of birch.*

birds /bûrdz/ *n.* plural of **bird.** *The birds flew south together.*

blew /blōō/ *v.* (**blows, blew, blown, blow•ing**) moved, driven, or forced by air. *Andre blew out the candles on the cake.*

blind¹ /blīnd/ *adj.* not able to see. *Many blind persons know how to read braille.*

blind² /blīnd/ *n.* a window shade. *Please raise the blind and let in the sunshine.*

block /blŏk/ *n.* **a.** a solid piece of wood, stone, metal, etc. *Children play with blocks.* **b.** a part of a town or city surrounded by four streets. *The new shopping center covers a city block.*

blood /blŭd/ *n.* the red liquid that flows through the bodies of people and animals. *Blood carries food and oxygen and carries away waste products.*

bloom¹ /blo͞om/ *n.* the flower of a plant. *The rose is a fragrant bloom.*

bloom² /blo͞om/ *v.* to have flowers. *Fruit trees bloom in April and May.*

blow /blō/ *v.* (**blows, blew, blown, blow•ing**) **a.** to move rapidly. *We could hear the wind blow.* **b.** to be moved or stirred by the wind. *The falling leaves are blowing around.* **c.** to cause to make a sound by forcing air through. *Blow the horn again.*

board¹ /bôrd/ or /bōrd/ *n.* **a.** a long, flat piece of sawed wood. *Boards are used in building houses.* **b.** a flat piece of wood or other material used for a special purpose. *The game of checkers is played on a board.*

board² /bôrd/ or /bōrd/ *v.* to get on a plane, train, ship, or bus. *The passengers waited to board the airplane.*

boats /bōts/ *n.* (**boat** *sing.*) small vessels for traveling on water. *They docked the boats at the pier.*

boil /boil/ *v.* **a.** to bubble and send out steam. *When water is heated enough, it boils.* **b.** to heat a liquid until bubbles rise. *He boiled the soup.* **c.** to cook in boiling water. *My mother boiled eggs for breakfast.*

boot /bo͞ot/ *n.* a cover for the foot and leg. *Sean and I have rubber boots.*

bor•der /bôr′ dər/ *n.* **a.** an outer edge. *The cabin was built on the border of the forest.* **b.** the imaginary line that divides one state or country from another. *We crossed the border when we visited Canada.*

bore•dom /bôr′ dəm/ or /bōr′ dəm/ *n.* a weary feeling because something is not interesting. *He fell asleep from boredom.*

bor•row /bŏr′ ō/ or /bôr′ ō/ *v.* to get something to use for a while before returning or repaying it. *May I borrow your spelling book?*

boss /bôs/ or /bŏs/ *n.* (**boss•es** *pl.*) the person in charge; the manager. *A good boss knows how to get along with people.*

bot•tom¹ /bŏt′ əm/ *n.* the lowest part. *The sled flew to the bottom of the hill.*

bot•tom² /bŏt′ əm/ *adj.* lowest. *Look on the bottom shelf for your book.*

bought /bôt/ *v.* (**buy, bought, buy•ing**) purchased. *Ava bought a pair of shoes.*

bounce /bouns/ *v.* (**bounc•es, bounced, bounc•ing**) to hit against a surface and spring back. *The rubber ball bounced off the wall.*

braid /brād/ *n.* three or more strands of hair or cloth woven together. *Marie's braid is ten inches long.*

branch /brănch/ *n.* (**branch•es** *pl.*) **a.** a limb of a tree, growing from the trunk or from another limb. *Children climb the branches of large trees.* **b.** a division of a large thing. *This small stream is a branch of the main river.*

brav•er /brāv′ ər/ *adj.* the comparative form of **brave.** having more courage; having less fear. *If you want to swim across the lake, then you are braver than I am.*

brav•est /brāv′ ĕst/ *adj.* the superlative form of **brave.** having the most courage; having the least fear. *Tony is the bravest of all of us.*

break /brāk/ *v.* (**breaks, broke, bro•ken, break•ing**) **a.** to come apart; to separate into pieces. *Fine china breaks easily.* **b.** to fail to keep or carry out. *Don't break the rules.* **c.** to go beyond; to do better than. *Will the runner break the record?*

breath /brĕth/ *n.* the air breathed into the lungs and then let out. *Take a deep breath.*

brick /brĭk/ *n.* a block of baked clay used for building or paving. *Many houses and apartment buildings are built with bricks.*

Spelling Dictionary

bridge /brĭj/ n. a structure built over a river or a valley for people or vehicles to cross. *Thousands of cars a day cross the Mississippi River on bridges.*

bridge

brief /brēf/ adj. short; quick; direct. *Our meeting was brief.*

bright /brīt/ adj. **a.** shining; giving light; reflecting light. *See how bright the car is when it is polished.* **b.** clear; brilliant. *She wore a bright red dress.*

bright • ly /brīt′ lē/ adv. in a shiny way; in a bright way. *The star shone brightly in the night sky.*

bring /brĭng/ v. (**brings, brought, bring•ing**) to carry from somewhere else. *Please bring my book with you.*

broil /broil/ v. to cook directly under heat, usually in an oven. *Mom likes to broil our steaks in the oven.*

broke /brōk/ past tense of **break**.

brook /bro͝ok/ n. a small stream of water. *The children waded in the brook.*

broth • er /brŭth′ ər/ n. a boy or man having the same parents as another person. *The girl had three brothers.*

brush¹ /brŭsh/ n. (**brush•es** pl.) the stiff hairs, straw, wire, etc., set in a stiff back or attached to a handle. *I have a new comb and brush.*

brush² /brŭsh/ v. to smooth or clean with a brush. *Brush your teeth after eating.*

Pronunciation Key

ă	pat	ŏ	pot	th	thin
ā	pay	ō	toe	*th*	this
âr	care	ô	paw, for	hw	which
ä	father	oi	noise	zh	vision
ě	pet	ou	out	ə	about,
ē	be	o͝o	took		item,
ĭ	pit	o͞o	boot		pencil,
ī	pie	ŭ	cut		gallop,
îr	pier	ûr	urge		circus

bub • ble /bŭb′ əl/ n. a thin, round film of liquid that forms a ball around a pocket of gas or air. *The slightest touch can pop a bubble.*

buck • et /bŭk′ ĭt/ n. a pail; a container for carrying liquids, sand, or other substances. *Please put the mop in the bucket.*

bun • ny /bŭn′ ē/ n. (**bun•nies** pl.) a pet name for a rabbit. *We saw a bunny hiding in the bushes.*

burn¹ /bûrn/ v. **a.** to be on fire. *We watched the logs burn.* **b.** to destroy by heat or fire. *The city burns its garbage.* **c.** to damage or hurt by fire, heat, wind, etc. *The sun burned her arms.*

burn² /bûrn/ n. an injury or sore made by something very hot. *He had a burn on his finger from the hot stove.*

bus /bŭs/ n. (**bus•es** pl.) a large motor vehicle that can carry many passengers. *We take a bus to school.*

bush /bo͝osh/ n. (**bush•es** pl.) a plant smaller than a tree, with many branches growing near the ground; a shrub. *Roses grow on bushes.*

bush • el /bo͝osh′ əl/ n. a unit of measure for dry goods such as grains, fruits, and vegetables. *The farmer gave us a bushel of apples.*

bus • y /bĭz′ ē/ adj. (**bus•i•er, bus•i•est; bus•i•ly** adv.) **a.** at work; active. *We will be busy until dark cleaning up the backyard.* **b.** full of work or activity. *The first day of school is always busy.*

but • ton /bŭt′ n/ *n.* a small, flat, hard, round piece used to fasten two parts of a garment by fitting through a slit. *The top button on my coat is loose.*

buzz¹ /bŭz/ *n.* the humming sound made by some insects. *The country air was still except for the buzz of the bees among the flowers.*

buzz² /bŭz/ *v.* to make a humming sound. *The wasps buzzed around their nest.*

cab • in /kăb′ ĭn/ *n.* a small house, often built of logs. *Abraham Lincoln lived in a cabin.*

cake /kāk/ *n.* a sweet, breadlike food made from batter. *The cake is mixed and ready to bake.*

calf /kăf/ *n.* (**calves** *pl.*) a young cow. *The calf was only three days old, so he stayed close to his mother.*

calves /kăvz/ plural of **calf**.

cam • el /kăm′ əl/ *n.* a large animal with one or two humps on its back. *Camels can go without drinking water for many days.*

camp¹ /kămp/ *n.* a place in the country where people live in tents or in simple buildings. *My sister goes to camp every summer.*

camp² /kămp/ *v.* to live outdoors for a time, especially in a tent. *On our trip we camped out every night.*

can /kăn/ or /kən/ *v.* (**could**) **a.** to be able to. *A cheetah can run fast.* **b.** to know how to. *Susan can play the drums.*

can • not /kăn′ ŏt/ or /kə nŏt′/ *v.* is or are not able to. *They cannot come with us.*

can't /kănt/ cannot.

care¹ /kâr/ *n.* **a.** protection; close attention. *A baby needs loving care.* **b.** anxiety; concern; worry. *Too much care can cause health problems.*

care² /kâr/ *v.* (**cares, cared, car•ing**) **a.** to feel anxiety, interest, or worry. *I don't care who wins.* **b.** to love or like someone. *He cares deeply for his children.*

care • ful • ly /câr′ fəl lē/ *adv.* (**care•ful** *adj.*) in a careful way; cautiously. *He carefully crossed the busy street.*

care • less • ly /câr′ lĭs lē/ *adv.* (**care•less** *adj.*) recklessly; in a careless way. *She carelessly tossed the litter into the street.*

car • rot /kăr′ ət/ *n.* a long, tapering, orange vegetable. *I chopped a carrot for the soup.*

car • ry /kăr′ ē/ *v.* (**car•ries, car•ried, car•ry•ing**) to take from one place to another. *Will you carry this package home?*

cas • tle /kăs′ əl/ *n.* a large building with high walls, towers, and sometimes a moat. *Kings and queens often live in castles.*

catch¹ /kăch/ *v.* (**catch•es, caught, catch•ing**) **a.** to get; to take and hold onto; to seize. *Watch that boy catch the ball!* **b.** to get to in time. *If you run, you can catch the bus.* **c.** to be held by something. *I always catch my coat on that nail.*

catch² /kăch/ *n.* (**catch•es** *pl.*) a thing that fastens or holds. *The catch on her dress was broken.*

cat • er • pil • lar /kăt′ ər pĭl′ ər/ *n.* the wormlike form, or larva, of a moth or butterfly. *The caterpillar spins a cocoon.*

caught /kôt/ *v.* (**catches, caught, catch•ing**) seized or retrieved; captured. *Tonight we caught five fireflies.*

cav • i • ty /kăv′ ĭ tē/ *n.* (**cav•i•ties** *pl.*) a small hollow caused by decay in a tooth. *If you brush your teeth properly, you won't have many cavities.*

ce • dar /sē′dər/ n. **a.** a type of tree known for its fragrant wood. **b.** a reddish wood. *Cedar is used to make trunks and closets.*

cell /sĕl/ n. one of the tiny parts of living matter of which all animals and plants are made. *Some animals and plants are made up of only one cell.*

cel • lar /sĕl′ər/ n. an underground room, used for storage. *The family next door fixed up the cellar as a playroom for their children.*

ce • ment /sĭ mĕnt′/ n. a powdered mixture of rock and clay that hardens into concrete when mixed with water. *Cement is used to build sidewalks.*

cent /sĕnt/ n. the smallest coin of the United States; a penny. *One hundred cents make a dollar.*

cen • ter /sĕn′tər/ n. **a.** a point in the middle. *Stand in the center of the circle.* **b.** a main area or place where people gather. *The town has a new shopping center.*

chain /chān/ n. **a.** a number of links or rings fastened together. *She strung the beads on a gold chain.* **b.** a series of things that are connected or joined. *The Rocky Mountains are a chain of mountains.*

chair /châr/ n. a piece of furniture with legs and a back that holds one seated person. *Let Grandfather sit in the rocking chair.*

chance /chăns/ n. a risk. *Sometimes you just have to take a chance and try something new.*

change¹ /chānj/ v. (**chang•es, changed, chang•ing**) to make or become different. *She changed her mind.*

change² /chānj/ n. **a.** making or becoming different. *Watch for a change in the weather tomorrow.* **b.** small coins. *John has a pocketful of change.*

Pronunciation Key

ă	pat	ŏ	pot	th	thin
ā	pay	ō	toe	th	this
âr	care	ô	paw, for	hw	which
ä	father	oi	noise	zh	vision
ĕ	pet	ou	out	ə	about,
ē	be	ŏŏ	took		item,
ĭ	pit	ōō	boot		pencil,
ī	pie	ŭ	cut		gallop,
îr	pier	ûr	urge		circus

chase¹ /chās/ v. (**chas•es, chased, chas•ing**) **a.** to run after, trying to catch. *The hounds chased the fox.* **b.** to drive away. *She chased the cat away from the bird's nest.*

chase² /chās/ n. a chasing. *It was a fine chase, but the fox got away.*

check¹ /chĕk/ v. to make sure of the correctness of. *Be sure to check your test before you hand it in.*

check² /chĕk/ n. **a.** a mark (✓) meaning something is satisfactory. *Make a check if the answer is correct.* **b.** a bill in a restaurant. *The check for our dinners was twelve dollars.* **c.** a written order from a bank to pay money to a certain person or place. *Make out a check for twenty dollars.*

check • up /chĕk′ŭp′/ n. a complete physical examination. *Everyone should have a regular checkup.*

cheese /chēz/ n. a food made from the thick part of milk. *I like sandwiches made with cheese.*

cher • ry /chĕr′ē/ n. (**cher•ries** pl.) a small, round red or white fruit with a stone or seed in the center. *Some cherries taste sweet, and some taste sour.*

chew /chōō/ v. to bite and grind with the teeth. *Chew your food well before you swallow it.*

Spelling Dictionary

child /chīld/ *n.* (**chil•dren** *pl.*) **a.** a baby. *The child is just learning to walk.* **b.** a young boy or girl. *Who is the child playing the flute?* **c.** a son or daughter. *I met Mrs. Keefe and her child in the store.*

chil•dren /chĭl′ drən/ plural of **child.**

chill•y /chĭl′ ē/ *adj.* cool; somewhat cold. *In the fall the mornings are usually chilly.*

chin /chĭn/ *n.* the part of the face beneath the bottom lip. *You move your chin when you chew.*

chirp /chûrp/ *v.* to make a short, sharp sound. *Some sparrows chirp.*

choice /chois/ *n.* a decision; a selection. *For dinner we will go to a restaurant of your choice.*

choose /chōōz/ *v.* (**choos•es, chose, chos•en, choos•ing**) **a.** to pick out. *Choose the kind of candy you want.* **b.** to prefer. *I do not choose to tell you my age.*

chop /chŏp/ *v.* (**chops, chopped, chop•ping**) to cut by hitting with a sharp tool like an ax. *We need to chop wood for our campfire.*

chore /chôr/ or /chōr/ *n.* an odd job; a task around the home. *One of my chores is mowing the lawn.*

chuck•le /chŭk′ əl/ *n.* a small, quiet laugh. *His funny speech caused chuckles in the audience.*

church /chûrch/ *n.* (**church•es** *pl.*) **a.** a building for public worship. *That church has stained-glass windows.* **b.** a religious service. *Church begins at ten o'clock.*

ci•der /sī′ dər/ *n.* the juice made from apples. *Hot apple cider is nice after a day out in the cold.*

cir•cle /sûr′ kəl/ *n.* a closed curve that forms a perfectly round figure. *Every part of a circle is the same distance from the center.*

cir•cus /sûr′ kəs/ *n.* (**cir•cus•es** *pl.*) a show featuring acts with animals, clowns, and acrobats. *A circus may be held under a tent.*

city /sĭt′ ē/ *n.* (**cit•ies** *pl.*) a large and important town. *Some large cities in the United States are New York, Chicago, Los Angeles, Philadelphia, and Detroit.*

clap[1] /klăp/ *v.* (**claps, clapped, clap•ping**) to strike the hands together. *After the play we all began to clap.*

clap[2] /klăp/ *n.* a sudden loud noise or crash. *I heard a clap of thunder.*

class /klăs/ *n.* (**class•es** *pl.*) **a.** a group of students meeting regularly with a teacher. *My English class is the first class of the day.* **b.** persons, animals, or things thought of as a group because they are alike. *Dogs belong to the class of mammals.*

class•room /klăs′ rōōm′/ or /klăs′ rŏŏm′/ *n.* a room in a school or college where classes meet. *The children decorated their classroom.*

clean /klēn/ *adj.* free from dirt. *Put on clean clothes for the party.*

clean•ly[1] /klĕn′ lē/ *adj.* (**clean•li•er, clean•li•est**) always and carefully neat and clean. *The cleanly house was pleasant to visit.*

clean•ly[2] /klēn′ lē/ *adv.* neatly; carefully. *Use a cold knife to cut cleanly through the cheesecake.*

clerk /klûrk/ *n.* **a.** a person who works in an office. *A clerk does general office work.* **b.** a person who sells things in a store. *My sister has a summer job as a clerk in a drugstore.*

click[1] /klĭk/ *n.* a short, sharp sound. *The camera made a click as I pressed the button to take the picture.*

click[2] /klĭk/ *v.* to make a short, sharp sound. *The catch clicked shut.*

cliff /klĭf/ *n.* a high, steep rock with a side that goes almost straight up. *Cliffs are difficult to climb.*

clock /klŏk/ *n.* a device made for telling time. *Can you see the hands move on that clock?*

close¹ /klōz/ v. (clos•es, closed, clos•ing) to shut. *Close the door when you leave.*

close² /klōs/ adj. (clos•er, clos•est; close•ly adv.) near. *We planted the tree close to the house.*

cloth /klôth/ or /klŏth/ n. a material made by weaving threads of cotton, wool, silk, nylon, etc. *Most of our clothes are made of cloth.*

cloud /kloud/ n. a large gray or white mass of tiny water drops floating in the sky. *That big cloud may bring rain.*

cloud•y /klou′ dē/ adj. (cloud•i•er, cloud•i•est; cloud•i•ly adv.) full of clouds. *The sky was gray and cloudy.*

clo•ver /klō′ vər/ n. a sweet-smelling plant with leaves growing in three parts. *I feed my rabbit clover.*

clover

coast /kōst/ n. the seashore; land along the sea or ocean. *There are many beaches along the coast of the Pacific Ocean.*

coat /kōt/ n. an outer garment with sleeves. *In winter I wear a heavy coat over my other clothes.*

coin /koin/ n. a piece of metal money. *Pennies, nickels, dimes, and quarters are coins.*

col•lar /kŏl′ ər/ n. the part of a shirt or coat that circles the neck. *He loosened his tie and his collar.*

col•o•ny /kŏl′ ə nē/ n. (col•o•nies pl.) a group of people with similar interests who live in a particular area. *The Pilgrims' colony grew as more people arrived.*

Pronunciation Key

ă	pat	ŏ	pot	th	thin
ā	pay	ō	toe	*th*	*th*is
âr	care	ô	paw, for	hw	which
ä	father	oi	noise	zh	vision
ě	pet	ou	out	ə	about,
ē	be	ŏŏ	took		item,
ĭ	pit	ōō	boot		pencil,
ī	pie	ŭ	cut		gallop,
îr	pier	ûr	urge		circus

col•or¹ /kŭl′ ər/ n. a hue, tint, or shade caused by the effect of light rays on the eyes. *All colors are combinations of red, yellow, and blue.*

col•or² /kŭl′ ər/ v. to change the color. *The children like to color the pictures in their coloring books.*

come /kŭm/ v. (comes, came, come, com•ing) **a.** to move toward. *The dark clouds are coming this way.* **b.** to arrive. *What time does the bus come?*

com•pare /kəm pâr′/ v. (com•pares, com•pared, com•par•ing) to examine things for similarities or differences. *If you compare prices, you can save money when you shop.*

cool¹ /kōōl/ adj. **a.** not hot; somewhat cold. *We were hoping for a cool day for the game.* **b.** calm; unexcited; in control of one's emotions. *A pilot must remain cool at all times.*

cool² /kōōl/ v. to make cool; to become cool. *If you add ice, your drink will cool faster.*

corn /kôrn/ n. a grain that grows in kernels or seeds on large ears. *We ate corn and peas for dinner.*

cor•ner¹ /kôr′ nər/ n. **a.** the place where two lines, edges, or sides of something come together. *A square has four corners.* **b.** the place where two or more streets come together. *The bus stops at the corner of Sixth and Main.*

cor•ner² /kôr′ nər/ adj. on or at a corner. *Jerry lives in the corner house.*

cost[1] /kôst/ or /kŏst/ v. to be for sale for; to be worth. *How much does one tomato cost?*

cost[2] /kôst/ or /kŏst/ n. the price that is to be paid. *The cost of a meal in a restaurant is going up.*

cot /kŏt/ n. a light bed that can be folded up. *Many cots are made of canvas on a metal or wood frame.*

cot•ton[1] /kŏt′ n/ n. a. the soft white fibers that surround the tiny seeds of certain plants. *Cotton is grown mainly to make cloth.* b. the thread or cloth made of cotton fibers. *Cotton is spun on large machines in mills.*

cot•ton[2] /kŏt′ n/ adj. made of cotton. *Cotton shirts are not as warm as wool shirts.*

could /kŏŏd/ a. past tense of **can.** b. used to suggest possibility. *We could do better.* c. used to suggest politeness. *Could you help us with this?*

could•n't /kŏŏd′ nt/ could not; not able to. *Why couldn't you go to the party?*

count /kount/ v. a. to name the numbers in order. *Our baby is learning to count already.* b. to add to find the total. *He counted the quarters in his bank.*

cou•ple /kŭp′ əl/ n. a. two of anything; a pair. *He had only a couple of dollars.* b. a man and woman together. *Mary and Jack make an attractive couple.*

cov•er[1] /kŭv′ ər/ n. a. the outside of a book. *Our math book has a red cover.* b. a lid or top. *Put the cover on the pot.* c. anything put on to protect, keep warm, etc. *A blanket is a cover for a bed.*

cov•er[2] /kŭv′ ər/ v. to put something on or over a person or thing. *We covered our books with heavy paper.*

crawl /krôl/ v. a. to move slowly along the ground by pulling the body. *Worms and caterpillars crawl.* b. to move on hands and knees. *Babies crawl before they walk.* c. to move slowly. *The traffic crawled along the crowded highway.*

crew /krōō/ n. the persons who run a boat, ship, train, or airplane. *A crew takes orders from a captain or other officer.*

cries /krīz/ a form of **cry.**

crop /krŏp/ n. food plants that are grown and harvested. *The farmer plants crops in the spring.*

cross /krôs/ or /krŏs/ v. a. to draw a line across. *Careful writers cross the letter "t" properly.* b. to go from one side to the other. *Wait for the traffic to clear, and then cross the street.*

cross•walk /krôs′ wôk′/ or /krŏs′ wôk′/ n. an area marked off for persons to use when crossing a street. *Always cross at a crosswalk.*

crouch /krouch/ v. (**crouch•es, crouched, crouch•ing**) to bend your legs and get close to the ground. *Crouch down to look under the table.*

crow /krō/ n. a large black bird with a harsh cry. *Crows sometimes eat most of the corn in a cornfield.*

crown /kroun/ n. a. a decorated covering for the head, worn by kings, queens, and others. *The king wears his crown only on very special occasions.* b. the upper part of a tooth. *I had a cavity in the crown of my tooth.*

cry[1] /krī/ v. (**cries, cried, cry•ing**) to weep; to shed tears and make sounds of sadness and pain. *The baby cried all night and kept us awake.*

cry[2] /krī/ n. (**cries** pl.) a sound of pain, unhappiness, etc. *The baby's cry woke us up.*

cuff /kŭf/ n. the fold of material turned over at the end of a sleeve or turned up at the bottom of a trouser leg. *I found the missing coin in my pants cuff.*

cul•ture /kŭl′ chər/ n. the beliefs, arts, and customs of a civilization at a certain stage of being. *The Roman culture borrowed much of its art from the Greeks.*

cup /kŭp/ *n.* a small, hollow container used for drinking. *Pour some milk into my cup, please.*

curl¹ /kûrl/ *v.* **a.** to twist or turn into rings or spirals. *She curls her hair every night.* **b.** to coil. *The cowboy's lasso was curled around the saddle.*

curl² /kûrl/ *n.* a lock of hair forming a ring. *Her head is covered with curls.*

curve /kûrv'/ *n.* a bend in a road; the part of a road that is not straight. *That curve in the road is dangerous!*

curv•ing /kûr' vĭng/ *v.* (**curves, curved, curv•ing**) bending; going in a way that is not straight. *The road is curving to the right and then to the left.*

cus•tom /kŭs' təm/ *n.* a usual practice among a certain group of people; the ordinary, accepted way of doing something. *Shaking hands when you meet someone is a custom in our country.*

dam /dăm/ *n.* a structure of earth, concrete, etc., that holds back water in a river or a stream and controls its flow. *Dams produce electricity and supply water for irrigation.*

dance¹ /dăns/ *v.* (**danc•es, danced, danc•ing**) to move, walk, step, etc., in time to music. *Can you dance to this song?*

dance² /dăns/ *n.* **a.** a particular series of steps done in time to music. *Can you do that new dance?* **b.** a party or gathering of people for dancing. *There will be a dance in the gymnasium on Friday night.*

danc•er /dăns' ər/ *n.* a person who participates in the various forms of dance. *The ballet dancer twirled on stage.*

dash¹ /dăsh/ *v.* (**dash•es, dashed, dash•ing**) to move quickly; to rush. *We dashed to the store, but it had closed.*

dash² /dăsh/ *n.* (**dash•es** *pl.*) a punctuation mark (—) used to show a break in thought or that something has been left out. *A dash shows that a sentence is incomplete or that a sharp contrast is being made.*

daw•dle /dôd' l/ *v.* (**daw•dles, daw•dled, daw•dling**) to waste time by lingering or moving slowly. *Don't dawdle on the way to school.*

dawn /dôn/ *n.* the first appearance of light in the morning. *Dawn came at six o'clock this morning.*

dear /dîr/ *adj.* greatly loved. *She gave the book to a dear friend.*

deer /dîr/ *n.* (**deer** *pl.*) a graceful animal with hooves. *The male deer has antlers.*

de•frost /dē frôst'/ or /dē frôst'/ *v.* to remove ice from; to thaw. *Defrost the meat before baking it.*

de•gree /dĭ grē'/ *n.* a unit used to measure temperature. *Water freezes at thirty-two degrees Fahrenheit.*

de•lay¹ /dĭ lā'/ *v.* to put off until a later time; to postpone. *The referee is going to delay the game until it stops raining.*

de•lay² /dĭ lā'/ *n.* a putting off until a later time; a postponement. *The train had a two-hour delay.*

depth /dĕpth/ *n.* the distance from the top of something to the bottom of something. *The scientist studied the depth of the ocean.*

des•ert /dĕz′ ərt/ *n.* a dry, sandy region in which little or nothing grows. *Camels are the only large animals that can survive in the desert.*

desk /dĕsk/ *n.* a piece of furniture somewhat like a table, having a flat top for writing and usually having drawers. *Office workers, teachers, and students have desks.*

dew /dōō/ or /dyōō/ *n.* water droplets that form at night on cool surfaces. *In the morning you may see dew on the leaves.*

did•n't /dĭd′ nt/ did not.

dig /dĭg/ *v.* (**digs, dug, dig•ging**) to make a hole in the ground; to break up the soil. *Dogs dig holes with their front paws.*

dime /dīm/ *n.* a silver coin used as money by the United States and by Canada. *A dime is worth ten cents.*

din•ner /dĭn′ ər/ *n.* the main meal of the day. *Some people have dinner at noon, and other people have dinner in the evening.*

dirt /dûrt/ *n.* **a.** mud, dust, soot, or any other thing that can soil skin, clothes, and furniture. *You have a smudge of dirt on your face.* **b.** earth; soil. *We put some dirt into the flowerpot.*

di•vide /dĭ vīd′/ *v.* (**di•vides, di•vid•ed, di•vid•ing**) **a.** to separate; to keep apart. *The expressway has a high wire fence that divides northbound traffic from southbound.* **b.** to separate into equal parts by using arithmetic. *24 divided by 8 is 3.*

does /dŭz/ *v.* (**does, did, done, do•ing**) **a.** performs or carries out a job. *My dad does the cooking.* **b.** acts or behaves. *She does very well playing quietly.*

does•n't /dŭz′ ənt/ does not.

dog /dôg/ or /dŏg/ *n.* a four-legged animal that makes a good pet. *Some dogs watch houses or tend sheep.*

dol•lar /dŏl′ ər/ *n.* a silver coin or a piece of paper money worth one hundred cents, or ten dimes, or twenty nickels. *When we write "$1.00," we mean "one dollar."*

don't /dōnt/ do not.

doo•dle /dōōd′ l/ *v.* to write or draw aimlessly; to scribble. *I sometimes doodle while talking on the phone.*

down•town¹ /doun′ toun′/ *adv.* in or toward the main business part of a city. *We all went downtown to shop.*

down•town² /doun′ toun′/ *n.* the business part of a city. *The downtown was decorated for the big parade.*

drain¹ /drān/ *v.* (**drains, drain•ing, drained**) to flow water or waste through a pipe. *Remember to drain the water in the tub after your bath.*

drain² /drān/ *n.* a pipe for flowing water or waste. *The drain in our sink is clogged.*

draw /drô/ *v.* (**draws, drew, drawn, draw•ing**) to make a design, picture, etc. *The artist drew an outline before he painted the picture.*

draw•er /drô′ ər/ *n.* a box, with handles, that slides in and out of a dresser or desk. *My socks are in the top drawer.*

dream¹ /drēm/ *n.* the thoughts, feelings, and pictures that occur in a person's mind while sleeping. *Her dream was about flying in an airplane.*

dream² /drēm/ *v.* **a.** to have a dream while sleeping. *He dreamed about food because he was hungry.* **b.** to suppose or imagine that a thing could happen. *We never dreamed that we'd win.*

dress¹ /drĕs/ *n.* (**dress•es** *pl.*) an outer garment worn by a woman or a girl. *She wore a long white dress for the wedding.*

dress² /drĕs/ *v.* to clothe; to put clothes on. *Mother dressed the baby after his nap.*

drew /drōō/ past tense of **draw**.

drive¹ /drīv′/ *v.* (**drives, drove, driv•en, driv•ing**) to make a car or working animal go. *Who is going to drive me home?*

drive² /drīv′/ *n.* a trip in a car. *We took a drive last Sunday.*

driv•er /drī′ vər/ *n.* any person who drives a vehicle or an animal. *The bus driver collected our fares when we got on.*

drop¹ /drŏp/ *n.* **a.** a small amount of liquid formed in a rounded mass. *A single drop of water was on the leaf.* **b.** a sudden fall. *After the fire, there was a sharp drop in the value of the house.*

drop² /drŏp/ *v.* (**drops, dropped, drop•ping**) to fall or let fall. *I dropped a dish as I was drying it.*

drug•store /drŭg′ stôr′/ or /drŭg′ stōr′/ *n.* a store where medicines and other items are sold. *You can buy toothpaste at the drugstore.*

drum /drŭm/ *n.* a musical instrument that consists of a hollow cylinder with a skin or fabric stretched taut over one or both ends. *The marchers kept time to the beat of a drum.*

drum

dull /dŭl/ *adj.* **a.** not sharp; not pointed; blunt. *We couldn't chop the wood because the ax was dull.* **b.** uninteresting; boring. *It was such a dull book that I fell asleep reading it.*

Pronunciation Key

ă	pat	ŏ	pot	th	thin
ā	pay	ō	toe	*th*	this
âr	care	ô	paw, for	hw	which
ä	father	oi	noise	zh	vision
ě	pet	ou	out	ə	about,
ē	be	ŏŏ	took		item,
ĭ	pit	ōō	boot		pencil,
ī	pie	ŭ	cut		gallop,
îr	pier	ûr	urge		circus

dust /dŭst/ *n.* a light powder of dirt. *I could see the dust on the old table.*

du•ty /dōō′ tē/ or /dyōō′ tē/ *n.* (**du•ties** pl.) a thing that a person ought to do. *He felt that it was his duty to tell the police about the thief's hiding place.*

ear•ly¹ /ûr′ lē/ *adv.* **a.** at or near the beginning of something. *I became tired very early in the race.* **b.** sooner than usual; before the usual time. *I will have to get up early to go fishing tomorrow.*

ear•ly² /ûr′ lē/ *adj.* (**ear•li•er, ear•li•est**) coming or happening at the beginning of something. *We took the early train.*

earn /ûrn/ *v.* **a.** to receive in return for performing a service, doing work, etc. *I earned four dollars today for mowing grass.* **b.** to deserve as a result of performing a service, doing work, etc. *After studying for two hours, we felt we had earned a break.*

earth /ûrth/ *n.* **a.** the third planet from the sun; the planet on which we live. *The earth revolves around the sun.* **b.** ground; soil. *Plant these seeds in black earth.*

Spelling Dictionary

earth•worm /ûrth' wûrm'/ *n.* a common worm that burrows in the ground. *We found many earthworms while digging in the garden.*

eas•i•ly /ē' zə lē/ *adv.* without trying hard; in an easy way. *He easily carried the light box.*

east[1] /ēst/ *n.* the direction to your right as you face north; the direction from which the sun rises. *We saw a glow of light in the east before dawn.*

east[2] /ēst/ *adv.* to the east. *We walked east until we came to the hotel.*

east[3] /ēst/ *adj.* from the east. *An east wind brought rain and colder temperatures.*

eight•een /ā tēn'/ *n.* the next number after seventeen; ten plus eight; 18. *He will turn eighteen next week.*

eighth[1] /ātth/ *adj.* coming next after the seventh. *The eighth float in the parade won first prize.*

eighth[2] /ātth/ *n.* a single one of eight equal parts. *Pies are often cut into eighths.*

ei•ther /ē' thər/ or /ī'-/ *adj.* one or the other of two. *I couldn't run faster than either one of my friends.*

e•lect /ĭ lĕkt'/ *v.* to choose or select for an office by voting. *We will elect our class president soon.*

e•lec•tric /ĭ lĕk' trĭk/ *adj.* **a.** having to do with electricity. *Our lighting depends upon an electric current.* **b.** worked by electricity. *We have an electric clock in our schoolroom.*

el•e•phant /ĕl' ə fənt/ *n.* a large, gray four-footed animal that has long white tusks and a long trunk with which it can grasp or carry objects. *Elephants are found in Africa and in India.*

elf /ĕlf/ *n.* (**elves** *pl.*) a tiny, make-believe being that is full of mischief. *The elf wore a green, pointed hat.*

elm /ĕlm/ *n.* a tall tree that has hard wood. *Elm trees give good shade.*

elves /ĕlvz/ plural of **elf.**

emp•ty /ĕmp' tē/ *adj.* (**emp•ti•er, emp•ti•est**) the opposite of full; not having anything or anyone in it. *Put this hat into the empty box.*

end•point /ĕnd' point'/ *n.* one of the two points that mark the ends of a segment of line; a point that marks the end of a ray. *This is one endpoint of the line.*

en•e•my /ĕn' ə mē/ *n.* (**en•e•mies** *pl.*) **a.** a person or a group that hates or fights another person or group. *Nations at war with each other are enemies.* **b.** anything that harms something else. *Cats are natural enemies of mice.*

en•gine /ĕn' jĭn/ *n.* a machine that changes fuel and energy into motion. *Most automobile engines use gasoline.*

e•qual[1] /ē' kwəl/ *adj.* of the same value, size, rank, amount, etc. *The two boys are of equal weight; they both weigh seventy pounds.*

e•qual[2] /ē' kwəl/ *v.* to be of the same value, size, rank, or amount as; to match. *Twelve inches equal one foot.*

e•rase /ĭ rās'/ *v.* (**e•ras•es, e•rased, e•ras•ing**) to wipe or rub out. *Will you please erase the board?*

e•ven[1] /ē' vən/ *adj.* **a.** flat; smooth. *The even surface of the road made driving very easy.* **b.** able to be divided by two without a remainder. *Some even numbers are 2, 4, 6, 8, 10, and 12.*

e•ven[2] /ē' vən/ *adv.* still; yet; by comparison. *This tree is tall, but that one is even taller.*

ev•er /ĕv' ər/ *adv.* at any time. *Have you ever traveled to Europe?*

eve•ry /ĕv' rē/ *adj.* each; all of a group. *Every child should visit the dentist regularly.*

eve•ry•day /ĕv' rē dā'/ *adj.* ordinary; all right for the usual day or event. *You should wear your everyday clothes to play outside.*

eve•ry•thing /ĕv' rē thĭng'/ *pron.* all things; each thing. *Everything is going right for me.*

eve•ry•where /ĕv′ rē hwâr′/ or /ĕv′ rē wâr′/ *adv.* in all places. *The bird-watcher saw birds everywhere.*

ex•plore /ĭk splôr′/ or /ĭk splōr′/ *v.* (**ex•plores, ex•plored, ex•plor•ing**) to travel in unknown lands; to journey in a strange place with hopes of discovery. *Many people explored America before the country was settled.*

face¹ /fās/ *n.* the front part of the head; that part of the head on which the eyes, nose, and mouth are located. *Her face was covered by a funny mask.*

face² /fās/ *v.* (**fac•es, faced, fac•ing**) to be turned toward; to have the front toward. *Our school faces the street.*

fac•ing /fā′ sĭng/ *v.* (**fac•es, faced, fac•ing**) **a.** looking in a certain direction. *Our beach house is facing the sea.* **b.** meeting a situation; confronting. *I will be facing the contest judges tomorrow.*

fac•to•ry /făk′ tə rē/ *n.* (**fac•to•ries** *pl.*) a building or a group of buildings in which something is manufactured. *He worked in a factory that makes farm machinery.*

fair /fâr/ *adj.* **a.** in keeping with the rules; according to what is accepted as right. *If you want to play on the team, you must learn fair play.* **b.** light in color. *She has fair hair and dark eyes.*

fair•y tale /fâr′ ē tāl′/ *n.* a made-up story, usually with fairies, elves, or other magical characters. *Cinderella is a famous fairy tale.*

fam•i•ly /făm′ ə lē/ or /făm′ lē/ *n.* (**fam•i•lies** *pl.*) **a.** a group that includes a parent or parents and their children. *Greg went to the movies with his family.* **b.** a group of people who are related to each other. *The Allen family has lived for years in this town.*

Pronunciation Key

ă	pat	ŏ	pot	th	thin
ā	pay	ō	toe	*th*	this
âr	care	ô	paw, for	hw	which
ä	father	oi	noise	zh	vision
ĕ	pet	ou	out	ə	about,
ē	be	ŏŏ	took		item,
ĭ	pit	ōō	boot		pencil,
ī	pie	ŭ	cut		gallop,
îr	pier	ûr	urge		circus

fan /făn/ *n.* anything used to move the air. *When it got hot I turned on the fan.*

fan•cy /făn′ sē/ *adj.* (**fan•ci•er, fan•ci•est; fan•ci•ly** *adv.*) decorated or ornamented; not plain. *Sue wore a fancy dress to the dance.*

far•a•way /fär′ ə wā/ *adj.* distant. *Movies show scenes of faraway places.*

fare /fâr/ *n.* money charged for a trip. *You pay a fare to ride in a bus, taxi, train, or airplane.*

fare•well /fâr wĕl′/ *n.* a wish of well-being at parting; a good-bye. *On my last day at work, I was given a warm farewell.*

fa•ther /fä′ thər/ *n.* the male parent. *My father is a very kind man.*

feel•ing /fē′ lĭng/ *n.* an emotion; what is felt in our minds. *On the morning of her birthday, Christine had a feeling of excitement.*

feet /fēt/ *n.* plural of **foot**. *These boots keep my feet dry and warm.*

fence /fĕns/ *n.* a barrier or enclosure of wood, wire, stone, etc., to keep people or animals from going into or out of a certain property. *Fences prevent animals from wandering off.*

fer•ry /fĕr′ ē/ *n.* (**fer•ries** *pl.*) a boat used to transport people or goods across a narrow body of water. *The ferry takes cars across the channel every day.*

fif•teen /fĭf tēn′/ *n.* one more than fourteen; ten plus five; 15. *He got fifteen right and none wrong.*

Spelling Dictionary

339

fifth[1] /fĭfth/ *n.* one of five equal parts. *Each of the five people had one fifth of the cake.*

fifth[2] /fĭfth/ *adj.* coming after four others; the fifth in order. *Henry was the fifth person in line.*

fif•ty-nine /fĭf′ tē nīn′/ *n.* one more than fifty-eight; fifty plus nine; 59. *She stopped counting when she reached fifty-nine.*

fight[1] /fīt/ *n.* a struggle to beat or overcome someone or something by force. *The boys stopped the fight between the two dogs.*

fight[2] /fīt/ *v.* (**fights, fought, fight•ing**) **a.** to try to overcome by force. *Boxers wear padded gloves when they fight.* **b.** to work hard in helping overcome. *Doctors fight disease.*

fill•ing /fĭl′ ĭng/ *n.* a material used to fill something. *The dentist put two metal fillings in my teeth.*

find /fīnd/ *v.* (**finds, found, find•ing**) **a.** to come upon accidentally; to locate an object by chance. *You may find my brother at the supermarket.* **b.** to look for and get back a lost object. *We will find my watch.*

fin•ish /fĭn′ ĭsh/ *v.* to come or bring to an end; to complete or become completed. *The movie finished at 9:30. Finish your dinner.*

fire•fight•er /fīr′ fī′ tər/ *n.* a person whose job is to put out fires. *The firefighter wears a helmet to protect her head.*

firm /fûrm/ *adj.* hard; solid. *They left the muddy road and walked on firm ground.*

first aid /fûrst′ ād′/ *n.* emergency help given to a person before a doctor comes. *We are learning first aid at school.*

fish[1] /fĭsh/ *n.* (**fish** or **fish•es** *pl.*) an animal that lives in water, has fins, and breathes through gills. *Most fish have scales covering their bodies.*

fish[2] /fĭsh/ *v.* (**fish•es, fished, fish•ing**) to try to catch fish. *Tracy and her father go to the lake each summer to fish.*

flag /flăg/ *n.* **a.** a piece of cloth with certain colors and designs. *A flag may stand for a country, a state, a city, or an organization.* **b.** a piece of cloth used as a signal. *A red flag often means "danger."*

flame[1] /flām/ *n.* the glow of burning; the visible part of the fire. *The flames from the forest fire shot upward.*

flame[2] /flām/ *v.* (**flames, flamed, flam•ing**) to burn with a flame; to blaze. *The campfire flamed when we added a sheet of paper.*

flash[1] /flăsh/ *n.* (**flash•es** *pl.*) **a.** a light that appears suddenly and briefly. *A flash of lightning appeared in the distance.* **b.** a very short time. *I'll be there in a flash.*

flash[2] /flăsh/ *v.* to give off a sudden, brief light. *The light on an answering machine will flash when there is a message.*

flat•ter /flăt′ ər/ *adj.* the comparative form of **flat**. smoother and more level. *This rock is flatter than that rock.*

flat•test /flă′ təst/ *adj.* the superlative form of **flat**. the smoothest and the most level. *The desert is the flattest place around here.*

flight /flīt/ *n.* a scheduled trip on an airplane. *The next flight to Chicago departs at 3:05.*

float[1] /flōt/ *v.* to stay or move in or on top of air, water, or other liquid. *Ice floats in water.*

float[2] /flōt/ *n.* **a.** something that floats. *The float on a fishing line bobs up and down.* **b.** a decorated truck or wagon used in a parade. *Elena rode on the float.*

flock¹ /flŏk/ *n.* a group of animals or birds that stay together. *There are fifty sheep in the flock.*

flock² /flŏk/ *v.* to gather in large numbers. *People flocked to see the movie star.*

floss¹ /flôs/ or /flŏs/ *n.* a strong thread used for cleaning between the teeth. *Do you use dental floss?*

floss² /flôs/ or /flŏs/ *v.* (**floss•es, flossed, floss•ing**) to use such thread to clean the teeth. *Everyone ought to floss regularly.*

flow¹ /flō/ *v.* to move in a stream, as water does. *A river flows to the ocean.*

flow² /flō/ *n.* a smooth, even, steady movement. *The flow of the sea is restful to watch.*

fluff•y /flŭf′ ē/ *adj.* (**fluff•i•er, fluff•i•est**) light and soft. *I like fluffy pillows.*

foam /fōm/ *n.* a quantity of small bubbles. *The big waves of the ocean have foam on top.*

fog•horn /fôg′ hôrn/ or /fŏg′ hôrn/ *n.* a loud horn used to warn ships of danger, especially during a dense fog. *Ships sound their foghorns to let other ships know they are coming.*

fold /fōld/ *v.* to close or bend parts of something together in order to fit it into a smaller space. *When we take down the flag, we fold it into the shape of a triangle.*

folk•tale /fōk′ tāl/ *n.* a story made up by and handed down among the people of a certain area. *The legend of Paul Bunyan is a famous folktale of the upper Midwest.*

fol•low /fŏl′ ō/ *v.* **a.** to go or come after. *Please follow me to your table.* **b.** to walk or move along. *Follow this path to the park.*

fool /fool/ *v.* to trick or attempt to trick someone. *Her costume fooled me into thinking she was someone else.*

Pronunciation Key

ă	pat	ŏ	pot	th	thin
ā	pay	ō	toe	*th*	this
âr	care	ô	paw, for	hw	which
ä	father	oi	noise	zh	vision
ĕ	pet	ou	out	ə	about,
ē	be	ŏŏ	took		item,
ĭ	pit	ōō	boot		pencil,
ī	pie	ŭ	cut		gallop,
îr	pier	ûr	urge		circus

foot /foot/ *n.* (**feet** *pl.*) **a.** the part of the body at the end of the leg. *Start the dance with your left foot.* **b.** a measure of length. *Twelve inches make a foot.*

foot•hill /foot′ hĭl′/ *n.* a low hill at the base or edge of a mountain range. *We saw deer in the foothills.*

foothill

foot•print /foot′ prĭnt′/ *n.* a mark made by a foot. *We followed their footprints in the snow.*

for /fôr/ *prep.* **a.** with the purpose of. *We are going for a bike ride.* **b.** sent or given to. *This letter is for you.* **c.** because of. *We jumped for joy.* **d.** in favor of. *Everyone voted for the trip to the zoo.*

for•est /fôr′ ĭst/ *n.* an area covered with trees; a woods. *We found pine cones in the forest.*

Spelling Dictionary

for•get /fər gĕt′/ or /fôr gĕt′/ v. (**for•gets, for•got, for•got•ten** or **for•got, for•get•ting**) **a.** to have no memory of; to be unable to recall. *I forget where I left my books.* **b.** to neglect to because of carelessness, lack of interest, etc. *I forgot to do my home-work last night.*

form¹ /fôrm/ n. **a.** the shape of some-thing. *We saw a cloud in the form of an elephant.* **b.** a particular kind or variety of something. *Steam is a form of water.* **c.** a paper containing blank spaces to be filled in. *Mark your answers on the answer form, not in the test book.*

form² /fôrm/ v. to give a shape to some-thing. *Potters form dishes out of clay.*

for•ty /fôr′ tē/ n. one more than thirty-nine; four times ten; 40. *Her father's age is forty.*

foul /foul/ adj. (**foul•er, foul•est**) being outside the game lines, as in baseball. *The foul ball flew into the dugout.*

found /found/ past tense of **find**.

four /fôr/ or /fōr/ n. one more than three; 4. *We need four to play this game.*

fowl /foul/ n. (**fowl** or **fowls** *pl.*) large birds used as food, such as turkeys, chickens, and ducks. *The county fair has a building housing several types of fowl.*

foxes /fŏks′ ĭs/ n. (**fox** *sing.*) wild ani-mals like dogs but with bushy tails. *The hiker uncovered where the foxes like to hide.*

fresh /frĕsh/ adj. **a.** newly made, grown, or gathered. *Mother baked fresh bread this morning.* **b.** clean. *Breathe this fresh air.*

friend /frĕnd/ n. a person that one likes. *Julio is a good friend who is always ready to cheer me up.*

friends /frĕnds/ n. plural of **friend**. *My friends are coming over this weekend for a slumber party.*

fun•ny /fŭn′ ē/ adj. (**fun•ni•er, fun•ni•est; fun•ni•ly** *adv.*) **a.** comical; causing laughs; humorous. *The movie was so funny that our sides hurt from laughing so much.* **b.** strange; unusual; peculiar. *That is a funny way to act.*

fur /fûr/ n. the thick, soft hair that is on the bodies of many animals. *We brush the cat's fur to keep it shiny.*

fur•ry /fûr′ ē/ adj. covered with fur. *A mouse is a small furry animal.*

fuzz•y /fŭz′ ē/ adj. (**fuzz•i•er, fuzz•i•est**) **a.** having a furry texture. *These young chicks are fuzzy.* **b.** blurred; out of focus. *Hold still while I take the picture so it won't be fuzzy.*

gadg•et /găj′ ĭt/ n. a small mechani-cal object with a practical use but often thought of as a novelty. *This gadget is used to open a can.*

gain¹ /gān/ v. to get; to acquire; to obtain. *Keisha gained business experi-ence from her paper route.*

gain² /gān/ n. an increase. *The owner of the ball park reported a gain in atten-dance.*

gal•lon /găl′ ən/ n. a measurement of liquid volume. *Four quarts make a gallon.*

geese /gēs/ plural of **goose**.

germ /jûrm/ n. a living thing that may cause a disease. *Germs are too small to be seen without a microscope.*

gi•raffe /jĭ răf′/ n. an African animal with a long neck, long legs, and a spot-ted skin. *A giraffe eats leaves from trees.*

girls /gûrlz/ n. plural of **girl**. *The girls sang "Happy Birthday" to their older brother.*

give /gĭv/ v. (gives, gave, giv•en, giv•ing) a. to hand over to another as a present. *Thank you for giving me the watch.* b. to let have. *Give me your hand and I'll pull you up.* c. to provide. *Let's give a show for parents' night.*

glad • ly /glăd′ lē/ adv. in a happy or joyful manner. *He gladly accepted the award.*

globe /glōb/ n. a round model of the earth, with a map on the outside showing oceans, countries, etc. *The children pointed out on the globe the route by which Columbus reached America.*

glo • ry /glôr′ ē/ or /glōr′ ē/ n. (glo•ries pl.) great honor or praise. *The winner was embarrassed by all the glory.*

gloss • y /glô′ sē/ or /glŏs′ ē/ adj. (gloss•i•er, gloss•i•est) smooth and shiny. *The glossy paper is really smooth.*

goat /gōt/ n. a horned animal about the size of a sheep. *The mountain goat is wild and very quick in climbing rocks.*

goods /go͝odz/ n. pl. things that are bought or made to be sold. *Department stores have many goods for sale.*

goose /go͞os/ n. (geese pl.) a swimming bird that looks like a duck, but has a larger body and a longer neck. *The male goose is called a gander.*

go • ril • la /gə rĭl′ ə/ n. an ape related to the chimpanzee, but less erect and much larger. *The gorilla named Coco learned sign language.*

grabbed /grăbd/ v. (grabs, grabbed, grab•bing) took or grasped suddenly. *The cat scratched me because I grabbed its tail.*

grace /grās/ n. beauty and ease of movement. *Ballet dancers need to have grace and flexibility.*

grade /grād/ v. (grades, graded, grading) to check over; to evaluate. *He took the homework papers home to grade.*

Pronunciation Key

ă	pat	ŏ	pot	th	thin
ā	pay	ō	toe	*th*	this
âr	care	ô	paw, for	hw	which
ä	father	oi	noise	zh	vision
ĕ	pet	ou	out	ə	about,
ē	be	o͝o	took		item,
ĭ	pit	o͞o	boot		pencil,
ī	pie	ŭ	cut		gallop,
îr	pier	ûr	urge		circus

grain /grān/ n. a. the seeds of a cereal plant such as wheat, oats, or corn. *People eat grain in the form of cornflakes, oatmeal, and wheatflakes.* b. a tiny piece of sand, sugar, or salt. *I spilled a few grains of salt on the table.*

gram /grăm/ n. a unit of mass in the metric system. *It takes about twenty-eight grams to make one ounce.*

grand /grănd/ adj. a. large; beautiful; costing much money. *The queen lived in a grand palace.* b. fine; wonderful. *You'll have a grand time at the party.*

grand • fa • ther /grănd′ fä′ thər/ or /grăn′ fä′ thər/ n. the father of one's mother or father. *One of my grandfathers lives here in town; my other grandfather lives in the country.*

grand • moth • er /grănd′ mŭth′ ər/ or /grăn′ mŭth′ ər/ n. the mother of one's father or mother. *My grandmother is coming to my birthday party.*

graph /grăf/ n. a diagram that shows the relationship between one thing and another. *Our graph shows how the price of a loaf of bread has increased over time.*

grasp /grăsp/ v. to clasp or embrace with the fingers or hands. *Grasp my hand and I will help you out of the pool.*

grass • land /grăs′ lănd′/ n. an area covered with grass; a pasture; a prairie. *The sheep grazed on the grassland.*

grate /grāt/ v. (**grates, grat•ed, grat•ing**) to break something down into small pieces by rubbing it against a rough surface. *He grated the onions and mixed them in with the meat.*

great /grāt/ adj. (**great•er, great•est; great•ly** adv.) **a.** large in size or number; big. *A great crowd of people was at the carnival.* **b.** more than is ordinary or expected. *You did a great job in cutting down the tree.* **c.** important; skilled; famous. *There have been many great presidents in our history.*

great•ly /grāt' lē/ adv. very much. *I greatly appreciate your help.*

green•house /grēn' hous'/ n. a heated building that has a glass roof and glass sides in which plants are grown. *Throughout the winter, flowers bloomed in the greenhouse.*

greenhouse

greet /grēt/ v. to welcome in a friendly way. *A taxi driver will greet us at the airport.*

greet•ing /grē' tĭng/ n. the words in a letter used to address someone. *The greeting in a friendly letter is followed by a comma.*

grew /groo/ v. past tense of **grow**. *The strawberries grew all over our backyard.*

grind /grīnd/ v. (**grinds, ground, grind•ing**) to crush into bits or small pieces. *I'll grind this tablet into powder.*

ground /ground/ n. **a.** the surface of the earth. *The model airplane crashed to the ground when it ran out of gas.* **b.** soil; earth. *The ground in this field is rich and fertile.*

grow /grō/ v. (**grows, grew, grown, grow•ing**) **a.** to become larger; to increase. *Our baby is growing so fast!* **b.** to live in a certain place. *Palm trees grow in the tropics.* **c.** to raise by planting seeds and caring for. *We grow tomatoes in our garden.*

gulf /gŭlf/ n. a large bay, or part of a sea or an ocean, that is partly enclosed by land. *The Gulf of Mexico is a part of the Atlantic Ocean.*

hail¹ /hāl/ n. small pieces of ice that may fall during a rainstorm. *Hail makes a noise on the top of a car.*

hail² /hāl/ v. to pour down hail. *It is raining and hailing at the same time.*

hair /hâr/ n. **a.** the mass of thin, thread-like strands that grow on a person's or an animal's skin. *Elizabeth has beautiful hair; she brushes it often.* **b.** any one of these strands. *Look at the hairs that dog left on the chair!*

hair•cut /hâr' kŭt'/ n. a cutting of the hair. *Tom got a very short haircut from the barber.*

half /hăf/ n. (**halves** pl.) one of two equal parts. *Which half of the sandwich do you want?*

hand•writ•ing /hănd' rī tĭng/ n. writing done by hand with a pen or a pencil. *Neat handwriting always makes a good impression.*

hap•pen /hăp' ən/ v. to take place; to occur. *Is anything happening tomorrow afternoon?*

hap • pi • ly /hăp′ ə lē/ *adv.* with joy or gladness; in a happy way. *The children happily played in the yard.*

hap • py /hăp′ ē/ *adj.* (**hap•pi•er, hap•pi•est; hap•pi•ly** *adv.*) feeling or showing pleasure; joyful. *The happy man whistled all day.*

hare /hâr/ *n.* an animal like a rabbit, but much larger. *A hare has strong legs and can run fast.*

has • n't /hăz′ ənt/ has not.

hatch /hăch/ *v.* (**hatch•es, hatched, hatch•ing**) to emerge from an egg or cocoon. *The bird's egg might hatch today.*

haul /hôl/ *v.* to pull with force; to drag. *The girls hauled their rowboat out of the water.*

have /hăv/ *v.* (**has, had, hav•ing**) used as a helping verb in addition to having the following meanings: **a.** to own; to possess. *They have a new house.* **b.** to accept; to take. *Have a piece of pie.* **c.** to be forced; to feel obliged. *I have to do my homework now.*

hawk /hôk/ *n.* a large bird with a strong curved beak, sharp claws, and good eyesight. *A hawk eats smaller birds and animals.*

he /hē/ *pron.* that boy or man. *He is a good piano player.*

heal /hēl/ *v.* to restore to health; to return to a healthy state. *Tim's broken finger should heal quickly.*

health • y /hĕl′ thē/ *adj.* (**health•i•er, health•i•est; health•i•ly** *adv.*) **a.** having good health. *The doctor said the baby was healthy.* **b.** good for the health. *Broccoli is a healthy food.*

hear /hîr/ *v.* (**hears, heard, hear•ing**) **a.** to take in sound through the ears. *We could hear every word clearly.* **b.** to listen to; to pay attention to. *Did you hear the principal's announcement?*

heard /hûrd/ past tense of **hear.**

Pronunciation Key

ă	pat	ŏ	pot	th	thin
ā	pay	ō	toe	*th*	this
âr	care	ô	paw, for	hw	which
ä	father	oi	noise	zh	vision
ĕ	pet	ou	out	ə	about,
ē	be	o͝o	took		item,
ĭ	pit	o͞o	boot		pencil,
ī	pie	ŭ	cut		gallop,
îr	pier	ûr	urge		circus

---

heart /härt/ *n.* **a.** the large hollow muscle that pumps blood throughout the body by contracting and expanding. *The heart keeps the blood in circulation.* **b.** something looking like a heart. *A deck of cards has thirteen cards with hearts on them.*

heat[1] /hēt/ *n.* hotness; great warmth. *Fire gives off heat.*

heat[2] /hēt/ *v.* to make or become warm. *The furnace heats the house.*

here /hîr/ *adv.* **a.** in or at this place. *We like living here.* **b.** to or into this place. *Please come here.*

here's /hîrz/ here is.

her • self /hər sĕlf′/ *pron.* **a.** her own self. *Jennifer fell down and hurt herself.* **b.** the person or self she usually is. *Beth isn't acting like herself today.*

he's /hēz/ he is; he has.

hic • cup /hĭk′ əp/ *n.* an uncontrollable intake of breath that causes a clicking sound. *Beth covered her mouth to muffle her hiccup.*

hid • den[1] /hĭd′ n/ *adj.* concealed; secret. *The explorers searched for the hidden treasure.*

hid • den[2] /hĭd′ n/ *v.* a form of **hide.**

hide /hīd/ *v.* (**hides, hid, hid•den, hid•ing**) to put or keep out of sight. *Hide the ribbon somewhere in the room, and we'll try to find it.*

high[1] /hī/ *adj.* **a.** tall; far above the ground. *Walnuts fell from a high branch.* **b.** greater than usual; more than normal. *Prices at this store are high.*

high[2] /hī/ *n.* a high amount, as in temperature. *Yesterday's high was ninety-eight degrees.*

high•land /hī' lənd/ *n.* a hilly area that is higher than the land around it. *The shepherd led the flock up to the highland.*

high•light /hī' līt'/ *n.* the best part of something. *Swimming was the highlight of our day.*

hill•side /hĭl' sīd'/ *n.* the side of a hill. *In winter we coast down the hillside on our sleds.*

him•self /hĭm sĕlf'/ *pron.* **a.** his own self. *My little brother tied his shoes all by himself.* **b.** the person or self he usually is. *Jason looked more like himself after the doctor took the cast off his arm.*

hiss[1] /hĭs/ *v.* (**hiss•es, hissed, hiss•ing**) to make a sound like s-s-s-s. *We all love to hiss the villain.*

hiss[2] /hĭs/ *n.* (**hiss•es** *pl.*) a sound like s-s-s-s. *The goose gave an angry hiss.*

hoarse /hôrs/ or /hōrs/ *adj.* (**hoars•er, hoars•est**) low or rough in sound or voice. *My voice was hoarse from cheering so loudly at the football game.*

hob•by /hŏb' ē/ *n.* (**hob•bies** *pl.*) something you do for fun. *Sue's favorite hobby is sewing.*

hol•i•day /hŏl' ĭ dā'/ *n.* a day on which a special event is celebrated. *Independence Day is the favorite holiday of many people.* [Middle English *holidai, holy day*]

hol•ly /hŏl' ē/ *n.* (**hol•lies** *pl.*) a shrub or tree that has evergreen leaves and red berries. *This holiday wreath is made of holly.*

hon•ey /hŭn' ē/ *n.* a sweet, sticky, yellow liquid made by honeybees. *Honey tastes good on toast.*

hoofs /hoofs/ or /ho͞ofs/ *n. pl.* (**hoof** *sing.*) the curved coverings of horn that protect the feet of animals. *The cow's hoofs were muddy.*

hop /hŏp/ *v.* (**hops, hopped, hop•ping**) to move by jumping. *Rabbits hop from place to place.*

hope /hōp/ *v.* (**hopes, hoped, hop•ing**) to expect and desire; to wish. *We hoped Brad would win.*

horse /hôrs/ *n.* a large, hoofed animal used for riding and pulling loads. *A colt is a young horse.*

hot /hŏt/ *adj.* (**hot•ter, hot•test**) **a.** very warm; having a high temperature. *I like taking hot baths.* **b.** sharp to the taste; peppery, spicy. *Do you prefer hot or mild sauce?*

hour•ly[1] /our' lē/ *adv.* every hour. *The bells in our school ring hourly.*

hour•ly[2] /our' lē/ *adj.* for every hour. *She receives an hourly wage of six dollars.*

house /hous/ *n.* a building in which to live. *The fine old house is for sale.*

house•fly /hous' flī'/ *n.* (**house•flies** *pl.*) a common two-winged flying insect. *There's a housefly in that spiderweb.*

how•ev•er /hou ĕv' ər/ *conj.* nevertheless. *I've never tasted eggplant before; however, it looks delicious.*

hugged /hŭgd/ *v.* (**hugs, hug•ged, hug•ging**) to press tightly, especially in the arms. *Sarah hugged her teddy bear.*

hun•dred /hŭn' drĭd/ *n.* ten times ten; 100. *Hundreds of children signed up for camp.*

hun•ger /hŭng' gər/ *v.* **a.** to want for food. *During our long hiking trip, we began to hunger for home-cooked meals.* **b.** to want for knowledge.

hun•gry /hŭng′ grē/ *adj.* (**hun•gri•er, hun•gri•est; hun•gri•ly** *adv.*) wanting food; needing food. *The hungry children ate fifty sandwiches.*

hunt•er /hŭn′ tər/ *n.* a person or animal who hunts. *The hawk's keen eyesight makes it a good hunter.*

hur•ry¹ /hûr′ ē/ or /hŭr′ ē/ *v.* (**hur•ries, hur•ried, hur•ry•ing**) to act quickly; to move fast. *Hurry or you'll be late!*

hur•ry² /hûr′ ē/ or /hŭr′ ē/ *n.* haste; a rush; a fast action. *Why are you in such a hurry?*

hurt /hûrt/ *v.* (**hurts, hurt, hurt•ing**) **a.** to cause pain to. *The sting of the bee hurt his arm.* **b.** to suffer pain. *Does your head hurt?*

ice /īs/ *n.* water that has been frozen solid by cold. *Ice keeps food and drinks cool.*

I'd /īd/ I would; I should; I had.

I'll /īl/ I shall; I will.

I'm /īm/ I am.

inch /ĭnch/ *n.* (**inch•es** *pl.*) a measure of length equal to one-twelfth of one foot. *Michelle is forty-six inches tall.*

is•n't /ĭz′ ənt/ is not.

its /ĭts/ *pron.* of or belonging to it. *The bird left its nest.*

it's /ĭts/ it is; it has.

i•vo•ry /ī′ və rē/ or /īv′ rē/ *n.* (**i•vo•ries** *pl.*) **a.** a hard, white substance, like the tusks of an elephant. *The tabletop is made of ivory.* **b.** a creamy-white color. *Ivory is a nice color for my living room.*

Pronunciation Key

ă	pat	ŏ	pot	th	thin
ā	pay	ō	toe	*th*	this
âr	care	ô	paw, for	hw	which
ä	father	oi	noise	zh	vision
ĕ	pet	ou	out	ə	about,
ē	be	ŏŏ	took		item,
ĭ	pit	ōō	boot		pencil,
ī	pie	ŭ	cut		gallop,
îr	pier	ûr	urge		circus

jaw /jô/ *n.* the lowest part of the face; the part that holds the teeth. *When you yawn, your jaw drops.*

jel•ly /jĕl′ ē/ *n.* (**jel•lies** *pl.*) a food made by boiling fruit juices and sugar. *I like grape jelly.*

jel•ly•fish /jĕl′ ē fĭsh′/ *n.* (**jel•ly•fish** or **jel•ly•fish•es** *pl.*) a soft, bowl-shaped sea animal with an almost transparent body. *Some jellyfish will sting you if you touch them.*

jig•saw /jĭg′ sô′/ *n.* a saw with a narrow blade for cutting curved and ornamental patterns. *Dad used a jigsaw to make the fancy shelf.*

jog•ging /jŏg′ ĭng/ *v.* (**jogs, jogged, jog•ging**) running at a slow, regular pace. *I like jogging early in the morning before it gets hot outside.*

join /join/ *v.* **a.** to put together; to connect. *The caboose was joined to the last car of the train.* **b.** to become a member of. *Next year I will be able to join the Boy Scouts.* **c.** to combine with a group in doing something. *Would you like to join our game?*

joke /jōk/ *n.* something said or done to make someone laugh. *Rob told a funny joke.*

Spelling Dictionary

jump /jŭmp/ *v.* to leap off the ground. *It was fun to watch the horses jump over the fences.*

kan•ga•roo /kăng′ gə roo′/ *n.* a mammal found in Australia and surrounding islands with a small head, large ears, long powerful hind legs, and a long thick tail. *The mother kangaroo carries her young in a pouch.*

kangaroo

keen•ly /kēn′ lē/ *adv.* with great interest; eagerly. *We keenly looked forward to learning the new computer game.*

kept /kĕpt/ *v.* (**keeps, kept, keep•ing**) **a.** stored; put away; saved. *I kept all of my old homework.*

kind¹ /kīnd/ *adj.* gentle and caring. *They are always very kind to animals.*

kind² /kīnd/ *n.* type; sort; variety. *Which kind of ice cream would you like?*

king•dom /kĭng′ dəm/ *n.* a country, land, or territory ruled by a king or queen. *The queen declared a holiday throughout the kingdom.*

kit•ten /kĭt′ n/ *n.* a young cat. *The kitten chased a butterfly around the garden.*

knew /noo/ or /nyoo/ past tense of **know**.

knight /nīt/ *n.* during the Middle Ages, a warrior who was honored with a military rank by a king or lord. *The king called his knights together to plan the battle.*

knit•ting /nĭt′ ĭng/ *v.* (**knits, knit** or **knit•ted, knit•ting**) making by weaving yarn with long needles. *My mother is knitting a sweater for me.*

know /nō/ *v.* (**knows, knew, known, know•ing**) **a.** to understand; to have information about. *Do you know how fossils are made?* **b.** to be aware; to be sure. *We knew we had heard a noise.* **c.** to be acquainted with. *I've known them for years.* **d.** to have skill in. *Who knows how to play the piano?*

lad•der /lăd′ ər/ *n.* a series of steps placed between two long sidepieces, used for climbing. *The painter leaned the ladder against the wall.*

laid /lād/ past tense of **lay**.

land /lănd/ *n.* **a.** the part of the earth that is not water. *After the plane went up through the clouds, we could no longer see the land.* **b.** ground; earth; soil. *This rich land is good for planting corn.*

large /lärj/ *adj.* (**larg•er, larg•est; large•ly** *adv.*) big. *A whale is large.*

last /lăst/ *adj.* **a.** coming after all others; final. *The last train leaves at six o'clock.* **b.** before the present time; most recent. *I read this book last year.*

last•ly /lăst′ lē/ *adv.* at the end; finally. *Lastly, pour the batter into a cake pan and put it into the oven.*

late¹ /lāt/ *adj.* (**la•ter, la•test**) **a.** happening after the usual time. *We had a late summer this year.* **b.** near the end of a certain time. *Our tomatoes ripen in late summer.*

late² /lāt/ *adv.* after the usual or proper time. *The bus came late.*

Spelling Dictionary

late • ly /lāt′ lē/ *adv.* not long ago; recently. *Edna has lately been working harder than ever.*

la • va /lä′ və/ *n.* the hot, melted rock that comes from a volcano. *The lava flowed down the mountain.*

law /lô/ *n.* a rule. *Every state has a law against stealing.*

lawn /lôn/ *n.* ground covered with grass that is kept cut short. *Mr. Griffin's lawn is smooth and green.*

lay /lā/ *v.* (**lays, laid, lay•ing**) **a.** to put or place. *You can lay your book on the table.* **b.** to produce eggs. *Hens lay eggs.*

leaf /lēf/ *n.* (**leaves** *pl.*) one of the green, flat parts that grow on bushes, plants, and trees. *The caterpillar was eating a leaf.*

learn /lûrn/ *v.* **a.** to gain skill or knowledge in. *We learn spelling in school.* **b.** to memorize. *Can you learn this poem?* **c.** to find out. *When will we learn the results of the election?*

leave /lēv/ *v.* (**leaves, left, leav•ing**) **a.** to go away; to go from. *The train left ten minutes ago.* **b.** to let stay or be. *Leave your packages here while you shop.*

ledge /lĕj/ *n.* a narrow shelf or ridge, especially on a cliff or rock wall. *We saw an eagle's nest on a ledge high above.*

left¹ /lĕft/ past tense of **leave.**

left² /lĕft/ *adj.* located closer to the side opposite the right. *We took a left turn at the corner.*

left³ /lĕft/ *n.* the left side. *Her house is the one on the left.*

left⁴ /lĕft/ *adv.* in the direction to the left. *Go left after you reach the stoplight.*

lem • on /lĕm′ ən/ *n.* a juicy, yellow, sour fruit. *The lemon made Alex pucker.*

less¹ /lĕs/ *adj.* not so much. *It took less time to do my homework this week than last.*

less² /lĕs/ *adv.* to a smaller extent. *I was less happy than I looked.*

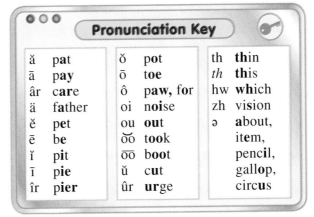

Pronunciation Key		
ă pat	ŏ pot	th thin
ā pay	ō toe	*th* this
âr care	ô paw, for	hw which
ä father	oi noise	zh vision
ĕ pet	ou out	ə about,
ē be	ŏŏ took	item,
ĭ pit	ōō boot	pencil,
ī pie	ŭ cut	gallop,
îr pier	ûr urge	circus

les • son /lĕs′ ən/ *n.* something to be taught or learned. *My brother is taking violin lessons.*

let's /lĕts/ let us.

let • ter /lĕt′ ər/ *n.* **a.** a symbol for a sound. *There are twenty-six letters in our alphabet.* **b.** a written or typed message sent by mail. *Mail your letter at the post office.*

lev • er /lĕv′ ər/ or /lē′ vər/ *n.* a bar used to lift objects. *The lever is rested on a support and pushed at one end to lift the other end.*

li • brar • y /lī′ brĕr′ ē/ *n.* (**libraries** *pl.*) a room or building containing books that may be read or borrowed. *A library is also used for research and studying.*

lift /lĭft/ *v.* to raise from a lower to a higher position. *This box is too heavy for me to lift.*

light¹ /līt/ *n.* **a.** rays of energy that help us see; the opposite of dark. *The sun gives light.* **b.** anything that gives light. *Turn off the light when you leave the room.*

light² /līt/ *adj.* not heavy; not having much weight. *In the summer we wear light clothes.*

line /līn/ *n.* **a.** a rope, cord, or wire. *Fishing line must be strong.* **b.** a long, thin mark. *Draw a line on your paper.* **c.** a row of persons or things. *There was a long line at the movie theater.*

li•on /lī′ ən/ *n.* a large, powerful, brownish-yellow member of the cat family. *A group of lions is called a pride.*

lip /lĭp/ *n.* either of the two edges of the mouth. *Your lips move when you speak.*

list¹ /lĭst/ *n.* a column of names, words, or numbers. *Please write "milk" on the grocery list.*

list² /lĭst/ *v.* to write or print in a column or columns. *List the spelling words on your paper.*

lit•er /lē′ tər/ *n.* a metric unit of volume used to measure both liquids and dry matter. *A liter of milk is about the same as a quart of milk.*

lit•tle¹ /lĭt′ l/ *adj.* **a.** small. *An elephant is big and an ant is little.* **b.** not much. *There is little food in the house.*

lit•tle² /lĭt′ l/ *n.* a small amount. *Patricia showed the teacher a little of her poetry.*

live /lĭv′/ *v.* (**lives, lived, liv•ing**) **a.** to be alive; to exist. *We live on the planet Earth.* **b.** to have one's home; to dwell. *Our aunt lives in Texas.*

liv•ing /lĭv′ ĭng/ *adj.* alive; not dead. *Biology is the study of living things.*

load¹ /lōd/ *n.* something that is carried. *The load was too heavy for the small car.*

load² /lōd/ *v.* to fill with something to be carried. *Load the truck with bricks.*

loaf /lōf/ *n.* (**loaves** *pl.*) a shaped or molded mass of bread; food baked in one large piece. *Grandma baked a loaf of bread.*

lob•by /lŏb′ ē/ *n.* (**lob•bies** *pl.*) a hall or waiting room in a hotel or other building. *Let's sit in the lobby and wait for Tanisha.*

log•ging /lô′ gĭng/ or /lŏg′ ĭng/ *n.* the work of cutting down trees and making them into logs. *Logging is a big industry.*

long•er /lông′ ər/ or /lŏng′ ər/ *adj.* having a greater length than something else. *This string is longer than that one.*

long•est /lông′ ĭst/ or /lŏng′ ĭst/ *adj.* having the greatest length than anything else. *She has the longest hair of anyone in her class.*

loop /lo͞op/ *n.* the curved shape of a line that dips and crosses itself. *We hung the crepe paper in loops.*

loose /lo͞os/ *adj.* (**loos•er, loos•est; loose•ly** *adv.*) not fastened tightly. *The bottom step is loose.*

lose /lo͞oz/ *v.* (**los•es, lost, los•ing**) **a.** to be unable to find. *Don't lose your key.* **b.** to fail to win. *Our team almost lost the game.*

lost¹ /lôst/ or /lŏst/ *v.* past tense of **lose**.

lost² /lôst/ or /lŏst/ *adj.* **a.** missing. *The children found the lost cat.* **b.** destroyed; ruined. *The lost trees will take years to replace.*

loud /loud/ *adj.* **a.** strong in sound; not soft or quiet. *My alarm clock is loud.* **b.** noisy. *The people in the next apartment have loud parties.*

love¹ /lŭv/ *n.* **a.** a deep, fond, affectionate feeling. *Helping people is a way of showing love.* **b.** a great liking. *He has a love of books.*

love² /lŭv/ *v.* (**loves, loved, lov•ing**) **a.** to have a deep affection for. *My parents love me.* **b.** to like very much. *Emily loves to play soccer.*

lov•ing /lŭv′ ĭng/ *adj.* caring; fond; showing love. *The loving mother held the baby.*

low•land /lō′ lənd/ *n.* an area that is lower and flatter than the land around it. *A marsh is often a lowland.*

lunch /lŭnch/ *n.* (**lunch•es** *pl.*) a light meal eaten around the middle of the day. *We have lunch at noon.*

ma•chine /mə shēn′/ *n.* **a.** a device for doing work. *Levers, pulleys, and wheels are simple machines.* **b.** a combination of parts, both moving and fixed, for doing work. *Do you know how to use a sewing machine?*

mag•net /măg′ nĭt/ *n.* an iron, steel, or alloy object that attracts iron. *He used a magnet to pick up the nails.*

mail¹ /māl/ *n.* packages, letters, postcards, etc., that are delivered through the post office. *Has the mail come yet?*

mail² /māl/ *v.* to send by mail; to place in a mailbox. *Did you mail my letter?*

main /mān/ *adj.* most important; chief; major. *Roast beef was the main course.*

main•ly /mān′ lē/ *adv.* for the most part; chiefly. *The book was mainly about history.*

make /māk/ *v.* (**makes, made, mak•ing**) **a.** to put together; to build; to create. *Let's make a tent out of blankets.* **b.** to cause; to bring about. *A horn makes a loud noise.* **c.** to equal; to add up to. *Two and three make five.*

ma•ple /mā′ pəl/ *n.* a tree with hard wood and a thin sap that is sometimes used in making syrup and sugar. *Maples are grown for both beauty and shade.*

math /măth/ *n.* the study of numbers and their relations to each other; mathematics. *We learned the times tables in math.*

may•be /mā′ bē/ *adv.* perhaps. *Maybe he hasn't left the train yet, and we can still find him.*

meal /mēl/ *n.* the food eaten at one time. *We had a big meal on Thanksgiving.*

Pronunciation Key

ă	pat	ŏ	pot	th	thin
ā	pay	ō	toe	*th*	this
âr	care	ô	paw, for	hw	which
ä	father	oi	noise	zh	vision
ĕ	pet	ou	out	ə	about,
ē	be	ŏŏ	took		item,
ĭ	pit	ōō	boot		pencil,
ī	pie	ŭ	cut		gallop,
îr	pier	ûr	urge		circus

mean¹ /mēn/ *v.* (**means, meant, mean•ing**) **a.** to indicate the idea of. *What does this word mean?* **b.** to have in mind as a purpose. *She didn't mean to get angry.*

mean² /mēn/ *adj.* unkind; wicked. *The man was mean to the children who walked on his lawn.*

meas•ure¹ /mĕzh′ ər/ *n.* a unit used in finding the length, size, or amount of something. *A mile, a pound, and a quart are common measures.*

meas•ure² /mĕzh′ ər/ *v.* (**meas•ures, meas•ured, meas•ur•ing**) to find the length, size, or amount of something. *They measured the floor for the new carpet.*

meat /mēt/ *n.* the flesh of an animal used as food. *Lean meat is better for you.*

med•i•cine /mĕd′ ĭ sĭn/ *n.* anything used to cure or prevent disease or improve health. *The doctor gave me some medicine to take.*

meet /mēt/ *v.* (**meets, met, meet•ing**) **a.** to come face to face with; to come together. *I'll meet you at the corner.* **b.** to be introduced to. *How did you meet her?* **c.** to gather as a group or club. *Our dance class meets on Tuesdays.*

mer•ry /mĕr′ ē/ *adj.* (**mer•ri•er, mer•ri•est; mer•ri•ly** *adv.*) full of happiness and cheer; joyful. *There was a merry crowd at the football game.*

me•ter /mē′ tər/ *n.* a unit of length in the metric system. *A meter is about thirty-nine inches.*

met•ric /mĕt′ rĭk/ *adj.* of or using the metric system. *Metric measurement is used in scientific experiments.*

mice /mīs/ plural of **mouse.**

mice

might /mīt/ (**may**) *v.* **a.** be allowed to. *Might we go tonight?* **b.** to be possible that. *I might buy the book.*

mild /mīld/ *adj.* **a.** not harsh; not severe; warm rather than cold. *We had a mild winter last year.* **b.** not sharp or biting to the taste. *We ordered mild sauce on our food.*

mill /mĭl/ *n.* **a.** a building with machinery in which something is manufactured. *Cloth is made in a textile mill.* **b.** a building in which grain is ground into flour. *The farmers brought their wheat to the mill.*

mine¹ /mīn/ *n.* a large hole, pit, or tunnel in the earth from which minerals can be taken. *We visited a coal mine in West Virginia.*

mine² /mīn/ *v.* (**mines, mined, min•ing**) to dig mines to locate and remove minerals. *The workers are mining coal.*

mi•nus¹ /mī′ nəs/ *prep.* less. *Eleven minus two is nine.*

mi•nus² /mī′ nəs/ *n.* (**mi•nus•es** *pl.*) a sign (−) that shows that the number following it is to be subtracted. *Did you notice the minus before the second number?*

miss /mĭs/ *v.* (**miss•es, missed, miss•ing**) **a.** to fail to hit, reach, or get. *Her arrow missed the target by ten feet.*

Miss /mĭs/ *n.* title used before an unmarried woman's last name. *When Miss Hansen got married, she became Mrs. Moore.*

mit•ten /mĭt′ n/ *n.* a glove worn in winter with a single covering for the fingers and a separate covering for the thumb. *Mittens keep our fingers warm.*

mod•el¹ /mŏd′ l/ *n.* **a.** a small copy of something. *Mr. Hill made a model of the bridge.* **b.** a person who wears clothes to show to others. *The model will look great in a blue suit.*

mod•el² /mŏd′ l/ *v.* to wear clothes to show to others. *Pam was asked to model a new coat.*

mon•ey /mŭn′ ē/ *n.* any metal or paper that is issued for use in buying and selling. *Do you have any money in your pocket?*

month /mŭnth/ *n.* one of the twelve parts into which a year is divided. *The first month is January.*

month•ly¹ /mŭnth′ lē/ *adj.* happening once a month. *Did you pay the monthly bills?*

month•ly² /mŭnth′ lē/ *adv.* once each month. *This magazine is published monthly.*

moon•light /mōōn′ līt′/ *n.* the light of the moon. *The moonlight helped the travelers find their way in the night.*

more /môr/ or /mōr/ *adj.* greater in number or amount. *You have more crayons than I do.*

morn•ing /môr′ nĭng/ *n.* the earliest part of the day, ending at noon. *We eat breakfast every morning.*

moss•y /mô′ sē/ or /mŏs′ ē/ *adj.* (moss•i•er, moss•i•est) covered with a soft, green plant (moss), or something like it. *There are mossy stones in the forest.*

most /mōst/ *adj.* greatest in amount, number, etc. *The team from Atlanta scored the most points.*

moth /môth/ or /mŏth/ *n.* an insect that usually flies at night and is very much like a butterfly. *The moths fluttered around the porch light.*

moth•er /mŭth′ ər/ *n.* the female parent. *The teacher wants to see my father and mother.*

mouse /mous/ *n.* (**mice** *pl.*) a small animal with white, gray, or brown fur, a long tail, and long, sharp front teeth. *Field mice make nests in the ground.*

mouth /mouth/ *n.* the opening in the head that contains the tongue and teeth and is used for taking in food and making sounds. *When you yawn, your mouth opens wide.*

Mr. /mĭs′ tər/ *n.* a title used before a man's last name. *Mr. Williams is our new neighbor.*

Mrs. /mĭs′ iz/ *n.* a title used before a married woman's last name. *Our teacher's name is Mrs. Sloane.*

Ms. /mĭz/ *n.* a title used before a woman's last name. *Ms. Velazquez is the president of our bank.*

mud•dy /mŭd′ ē/ *adj.* (mud•di•er, mud•di•est) covered with mud. *Take your muddy shoes off before you come inside.*

mule /myool/ *n.* a work animal that is part horse and part donkey. *Mules can carry heavy loads.*

Pronunciation Key

ă	pat	ŏ	pot	th	thin
ā	pay	ō	toe	*th*	this
âr	care	ô	paw, for	hw	which
ä	father	oi	noise	zh	vision
ĕ	pet	ou	out	ə	about,
ē	be	oŏ	took		item,
ĭ	pit	oō	boot		pencil,
ī	pie	ŭ	cut		gallop,
îr	pier	ûr	urge		circus

mul•ti•ply /mŭl′ tə plī/ *v.* (mul•ti•plies, mul•ti•plied, mul•ti•ply•ing) to add the same number to itself a certain number of times. *When 12 is multiplied by 3, it is the same as adding 12 + 12 + 12.*

mush•room /mŭsh′ roōm′/ or /mŭsh′ roŏm′/ *n.* an umbrella-shaped fungus. *Some mushrooms are edible, but some are poisonous.*

my•self /mī sĕlf′/ *pron.* (**our•selves** *pl.*) **a.** one's own self. *I guessed the answer by myself.* **b.** one's usual self. *When I was sick I didn't feel like myself.*

neat•ly /nēt′ lē/ *adv.* in an orderly way. *He neatly folded his shirts.*

neck•lace /nĕk′ lĭs/ *n.* an ornament worn around the neck. *She wore a pearl necklace with her dress.*

need /nēd/ *v.* to require; to have to have. *Most plants need lots of sunshine to grow.*

nerve /nûrv/ *n.* one of the fibers that carry messages and feelings between the brain and the rest of the body. *Nerves in the skin allow us to feel heat and cold.*

nest¹ /něst/ *n.* **a.** a place built by a bird for laying eggs. *The robin built its nest outside my window.* **b.** a place where insects or animals live. *Wasps build nests.*

nest² /něst/ *v.* to build and use a nest. *Birds nest in trees.*

nev•er /něv′ ər/ *adv.* not ever; not at any time. *Maria has never been late to school; she is always early.*

news /nōōz/ or /nyōōz/ *n.* **a.** information; things that a person has not heard about. *What is the news about your brother's new job?* **b.** recent happenings reported in newspapers and over television and radio. *We read the news in the paper.*

news•pa•per /nōōz′ pā′ pər/ or /nyōōz′–/ *n.* a printed paper that contains news, advertisements, cartoons, etc. *My grandfather likes to work the crossword puzzles in the newspaper.*

nice /nīs/ *adj.* (**nic•er, nic•est**) **a.** agreeable; pleasant. *Did you have a nice time at the picnic?* **b.** showing skill and care. *Kathy does a nice job of painting.*

nick•el /nĭk′ əl/ *n.* a small coin worth five cents. *A nickel is bigger than a penny.*

night /nīt/ *n.* the time between evening and morning; the time from sunset to sunrise when it is dark. *The stars shine at night.*

night•mare /nīt′ mâr′/ *n.* a scary dream that usually wakes up the sleeper. *Mike had a nightmare about falling off his bike.*

no•bod•y /nō′ bŏd′ ē/ or /nō′ bə dē/ *pron.* no one; no person. *Nobody is here at this time of day.*

nod /nŏd/ *v.* (**nods, nod•ded, nod•ding**) to bow the head and raise it quickly to say "yes" or "hello." *He nodded and waved to his friend.*

noise /noiz/ *n.* a sound, especially one that is loud and harsh. *The noise of the alarm clock startled me.*

none /nŭn/ *pron.* not any; not one. *None of us had the bus fare, so we walked.*

noon /nōōn/ *n.* the middle of the day; twelve o'clock in the daytime. *Our school serves lunch at noon.*

north¹ /nôrth/ *n.* the direction to your right when you face the sunset. *Cold winds blow from the north.*

north² /nôrth/ *adj.* to the north. *The north side of the house faces the highway.*

north³ /nôrth/ *adv.* toward the north. *Birds fly north in the spring.*

note•book /nōt′ bŏŏk′/ *n.* a book for notes of things to be learned or remembered. *I always carry a notebook to class.*

noth•ing /nŭth′ ĭng/ *n.* **a.** not anything. *We saw nothing we liked in that shop.* **b.** zero. *Six taken from six leaves nothing.*

nudge /nŭj/ *n.* a little push with the elbow. *Mom woke me up by giving me a nudge in my side.*

num•ber /nŭm′ bər/ *n.* **a.** the count or total sum of persons or things; the amount. *What is the number of students in your class?* **b.** a word or figure that tells how many. *Four is my favorite number.*

nurse /nûrs/ *n.* a person who cares for people who are sick or who need help. *Nurses work with doctors to help people stay well.*

oak /ōk/ *n.* a large tree having hard wood and nuts called acorns. *That tall tree is an oak.*

o•cean /ō′ shən/ *n.* **a.** the large body of salt water that covers much of the earth's surface; the sea. *Ships sail on the ocean.* **b.** any of its five main divisions—Atlantic, Pacific, Indian, Arctic, or Antarctic. *Which ocean is the largest?*

o'clock /ə klŏk'/ *adv.* of or according to the clock. *Our school day ends at three o'clock.*

oc•to•pus /ŏk' tə pəs/ *n.* (**oc•to•pus•es** or **oc•to•pi** *pl.*) a sea animal having a soft body and eight arms called tentacles. *An octopus uses its arms to grasp things.*

odd /ŏd/ *adj.* **a.** strange; not usual. *What an odd thing to say!* **b.** not able to be divided evenly by the number two. *The smallest odd numbers are 1 and 3.*

o•dor /ō' dər/ *n.* a strong smell. *The garbage had a bad odor.*

oh /ō/ *interj.* a sound that expresses surprise, interest, or sorrow. *Oh, no! I forgot my keys!*

oil /oil/ *n.* a greasy liquid obtained from animals, plants, or minerals. *Please put oil on the rusty wheel.*

oint•ment /oint' mənt/ *n.* a lotion for the skin. *This ointment will soothe your sunburn.*

once /wŭns/ *adv.* **a.** one time. *We met only once.* **b.** formerly. *Horses once were used to plow fields.*

o•pen¹ /ō' pən/ *v.* **a.** to move from a shut position. *Open the door.* **b.** to remove the outer cover. *Open the envelope.*

o•pen² /ō' pən/ *adj.* not closed or shut. *The cat climbed out an open window.*

or•ange /ôr' ĭnj/ or /ŏr' ĭnj/ *n.* **a.** a round, reddish-yellow, juicy fruit. *I ate an orange from Florida.*

or•der /ôr' dər/ *n.* **a.** a command; an instruction. *The sailors obeyed the captain's orders.* **b.** the way in which things follow one another. *These names are in alphabetical order.*

or•gan /ôr' gən/ *n.* **a.** a keyboard instrument that makes music by sending air through a set of pipes. *Who played the organ at the wedding?* **b.** a part of an animal or plant that has a special duty. *The eyes, heart, and stomach are organs.*

Pronunciation Key

ă	pat	ŏ	pot	th	thin
ā	pay	ō	toe	*th*	this
âr	care	ô	paw, for	hw	which
ä	father	oi	noise	zh	vision
ĕ	pet	ou	out	ə	about,
ē	be	ŏŏ	took		item,
ĭ	pit	ōō	boot		pencil,
ī	pie	ŭ	cut		gallop,
îr	pier	ûr	urge		circus

---

oth•er¹ /ŭth' ər/ *adj.* **a.** different. *I asked the salesman to call some other day.* **b.** remaining. *Can you write with your other hand?*

oth•er² /ŭth' ər/ *pron.* the remaining one; the other one. *Raise one hand, and then raise the other.*

out•fit /out' fĭt'/ *n.* the clothing and accessories for an event. *What do you think of my party outfit?*

o•ver¹ /ō' vər/ *prep.* **a.** above. *The reading lamp is over the bed.* **b.** on top of. *Put the cover over the basket.* **c.** more than. *The flight took over three hours.*

o•ver² /ō' vər/ *adv.* again. *Do this exercise over.*

o•ver³ /ō' vər/ *adj.* ended. *The rain is over.*

owe /ō/ *v.* (**owes, owed, ow•ing**) to have to pay or repay in return for something. *Brad owes Jon a dollar.*

owl /oul/ *n.* a bird with a large head, large eyes, and sharp claws. *Owls fly mostly at night.*

ox•en /ŏk' sən/ *n. pl.* (**ox** *sing.*) full-grown male cattle that cannot father young. *Two oxen pulled the plow.*

Spelling Dictionary

pace /pās/ *v.* (**pac•es, paced, pac•ing**) to walk with regular steps. *The leopard paced in its cage.*

pack•et /pǎk' ǐt/ *n.* a small bundle or parcel. *Mom carries a packet of tissues in her purse.*

page /pāj/ *n.* one side of a sheet of paper in a book, magazine, newspaper, or letter. *Kurt knew from the first page that he would like the book.*

paid /pād/ past tense of **pay.**

pail /pāl/ *n.* a round bucket with a handle. *We filled the pails with water.*

pain /pān/ *n.* an ache, hurt, or sore feeling. *The pain in Robin's arm soon went away.*

paint[1] /pānt/ *n.* a mixture used to color a surface. *Where's the jar of blue paint?*

paint[2] /pānt/ *v.* **a.** to cover a surface with paint. *They painted the fence.* **b.** to make a picture with paints. *Ms. Lindquist paints landscapes in her spare time.*

paint•brush /pānt' brŭsh'/ *n.* (**paint•brush•es** *pl.*) a brush for applying paint. *Please use the big paintbrush to paint the door.*

paint•ing /pān' tǐng/ *n.* a painted picture. *We saw many paintings in the art museum.*

pair /pâr/ *n.* **a.** two things of the same kind that go together; a set of two. *Carlos has a new pair of shoes.* **b.** a couple. *A pair of robins built their nest in a tree.*

pan•ther /pǎn' thər/ *n.* a black leopard. *The panther belongs to the feline family.*

part•ly /pärt' lē/ *adv.* in part; not completely. *My test is partly finished.*

passed /pǎst/ *v.* went by. *They passed the fire station on their way to the store.*

past /pǎst/ *n.* the time that has gone by. *In the distant past, dinosaurs lived on the earth.*

Past sounds like **passed.**

patches /pǎch' ǐs/ *n.* (**patch** *sing.*) a piece of cloth sewn over a hole or a tear. *My old pants have patches on them.*

pave /pāv'/ *v.* (**paves, paved, pav•ing**) to cover a road, street, etc., with a smooth, hard surface. *The dirt road will be paved next week.*

pay /pā/ *v.* (**pays, paid, pay•ing**) to give money to someone for goods or for something done. *Kim paid three dollars for her lunch.*

peace /pēs/ *n.* **a.** quiet and calm; stillness. *We like the peace of the country.* **b.** freedom from war. *Every thinking person wants peace.*

pea•cock /pē' kŏk'/ *n.* a large bird that spreads its beautiful green, blue, and gold feathers. *The peacock's feathers look like a fan.*

peacock

peak /pēk/ *n.* **a.** the pointed top of a mountain. *We hiked up to a snowy peak.* **b.** the highest point. *It rained hardest during the storm's peak.*

pea•nut /pē' nŭt'/ *n.* an edible seed. *I can't eat this peanut because I am allergic to it.*

pear /pâr/ *n.* a juicy fruit with a mild flavor. *A pear is usually larger at the bottom end.*

pearl /pûrl/ *n.* a white or off-white gem found in oysters. *The pearl on Jane's ring is very smooth.*

pen•cil /pĕn' səl/ *n.* a long, slender piece of wood with a center of black or colored writing material. *Pencils are used for writing and for drawing.*

pen•ny /pĕn' ē/ *n.* (**pen•nies** *pl.*) a cent. *One hundred pennies make a dollar.*

peo•ple /pē' pəl/ *n.* human beings; persons; men, women, boys, and girls. *People of all ages attended the fair.*

pep•per /pĕp' ər/ *n.* a hot-tasting powdered spice. *Pepper is used to season foods.*

pic•to•graph /pĭk' tə grăf'/ *n.* a diagram or chart that uses pictures to stand for words or numbers. *This pictograph shows the number of students in each class.*

pie /pī/ *n.* a baked food made of fruit, meat, or pudding within a crust. *Apple pie is his favorite food.*

piece /pēs/ *n.* a part; a segment. *Would you like a piece of my orange?*

pil•low /pĭl' ō/ *n.* a support used for the head in resting or sleeping; a cushion. *Do you like to sleep on a feather pillow?*

pi•lot /pī' lət/ *n.* a person who flies an airplane. *Airline pilots must have years of training.*

pint /pīnt/ *n.* a measure of volume equal to one half of a quart. *We bought a pint of cream.*

place¹ /plās/ *n.* **a.** a certain point; a spot. *The coolest place in town is near the river.* **b.** a space where something belongs. *Put the chair back in its place.* **c.** a seat or space for a person. *If you get there early, save me a place.*

place² /plās/ *v.* (**plac•es, placed, plac•ing**) to put in a particular position; to set. *Place your pencil on the desk.*

Pronunciation Key

ă	pat	ŏ	pot	th	thin
ā	pay	ō	toe	*th*	this
âr	care	ô	paw, for	hw	which
ä	father	oi	noise	zh	vision
ĕ	pet	ou	out	ə	about,
ē	be	ŏŏ	took		item,
ĭ	pit	ōō	boot		pencil,
ī	pie	ŭ	cut		gallop,
îr	pier	ûr	urge		circus

---

plain /plān/ *adj.* (**plain•ly** *adv.*) **a.** easy to see; clear. *The directions are plain.* **b.** simple; not fancy in appearance. *Tracy wore a plain blue dress.*

Plain sounds like **plane.**

plan¹ /plăn/ *n.* a way of doing something that is thought out in advance; a scheme. *Mark is excited about his plan for a vacation in California.*

plan² /plăn/ *v.* (**plans, planned, plan•ning**) to think out in advance. *Amy helped us plan the bake sale.*

plane /plān/ *n.* an airplane. *The big planes take off from the airport one minute apart.*

Plane sounds like **plain.**

plan•ning /plăn' ĭng/ *v.* (**plans, plan•ned, plann•ing**) thinking beforehand about how something should be done. *Will you be planning a party soon?*

planted /plăn' tĭd/ *v.* put into the ground so that it will grow. *We planted a lilac bush in our front yard.*

plat•ter /plăt' ər/ *n.* a large dish used for serving food. *The platter held three baked fish.*

play /plā/ *v.* **a.** to take part in a game or activity for fun. *Children like to play tag.* **b.** to perform on a musical instrument. *I can play the piano.* **c.** to act on the stage. *Jennifer wants to play the queen.*

play•ground /plā′ ground′/ n. a place for playing, used by children. *Swings and slides are in the playground.*

plot /plŏt/ n. a small section of ground. *Kevin and Jason each has his own plot.*

plunge /plŭnj/ v. (**plung•es, plunged, plung•ing**) to jump into; to rush into; to thrust oneself into water. *Greg always likes to plunge into our pool.*

plus¹ /plŭs/ prep. added to; and. *Four plus two is six.*

plus² /plŭs/ n. (**plus•es** pl.) a sign (+) that shows that the number following it is to be added. *Is that a plus or a minus?*

pock•et /pŏk′ ĭt/ n. a small bag sewn into clothing. *I carry my wallet in the pocket of my pants.*

point¹ /point/ n. **a.** a sharp end. *I like a pencil with a fine point.* **b.** a position; a place. *We are at this point on the map.* **c.** a unit of scoring. *She won the game by two points.*

point² /point/ v. to aim. *He pointed his arrow at the target.*

pool /pool/ n. a tank filled with water and used for swimming. *Peter swam across the pool.*

poor /poor/ adj. (**poor•er, poor•est**) not of good quality; not good enough. *The furniture fell apart because its quality was poor.*

pop•corn /pŏp′ kôrn′/ n. pl. (**pop•corn** sing.) kernels of corn that burst open when heated. *Do you like butter on your popcorn?*

po•ta•to /pə tā′ tō/ n. (**po•ta•toes** pl.) an oval or round vegetable grown underground. *The sweet potato is also called a yam.*

pounce /pouns/ v. (**pounc•es, pounced, pounc•ing**) to suddenly swoop or jump. *When the cat sees the mouse, it may pounce on it.*

pound /pound/ n. a measure of weight equal to sixteen ounces. *Buy a pound of flour for me.*

pres•i•dent /prĕz′ ĭ dənt/ n. the person who occupies the highest office in a nation, business, club, college, etc. *Lisa is president of the nature club.*

pret•ty /prĭt′ ē/ adj. (**pret•ti•er, pret•ti•est; pret•ti•ly** adv.) lovely; pleasing; pleasant to look at or to hear. *The garden was filled with pretty flowers.*

price /prīs/ n. the cost in money; the amount of money for which something is sold. *The price should be clearly labeled.*

prince /prĭns/ n. the son of a king or queen. *The prince in the story rode a white horse.*

prin•cess /prĭn′ sĭs/ or /prĭn′ sĕs′/ n. (**prin•cess•es** pl.) the daughter of a king or queen. *A princess sometimes wears a crown.*

prize /prīz/ n. a thing won in a contest. *Tony won the prize for spelling the most words correctly.*

proud /proud/ adj. **a.** having a proper regard for oneself. *Mr. Collins is a proud man who likes to do his job well.* **b.** having satisfaction and pleasure. *The proud mother watched her daughter graduate.*

pue•blo /pwĕb′ lō/ n. a flat-roofed village of the Southwest built of adobe and stone. *We watched a woman weaving outside the pueblo.*

pul•ley /pool′ ē/ n. a wheel with a furrow in the rim through which a rope moves, used to run a machine or lift a heavy object. *The men used a pulley to lift the big piano onto the truck.*

pup•py /pŭp′ ē/ n. (**pup•pies** pl.) a young dog; a pup. *The silly puppy tried to chase its own tail.*

put /poot/ v. (**puts, put, put•ting**) **a.** to place; to set. *Put the books on the desk.* **b.** to bring into a certain state. *Put the room in order.*

puz•zle /pŭz′ əl/ n. a game with a problem to be worked out. *We do word puzzles in school.*

rab•bit /răb′ ĭt/ *n.* a small, swift animal with long ears, soft fur, and a short tail. *Rabbits live in holes.*

rac•coon /ră kōōn′/ *n.* a small animal having gray fur, a bushy tail, and a mark on its face that looks like a black mask. *Raccoons live in trees.*

race /rās/ *n.* a contest of speed. *During the summer we went to the boat races.*

rail•way /rāl′ wā′/ *n.* a railroad. *Many people travel to work each day by railway.*

rain•bow /rān′ bō′/ *n.* a curved band of colored light in the sky, caused by the rays of the sun passing through drops of rain, mist, or spray. *We saw a rainbow where the waves broke against the rocks.*

raise /rāz/ *v.* (**rais•es, raised, rais•ing**) **a.** to put up; to lift. *Raise the window for more air.* **b.** to grow. *They raise oranges on that farm.*

rare /râr/ *adj.* not often found or seen. *My uncle saves rare postage stamps.*

rat•tle /răt′ l/ *v.* (**rat•tles, rat•tled, rat•tling**) **a.** to make a number of short, sharp sounds. *The windows rattle when the wind blows.* **b.** to move with short, sharp sounds. *The old car rattled over the bumpy road.*

raw /rô/ *adj.* not cooked. *Strawberries and radishes can be eaten raw.*

real /rē′ əl/ or /rēl/ *adj.* **a.** actual; true; not imagined; not made up. *My uncle told us a real story about his trip to Brazil.* **b.** genuine. *Her necklace is made of real pearls.*

re•al•ly /rē′ ə lē/ or /rē′ lē/ *adv.* truly; in fact. *Nancy can really run fast.*

rea•son¹ /rē′ zən/ *n.* **a.** a cause or explanation. *Your parents will write the reason for your absence.* **b.** logic; the power to think. *Use reason to solve the problem.*

rea•son² /rē′ zən/ *v.* to think in a sensible way; to use logic. *See if you can reason out the meaning of the word.*

red /rĕd/ *adj.* (**red•der, red•dest**) a bright color like that of a ruby or a strawberry. *Stop signs are always red.*

re•group /rē grōōp′/ *v.* to arrange differently; to put into a new grouping. *You must sometimes regroup numbers before you can subtract.*

rein•deer /rān′ dîr′/ *n.* (**rein•deer** or **rein•deers** *pl.*) an animal with antlers that resembles a caribou. *The reindeer pulled the sleigh.*

re•main /rĭ mān′/ *v.* **a.** to continue without change; to stay. *The nurse reported that the patient's condition remained good.* **b.** to be left over. *After the picnic only a few sandwiches remained.*

re•name /rē nām′/ *v.* (**re•names, re•named, re•nam•ing**) to call by a different name; give a new name to. *We can rename one ten as ten ones.*

re•port /rĭ pôrt′/ or /-pōrt′/ *n.* a detailed written or spoken account. *The newspaper report of the election listed the winners.*

re•source /rĭ sôrs′/ or /rē′ sōrs′/ *n.* **a.** an available supply of something that can bring wealth. *Oil is a natural resource.* **b.** anything that can be put to use. *Helping hands are our greatest resource.*

Spelling Dictionary

re•turn /rĭ tûrn′/ *v.* **a.** to come or go back. *We will return after the game is over.* **b.** to bring, send, or give back. *Return the book when you have finished reading it.*

re•view /rĭ vyōō′/ *v.* to study again; to go over. *She reviewed the chapter before she took the test.*

re•wind /rē wīnd′/ *v.* (**re•winds, re•wound, re•wind•ing**) to turn back. *Please rewind the videotape after you have finished watching the movie.*

rib•bon /rĭb′ ən/ *n.* a narrow strip of fabric, especially one used as a decoration. *She wore a yellow ribbon in her hair.*

right¹ /rīt/ *adj.* **a.** just; good. *Obeying the law is the right thing to do.* **b.** correct; true; accurate. *Allan's answers were all right.* **c.** located on the side opposite to left. *Raise your right hand.*

right² /rīt/ *adv.* **a.** correctly; accurately. *Do your work right.* **b.** straight on; directly. *He looked right at me.* **c.** to the right side. *Turn right at the second stop light.*

Right sounds like **write.**

rip•en /rī′ pən/ *v.* to become fully grown or developed. *The fruit will ripen in a few days.*

road /rōd/ *n.* a way or path between places; highway. *This is the road to my friend's house.*

rob•in /rŏb′ ĭn/ *n.* a bird with a reddish breast and a dark back. *We saw a robin on the lawn.*

robin

role /rōl/ *n.* a part or a character in a play. *Who will play the role of Peter Pan?*

roll /rōl/ *v.* **a.** to move by turning over and over. *The ball rolled down the hill.* **b.** to wrap something around itself. *She rolled the yarn into a ball and put it in a drawer.*

roof /rōōf/ or /rŏŏf/ *n.* **a.** the part that covers the top of a house or building. *Many houses have sloping roofs.* **b.** anything like a roof. *The peanut butter stuck to the roof of her mouth.*

roofs /rōōfs/ or /roofs/ *n. pl.* (**roof** *sing.*) covers of buildings. *The workers put new shingles on the roofs.*

root /rōōt/ or /rŏŏt/ *n.* the part of a plant that grows beneath the ground. *Many weeds have strong roots.*

round /round/ *adj.* **a.** shaped like a ball. *The earth is round.* **b.** shaped like a circle. *Our swimming pool is square, but theirs is round.*

row¹ /rō/ *n.* a line formed by a number of persons or things. *Who is sitting in the last row?*

row² /rō/ *v.* to move a boat by using oars. *He rowed across the lake and back.*

rub /rŭb/ *v.* (**rubs, rubbed, rub•bing**) to move something back and forth against another surface. *We had to rub hard to get all the dirt off.*

run /rŭn/ *v.* (**runs, ran, run, run•ning**) **a.** to move by lifting the legs quickly off the ground one after the other. *Teresa ran to second base.* **b.** to go along a certain path. *The road runs past the lake.* **c.** to flow. *Water runs downhill.*

rush¹ /rŭsh/ *v.* (**rush•es, rushed, rush•ing**) to move quickly, often with force. *The wind rushed past the windows.*

rush² /rŭsh/ *n.* an excited state of activity; hurry. *Jill was in a rush to get to school on time.*

sad /săd/ *adj.* (**sad•der, sad•dest; sad•ly** *adv.*) **a.** unhappy. *We were sad when our team lost.* **b.** causing unhappiness. *Do you cry when you read a sad book?*

safe /sāf/ *adj.* (**saf•er, saf•est**) free from risk or harm. *The sidewalk is a safe place to walk.*

safe•ly /sāf′ lē/ *adv.* in a creful or safe way. *During the storm, we arrived home safely.*

safe•ty /sāf′ tē/ *n.* freedom from injury or danger. *Police officers care about your safety.*

said /sĕd/ *v.* (**say, said, say•ing**) **a.** spoke; put into words. *He didn't hear what I said.* **b.** to give as an opinion. *I can't tell you what he said about your teacher.*

sail¹ /sāl/ *n.* a large sheet of heavy cloth used to move a boat through water by catching the wind. *The largest ships used to have thirty sails.*

sail² /sāl/ *v.* to move swiftly, especially in air or on water. *The ship sailed down the river.*

sale /sāl/ *n.* **a.** the selling of something; an exchanging of goods for money. *How much money would the sale of the house bring?* **b.** a special selling at prices lower than usual. *The store was crowded during the sale.*

sand /sănd/ *n.* tiny bits of stone in large amounts, found in the deserts and on shores along oceans, lakes, and rivers. *This beach has smooth sand.*

sand•wich /sănd′ wĭch/ *n.* (**sand•wich•es** *pl.*) two or more slices of bread, with a layer of meat, cheese, or other food placed between them. *I like a sandwich made of peanut butter and bananas.*

sang /săng/ past tense of **sing**.

Pronunciation Key

ă	pat	ŏ	pot	th	thin
ā	pay	ō	toe	*th*	this
âr	care	ô	paw, for	hw	which
ä	father	oi	noise	zh	vision
ĕ	pet	ou	out	ə	about,
ē	be	ŏŏ	took		item,
ĭ	pit	ōō	boot		pencil,
ī	pie	ŭ	cut		gallop,
îr	pier	ûr	urge		circus

save /sāv/ *v.* (**saves, saved, sav•ing**) **a.** to rescue; to make safe from danger. *We saved the cat that was up in the tree.* **b.** to put away; keep. *I save stamps for my collection.*

sav•ing /sā′ vĭng/ *v.* (**saves, saved, sav•ing**) putting aside or keeping. *Carla is saving money to buy a new coat.*

saw¹ /sô/ *n.* a tool or machine used to cut. *Dad used his saw to build a birdhouse.*

saw² /sô/ *v.* past tense of **see**. *I saw the Big Dipper last night.*

scarfs /skärfs/ *n. pl.* (**scarf** *sing.*) broad bands of material worn around the shoulders, neck, or head. *The women wore red scarfs to protect their heads.*

scene /sēn/ *n.* **a.** the time and place of a story or play. *The scene of the play is a mining town in the old West.* **b.** a division of an act of a play. *I appear in the second scene of the first act of the play.*

scent /sĕnt/ *n.* an odor; a smell. *The dogs followed the scent of the fox.*

school /skōōl/ *n.* **a.** a place for teaching and learning. *Children learn how to read in school.* **b.** the regular time when teaching and learning take place. *We had no school because of the storm.*

scoop¹ /skōōp/ *n.* a utensil for digging, dipping, or shoveling. *He used a scoop to get ice cream out of the tub.*

scoop² /skōōp/ *v.* to take out with a scoop. *I scoop ice cream at the corner store.*

score /skôr/ or /skōr/ n. **a.** the number of points made in a game. *The final score in the baseball game was 5 to 0.* **b.** a grade. *His score on the test was 93.*

scout /skout/ v. to explore; to make a search. *The hiker will scout a new trail.*

scrape /skrāp/ v. to scratch the surface of. *The basketball player scraped his knee when he fell.*

scratch[1] /skrăch/ v. to cut or scrape a surface. *You can tell that a diamond is genuine if it scratches glass.*

scratch[2] /skrăch/ n. (**scratch•es** pl.) a thin cut or mark. *The top of this old desk has many scratches.*

scream /skrēm/ v. to voice a sudden sharp cry; to produce harsh, high tones. *The scary movie made me scream.*

scrib•ble /skrĭb′ əl/ v. (**scrib•bles, scrib•bled, scrib•bling**) to write carelessly and in a hurry. *I barely had time to scribble a letter home last night.*

scrub /skrŭb/ v. (**scrubs, scrubbed, scrub•bing**) to wash or clean by rubbing hard. *At camp we had to scrub and mop the floors.*

sea horse /sē′ hôrs′/ n. a kind of small fish with a curling tail and a head that looks like a horse's head. *The sea horse lives in warm seas around the world.*

sea•shore /sē shôr′/ or /sē′ shôr′/ n. the land where the sea meets the shore. *Our family collected shells at the seashore.*

seat belt /sēt′ belt′/ n. a safety strap designed to hold a person securely in a seat. *The flight attendant asked the man to fasten his seat belt.*

se•cret /sē′ krĭt/ n. something kept from other people. *Please don't share my secret with anyone.*

se•cret•ly /sē′ krĭt lē/ adv. in a secret or hidden way. *Mr. Grant secretly bought his wife a gift.*

seed•ling /sēd′ lĭng/ n. a young plant or tree that has grown from a seed. *We plant our tomato seedlings in the spring.*

seem /sēm/ v. to look like; to appear to be. *The new family next door seems very nice.*

seg•ment /sĕg′ mənt/ n. any one of the parts into which a thing is divided. *The line segment extended from point A to point B.*

sell /sĕl/ v. (**sells, sold, sell•ing**) **a.** to exchange for money or other payment. *Matt sold his old radio for five dollars.* **b.** to keep for sale; to deal in. *A bakery sells bread, rolls, cookies, and cakes.*

send /sĕnd/ v. (**sends, sent, send•ing**) to cause or order to go. *The principal sent the children home early because of the storm.*

sent /sĕnt/ past tense of **send.**

sev•en /sĕv′ ən/ n. the next number after six; six plus one; 7. *I added seven and three.*

sev•en•teen /sĕv′ ən tēn′/ n. the next number after sixteen; ten plus seven; 17. *Some students finish high school at age seventeen.*

sev•enth[1] /sĕv′ ənth/ adj. coming next after the sixth. *The seventh day of the week is Saturday.*

sev•enth[2] /sĕv′ ənth/ n. one of seven equal parts. *Since there were seven of us, we divided the pizza into sevenths.*

sev•er•al /sĕv′ ər əl/ or /sĕv′ rəl/ pron. pl. an indefinite number more than two and fewer than many. *Several of my friends have brown hair.*

sew /sō/ v. (**sews, sewed, sewn, sew•ing**) to fasten with stitches made by a needle and thread. *He is sewing the buttons on the coat.*

shade[1] /shād/ n. shelter from heat or sun. *The shade made me feel cooler.*

shade[2] /shād/ v. (**shades, shad•ed, shad•ing**) to shelter from heat or sun. *I'd like to shade my deck with an awning.*

shag•gy /shăg′ ē/ adj. (shag•gi•er, shag•gi•est) covered with long, coarse, or tangled hair. *We washed the shaggy dog with lots of shampoo.*

shake /shāk/ v. (shakes, shook, shak•en, shak•ing) to move quickly up and down or from side to side. *Shake the can of orange juice before you open it.*

shall /shăl/ v. (should) **a.** am, is, or are going to. *I shall be there tomorrow.* **b.** must; am, is, or are obliged to. *You shall do your duty.*

shape /shāp/ n. **a.** form; appearance. *The shape of an apple is round.* **b.** condition. *Regular exercise will keep you in good shape.*

shark /shärk/ n. a large ocean fish that eats other fish. *A shark has strong, sharp teeth.*

sharp /shärp/ adj. (sharp•er, sharp•est; sharp•ly adv.) **a.** having a fine point or a thin edge for cutting. *The knife blade is sharp.* **b.** abrupt; sudden; not gradual. *Slow down the car for the sharp turn just ahead.*

she /shē/ pron. that girl or woman. *She likes to read.*

she's /shēz/ she is; she has.

sheep /shēp/ n. (sheep pl.) a hoofed animal with a thick, woolly coat. *Farmers raise sheep both for meat and for wool.*

shine /shīn/ v. (shines, shone or shined, shin•ing) **a.** to give off light. *That light shines right in my eyes.* **b.** to make bright; to polish. *I helped my sister shine the pots and pans.*

shin•y /shī′ nē/ adj. (shin•i•er, shin•i•est) bright. *We saw the shiny car quickly.*

ship•ping /shĭp′ ĭng/ n. the action or business of sending goods by ship, truck, train, or air. *Shipping is a major industry.*

ship•wreck /shĭp′ rĕk′/ n. a wrecked ship or its parts. *Pieces of the shipwreck were floating in the ocean.*

Pronunciation Key

ă	pat	ŏ	pot	th	thin
ā	pay	ō	toe	*th*	this
âr	care	ô	paw, for	hw	which
ä	father	oi	noise	zh	vision
ĕ	pet	ou	out	ə	about,
ē	be	o͝o	took		item,
ĭ	pit	o͞o	boot		pencil,
ī	pie	ŭ	cut		gallop,
îr	pier	ûr	urge		circus

---

shirt /shûrt/ n. a garment for the upper part of the body. *Most shirts have a collar and sleeves.*

shoe•lace /sho͞o′ lās′/ n. a strip of leather or other material for tying a shoe. *I have red shoelaces in my new shoes.*

shone /shōn/ v. (shines, shone, shin•ing) *The light shone on the painting.*

shook /sho͝ok/ past tense of **shake**.

shoot /sho͞ot/ v. (shoots, shot, shoot•ing) **a.** to fire a gun. *Mrs. Hill will shoot a pistol to start the race.* **b.** to send out swiftly. *The archer shot an arrow at the target.*

shop•ping /shŏp′ ĭng/ v. (shops, shopped, shop•ping) buying things. *We are shopping for shoes.*

shore•line /shôr′ līn′/ or /shōr′ līn′/ n. the line where the water meets the land. *We watched the surf along the shoreline.*

short /shôrt/ adj. **a.** not long or tall. *I look short next to my big brother.*

short•ly /shôrt′ lē/ adv. in a short time; soon. *We will go home shortly.*

shot[1] /shŏt/ past tense of **shoot**.

shot[2] /shŏt/ n. an injection through a needle. *Children get shots to prevent measles and polio.*

should /sho͝od/ v. **a.** have a duty to; ought to. *I should study tonight.* **b.** expect to. *We should be able to come.* **c.** past tense of **shall**.

shout /shout/ v. to call out loudly. *We shouted into the tunnel to hear the echo.*

show•er /shou′ ər/ *n.* **a.** a short fall of rain. *During the afternoon there were three showers.* **b.** a bath in which water comes down in a spray. *I take a shower every morning.*

shut•ter /shŭt′ ər/ *n.* a movable cover or screen for a window. *We need to replace our front window shutter.*

side /sīd/ *n.* **a.** a surface or a line that forms the edge of something. *A triangle has three sides.* **b.** a place or direction. *It's on the other side of town.*

side•walk /sīd′ wôk′/ *n.* a path for walking at the side of a street. *Let's skate on the sidewalk.*

sigh[1] /sī/ *v.* to let out a long, deep breath. *When Todd won, he sighed with relief.*

sigh[2] /sī/ *n.* the act of sighing. *She gave a sigh of sadness.*

sight /sīt/ *n.* **a.** the power or ability to see. *A pilot's sight must be good.* **b.** something that is seen. *The sunset last night was a lovely sight.*

sign /sīn/ *n.* **a.** something that stands for something else; a symbol. *The sign for adding is "+."* **b.** a board or space used for advertising or for information. *The traffic sign says "No Parking."*

sig•nal[1] /sĭg′ nəl/ *n.* a sign or movement that gives notice of something. *A red traffic light is a signal for "stop."*

sig•nal[2] /sĭg′ nəl/ *v.* to tell by using a signal. *The policewoman signaled the driver to stop.*

sil•ly /sĭl′ ē/ *adj.* (**sil•li•er, sil•li•est**) foolish; not sensible. *It's silly to go out in the cold without a coat.*

since[1] /sĭns/ *conj.* **a.** because. *Since I bought a new catcher's mitt, I'd like to give you the old one.* **b.** after the time that. *I haven't seen him since he moved away.*

since[2] /sĭns/ *prep.* ever after. *We've lived here since 1997.*

sing /sĭng/ *v.* (**sings, sang, sung, sing•ing**) **a.** to make music with the voice. *Molly likes to sing in the shower.* **b.** to perform or present in song. *Mr. Cortez sang a solo at the concert.* **c.** to make pleasant whistling sounds. *Birds sing.*

si•ren /sī′ rən/ *n.* a device used to make a loud warning sound. *The police siren got louder as it got closer.*

sis•ter /sĭs′ tər/ *n.* a girl or woman having the same parents as another person. *Steve has two sisters.*

sit /sĭt/ *v.* (**sits, sat, sit•ting**) to rest on the lower part of the body. *Dad always sits in this chair.*

six•teen /sĭks′ tēn′/ *n.* the next number after fifteen; ten plus six; 16. *You can get your driver's license when you are sixteen.*

sixth[1] /sĭksth/ *adj.* coming next after the fifth. *The sixth boy in line is my brother.*

sixth[2] /sĭksth/ *n.* one of six equal parts. *How can I divide this into sixths?*

six•ty-one /sĭks′ tē wŭn′/ *n.* the next number after sixty; sixty plus one; 61. *He will retire when he is sixty-one.*

size /sīz/ *n.* **a.** the amount of space that a thing takes up. *Look at the size of that elephant!* **b.** one of a series of measures. *Which size paintbrush do you need?*

skate[1] /skāt/ *n.* **a.** a shoe with a blade for moving over ice. *If the pond is frozen, we can use our skates.* **b.** a shoe with four wheels; a roller skate. *You can rent skates at the arena.*

skate[2] /skāt/ *v.* move along on skates. *Don't skate so fast.*

sketch /skĕch/ *n.* (**sketch•es** *pl.*) a simple, rough drawing that is made quickly. *The artist drew sketches of the people in the park.*

skill /skĭl/ *n.* the ability to do something well as a result of practice. *His skill in playing the violin may someday make him famous.*

skirt /skûrt/ *n.* **a.** the part of a dress that hangs below the waist. *She wore a dress with a long skirt.* **b.** a garment that hangs from the waist. *Many girls wear sweaters and skirts in the fall.*

skunk /skûngk/ *n.* a small animal with a bushy tail and dark fur that has a white stripe down the middle of its back. *A skunk can give off a bad smell.*

sled¹ /slĕd/ *n.* a low platform on runners that slides over ice and snow. *It is fun to coast down a hill on a sled.*

sled

sled² /slĕd/ *v.* (**sleds, sled•ded, sled•ding**) to travel on a sled. *We went sledding after the first snowfall.*

sleep¹ /slēp/ *v.* (**sleeps, slept, sleep•ing**) to rest the body and the mind by closing the eyes and losing awareness. *Did you sleep through the movie?*

sleep² /slēp/ *n.* a state of rest; not being awake. *Most people need at least eight hours of sleep each night.*

sleep•ing /slē′ pĭng/ *v.* (**sleeps, slept, sleep•ing**) resting the body and mind. *Uncle Joe was still sleeping at 10:00 A.M.*

slept /slĕpt/ past tense of **sleep**.

slice¹ /slīs/ *n.* a thin, flat piece cut from something. *Give everyone a slice of bread.*

slice² /slīs/ *v.* (**slic•es, sliced, slic•ing**) to cut into slices. *Mom sliced the watermelon.*

slid /slĭd/ past tense of **slide**.

slide¹ /slīd/ *v.* (**slides, slid, slid•ing**) to move smoothly and easily over a surface. *The skier slid over the snow.*

slide² /slīd/ *n.* a smooth surface on which a person can slide. *Children like to go down the slide at the playground.*

slight /slīt/ *adj.* not big; small; slender. *Although it looks sunny, there's a slight chance it will rain later today.*

slim /slĭm/ *adj.* (**slim•mer, slim•mest**) thin; slender. *The wind blew over the slim tree.*

slip•pers /slĭp′ ərz/ *n.* (**slip•per** *sing.*) low, comfortable shoes that can be slipped on and off easily. *Slippers keep your feet warm on cool nights.*

slow /slō/ *adj.* (**slow•ly** *adv.*) **a.** not fast or quick. *The turtle makes slow but steady progress.* **b.** behind time. *Your watch is slow.*

smile¹ /smīl/ *v.* (**smiles, smiled, smil•ing**) to look happy or amused by turning up the mouth at the corners. *The teachers smiled as we sang our songs.*

smile² /smīl/ *n.* the act of smiling; a smiling expression. *A smile can make your day brighter.*

smoke¹ /smōk/ *n.* a cloud that rises from something that is burning. *The smoke from the fireplace smells good.*

smoke² /smōk/ *v.* (**smokes, smoked, smok•ing**) to give out smoke. *The chimney is smoking.*

smooth /smo͞oth/ *adj.* having no bumps or rough spots. *The smooth highway made driving a pleasure.*

smooth•est /smo͞oth′ əst/ *adj.* the superlative form of **smooth**. (**smooth•er**) having the most even surface; the least rough or lumpy. *This is the smoothest blanket I have ever felt.*

snacks /snăks/ *n.* (**snack** *sing.*) small amounts of food eaten between meals. *Mom packed snacks of fruit and nuts for the long road trip.*

snake /snāk/ *n.* a long, crawling reptile that has scales and no legs. *Some snakes are poisonous.*

snow[1] /snō/ *n.* frozen water crystals that fall to the earth as soft white flakes. *Snow falls in winter.*

snow[2] /snō/ *v.* to fall as snow. *It has started to snow.*

soak /sōk/ *v.* **a.** to wet through; to make or become wet. *The heavy rain fell for two days, soaking the dry land.* **b.** to let stay in water or other liquid. *The baseball player soaked his sore arm in hot water.*

soap /sōp/ *n.* a substance used for washing. *Use plenty of soap when you wash your hands.*

sock•et /sŏk′ ĭt/ *n.* a hollow opening into which something fits. *The lamp flickered because the bulb was loose in the socket.*

soft /sôft/ or /sŏft/ *adj.* (**soft•ly** *adv.*) **a.** not hard. *We can dig easily in this soft ground.* **b.** smooth; not rough. *The baby has soft skin.* **c.** quiet; gentle; mild. *She has a soft voice.*

soil /soil/ *n.* ground; earth; dirt. *Plants grow in rich, dark soil.*

so•lo /sō′ lō/ *n.* a piece of music performed by one person. *Jim played a trumpet solo at the concert.*

some•one /sŭm′ wŭn′/ or /sŭm′ wən/ *pron.* somebody; some person. *Someone ought to fix that front door.*

some•thing /sŭm′ thĭng/ *pron.* a certain thing that is not specifically named. *Give the dog something to eat.*

some•where /sŭm′ hwâr′/ or /sŭm′ wâr′/ *adv.* at some place; to some place. *There is a pond somewhere in the park.*

song /sông/ or /sŏng/ *n.* a tune; a piece of music to be sung. *The principal asked us to sing another song.*

sor•ry /sŏr′ ē/ or /sôr′ ē/ *adj.* (**sor•ri•er, sor•ri•est; sor•ri•ly** *adv.*) feeling regret; full of sorrow or sadness. *I'm sorry; I didn't mean to bump you.*

sound[1] /sound/ *n.* anything that is heard; a noise. *The sound of the bells came softly on the breeze.*

sound[2] /sound/ *v.* to make a noise. *His snores sounded all through the house.*

south /south/ *n.* the direction to the left when a person faces the sunset. *A warm wind blew from the south.*

space /spās/ *n.* **a.** the area in which the planets and stars exist. *Earth travels in space around the sun.* **b.** room; a place. *There is no more space for passengers in the crowded train.*

speech /spēch/ *n.* (**speech•es** *pl.*) a talk given in public. *The President made a speech on television.*

spend /spĕnd/ *v.* (**spends, spent, spend•ing**) **a.** to pay out money. *Never spend more than you earn.* **b.** to pass time. *We spent the weekend at the beach.*

spent /spĕnt/ past tense of **spend**.

spice /spīs/ *n.* a seasoning used to add flavor to food. *Pepper is a spice.*

spin•ach /spĭn′ ĭch/ *n.* a leafy green vegetable. *Spinach provides iron, which a healthy body needs.*

spin•ning /spĭn′ ĭng/ *v.* (**spins, spun, spin•ning**) twirling something. *The woman was spinning cotton on the spinning wheel.*

splash¹ /splăsh/ *v.* **a.** to scatter and fall in drops. *Rain splashed on the pavement.* **b.** to make wet or dirty. *The car splashed me with mud as it sped past.*

splash² /splăsh/ *n.* (**splash•es** *pl.*) a scattering or throwing of a liquid. *The children made a splash as they jumped into the water.*

sponge /spŭnj/ *n.* a porous mass used for cleaning and washing. *I always wash my car with a sponge.*

sport /spôrt/ or /spōrt/ *n.* any game involving exercise; recreation. *Swimming is a common summer sport.*

spot¹ /spŏt/ *n.* a small mark of a different color. *There's a spot of paint on the rug.*

spot² /spŏt/ *v.* (**spots, spot•ted, spot•ting**) to see; to locate; to catch sight of. *How can we spot him in this big crowd?*

spot•ted /spŏt′ ĭd/ *adj.* having spots. *Heather wore a spotted blouse.*

sprain¹ /sprān/ *n.* a sudden twist of a joint with stretching or tearing of ligaments. *I couldn't run because of my ankle sprain.*

sprain² /sprān/ *v.* to injure by a sudden or severe twist. *You will sprain your ankle if you don't wear the right shoes.*

spray /sprā/ *n.* water or another liquid flying through the air. *The spray of the water got my shirt wet.*

spring¹ /sprĭng/ *v.* (**springs, sprang, sprung, spring•ing**) **a.** to jump; to leap. *The fox sprang at the rabbit.* **b.** to snap back into position. *A rubber band will spring back instantly.*

spring² /sprĭng/ *n.* **a.** a coil of wire or a strip of metal that goes back into shape after pressure is released. *Does your watch have a spring?* **b.** the season of the year that begins about March 21 and ends about June 21. *The weather begins to get warm in spring.*

Pronunciation Key

ă	pat	ŏ	pot	th	thin
ā	pay	ō	toe	*th*	this
âr	care	ô	paw, for	hw	which
ä	father	oi	noise	zh	vision
ĕ	pet	ou	out	ə	about,
ē	be	ŏŏ	took		item,
ĭ	pit	ōō	boot		pencil,
ī	pie	ŭ	cut		gallop,
îr	pier	ûr	urge		circus

stair /stâr/ *n.* a single step of a series of steps going up or down. *When we got to the last stair going up, we were out of breath.*

stamp /stămp/ *n.* a small, printed piece of paper for sticking on letters and packages to show that the postage has been paid. *You can buy a stamp at the post office.*

stand /stănd/ *v.* (**stands, stood, stand•ing**) **a.** to be or place upright. *Can you stand on one leg?* **b.** to endure; to put up with. *How can you stand such a mess?*

stare /stâr/ *v.* (**stares, stared, star•ing**) to look at with a steady gaze. *Mei Li stared at the painting, fascinated by the bright colors.*

star•fish /stär′ fĭsh′/ *n.* (**star•fish•es** or **star•fish** *pl.*) a small sea animal with a body shaped like a star. *We found a starfish on the beach.*

starfish

Spelling Dictionary

state /stāt/ *n.* **a.** the condition of. *The old house was in a bad state.* **b.** one of the fifty separate divisions of the United States. *Rhode Island is the smallest state.*

sta•tion /stā′ shən/ *n.* the place from which a service is provided or operations are directed. *The local radio station will broadcast the game.*

steam /stēm/ *n.* the vapor into which water is changed by heating. *We could see steam rising from the iron.*

steep /stēp/ *adj.* slanting sharply up and down. *That cliff is too steep to climb.*

stem /stĕm/ *n.* the part of a plant that grows up from the ground; a stalk. *Some roses have long stems.*

stew /stoo/ or /styoo/ *n.* a thick soup that is cooked slowly. *This stew has beef, potatoes, and carrots in it.*

stick /stĭk/ *n.* a long, thin piece of wood or other material. *We used a stick to stir the paint.*

sting[1] /stĭng/ *v.* (**stings, stung, sting•ing**) **a.** to prick or wound with a small point. *Bees and wasps sting.* **b.** to affect with a sharp pain. *Soap stings the eyes.*

sting[2] /stĭng/ *n.* a wound or pain caused by stinging. *The bee sting hurt for three days.*

stitch[1] /stĭch/ *n.* (**stitch•es** *pl.*) one complete movement of a threaded needle through cloth or other material. *Tie a knot after the last stitch.*

stitch[2] /stĭch/ *v.* (**stitch•es, stitched, stitch•ing**) to sew. *Can you stitch these quilt squares together?*

stone /stōn/ *n.* **a.** rock; hard mineral matter. *Our house is built of stone.* **b.** a small piece of this material; a bit of rock. *We threw stones into the water.* **c.** a gem. *Diamonds are precious stones.*

stop[1] /stŏp/ *v.* (**stops, stopped, stop•ping**) to halt or come to a halt. *The car stopped while we were going uphill.*

stop[2] /stŏp/ *n.* a halt or a short visit. *We made a stop at the grocery store.*

stop•light /stŏp′ līt/ *n.* a traffic light; a signal. *Turn right at the second stoplight.*

store /stôr/ or /stōr/ *n.* a place where things are sold. *Salim bought a hammer in the hardware store.*

storm /stôrm/ *n.* strong winds often accompanied by heavy amounts of rain, snow, hail, or sleet. *In summer a storm can bring thunder and lightning.*

stor•y /stôr′ ē/ or /stōr′ ē/ *n.* (**stor•ies** *pl.*) a tale or account of an adventure or happening. *Mr. Lee told us a story about his grandfather.*

strange /strānj/ *adj.* unusual; odd. *We were startled by the strange noise.*

straw[1] /strô/ *n.* **a.** the hollow stalks or stems of grain, such as wheat or oats, after the grain has been removed. *Straw is used to make baskets.* **b.** a thin hollow tube of plastic or paper. *Karen drank her milk through a straw.*

straw[2] /strô/ *adj.* made of straw. *She wore a straw hat.*

stray /strā/ *v.* (**strays, strayed, stray•ing**) to wander or roam. *My dog will stray if he isn't wearing his leash.*

stream /strēm/ *n.* a brook, creek, or small river. *The stream bubbled over the rocks.*

street /strēt/ *n.* a road in a city or town. *This street is always crowded during rush hour.*

stretch /strĕch/ *v.* **a.** to hold out; to extend. *Rachel stretched her hand across the table.* **b.** to draw out to full length; to extend to full size. *Jeff stretched after he woke up.*

string /strĭng/ *n.* a thin cord; a thick thread. *How much string do you need for your kite?*

strolled /strōld/ *v.* walked slowly and easily. *We strolled through the park.*

strong /strŏng/ or /strông/ *adj.* **a.** not weak; powerful. *We need someone strong to lift this box.* **b.** hard to break or knock down; lasting; tough. *You will need a strong rope.* **c.** not mild; sharp. *Some people like strong cheese.*

stud•y¹ /stŭd′ ē/ *v.* (stud•ies, stud•ied, stud•y•ing) to try to learn by thinking, reading, and practicing. *We study many subjects in school.*

stud•y² /stŭd′ ē/ *n.* (stud•ies *pl.*) an investigation; an examination. *Our school nurse made a study of our health habits.*

stuff¹ /stŭf/ *n.* things; objects of any kind. *Don't put any more stuff in the car.*

stuff² /stŭf/ *v.* to fill by packing things into. *We stuffed the box with old newspapers.*

sub•tract /səb trăkt′/ *v.* to take away. *If we subtract 7 from 10, we get 3.*

sud•den /sŭd′ n/ *adj.* (sud•den•ly *adv.*) **a.** not expected. *We got caught in the sudden rainfall.* **b.** quick; hasty. *Mr. Parker made a sudden decision.*

sug•ar /shŏŏg′ ər/ *n.* a sweet substance from sugar cane or sugar beets. *I like one teaspoon of sugar in my tea.*

sum•mer¹ /sŭm′ ər/ *n.* the warmest season of the year. *Summer comes between spring and fall.*

sum•mer² /sŭm′ ər/ *adj.* of summer; for summer. *Some summer days are very hot.*

sum•mit /sŭm′ ĭt/ *n.* **a.** the top of a mountain. *The climbers hope to reach the summit.*

sun•ny /sŭn′ ē/ *adj.* (sun•ni•er, sun•ni•est; sun•ni•ly *adv.*) bright with sunshine. *Let's play outside while it's still sunny.*

sun•shine /sŭn′ shīn/ *n.* the light from the sun. *Our cat loves to nap in the sunshine.*

Pronunciation Key

ă	pat	ŏ	pot	th	thin
ā	pay	ō	toe	*th*	this
âr	care	ô	paw, for	hw	which
ä	father	oi	noise	zh	vision
ĕ	pet	ou	out	ə	about,
ē	be	ŏŏ	took		item,
ĭ	pit	ōō	boot		pencil,
ī	pie	ŭ	cut		gallop,
îr	pier	ûr	urge		circus

---

sup•per /sŭp′ ər/ *n.* the last meal of the day. *We hurried home for supper.*

sure /shŏŏr/ *adj.* (sur•er, sur•est; sure•ly *adv.*) certain; positive. *Are you sure the clock shows the correct time?*

swal•low /swŏl′ ō/ *v.* (swal•lows, swal•lowed, swal•low•ing) to pass from mouth to throat to stomach; to gulp. *Swallow your food carefully.*

swam /swăm/ past tense of **swim**.

sweet /swēt/ *adj.* **a.** having the taste of sugar. *We ate sweet rolls for breakfast.* **b.** pleasing. *I think roses have a sweet smell.*

swim /swĭm/ *v.* (swims, swam, swum, swim•ming) to move in water by moving arms, legs, fins, etc. *Fish swim, but so do people.*

switch¹ /swĭch/ *n.* (switch•es *pl.*) in an electrical circuit, a device for making a connection. *When we turn the switch, the light goes on.*

switch² /swĭch/ *v.* **a.** to turn on or off. *Please switch the fan off.* **b.** to change. *Let's switch places; you stand here.*

switch•es /swĭch′ əs/ *n. pl.* (switch *sing.*) devices used for making, breaking, or changing electrical connections. *The light switches are on the front wall.*

tai•lor /tā′ lər/ *n.* a person whose job is making or altering clothing. *I took my dress to a tailor for alterations.*

take /tāk/ *v.* (**takes, took, tak•en, tak•ing**) **a.** to accept or receive. *Take one; they're free.* **b.** to carry. *We took three suitcases.* **c.** to travel on. *Let's take the bus.* **d. take up** to require; to use. *Boxes take up too much space.*

talk[1] /tôk/ *v.* (**talks, talked, talk•ing**) **a.** to speak; to say words. *My little sister just learned to talk.* **b.** to communicate. *Deaf people sometimes talk with their hands.*

talk[2] /tôk/ *n.* **a.** a conversation. *Tim and I had a long talk.* **b.** a short speech. *The scientist gave a talk about fossils.*

teach•er /tē′ chər/ *n.* a person who teaches. *Who is your piano teacher?*

tear[1] /târ/ *v.* (**tears, tore, torn, tear•ing**) to rip or pull apart. *We made shapes by tearing pieces of paper.*

tear[2] /târ/ *n.* a rip. *There's a tear in the elbow of my jacket.*

teeth /tēth/ *n. pl.* more than one tooth. *Did you brush your teeth this morning?*

tell /tĕl/ *v.* (**tells, told, tell•ing**) **a.** to say; to talk about. *Tell us a story.* **b.** to make known. *Don't tell the answer to anyone.*

tent /tĕnt/ *n.* a portable structure of canvas or other material supported by a pole or poles. *We sleep in tents when we go hiking.*

test[1] /tĕst/ *n.* an examination or trial, often consisting of a series of questions or problems. *There were twenty problems on the arithmetic test.*

test[2] /tĕst/ *v.* to try; to examine; to put to a test. *Our teacher tested us in history last week.*

thank /thăngk/ *v.* to say or show you are pleased and grateful. *I want to thank Grandfather for my game.*

that's /thăts/ that is; that has.

their /thâr/ *adj.* of, belonging to, or relating to them. *Is that your cat or their cat?*

there[1] /thâr/ *adv.* **a.** in or at that place. *Put the flowers over there.* **b.** to that place; into that place. *I went there last week.*

there[2] /thâr/ *pron.* used to introduce a sentence or clause in which the subject follows the verb. *There is a new student in our class.*

there's /thârz/ there is; there has.

they /thā/ *pron.* the ones spoken about. *Liz and Dennis said they would come.*

they're /thâr/ they are. *They're the best team ever.*

they've /thāv/ they have. *They've left you plenty of food.*

thick /thĭk/ *adj.* **a.** large in size from one side to its opposite; not thin. *The old castle door was very thick.* **b.** measuring in distance through; in depth. *The geography book is one inch thick.*

thing /thĭng/ *n.* **a.** any object; anything that exists and can be seen, heard, felt, etc. *He took his clothes and some other things to summer camp.* **b.** an action; a matter; an affair. *That was a good thing to do.*

think /thĭngk/ *v.* (**thinks, thought, think•ing**) **a.** to use the mind to reach decisions, form opinions, etc. *I can't think when there is noise all around me.* **b.** to have in mind as an opinion, idea, etc.; to believe. *She thought she knew the answer.*

thin•ner /thĭn′ ər/ *adj.* (**thin, thin•nest**) being more slender or less thick than something or someone else. *This bed sheet is thinner than the comforter.*

thin•nest /thĭn′ ĭst/ *adj.* (**thin, thin•ner**) being the most slender or least thick of anything or anyone. *That is the thinnest book I have ever seen!*

Spelling Dictionary

thirst /thûrst/ *n.* a desire for something to drink caused by a dry feeling in the mouth or throat. *The horses satisfied their thirst by drinking from a stream.*

thir • ty-two /thûr′ tē too′/ *n.* the next number after thirty-one; thirty plus two; 32. *There are only thirty-two cards in the deck.*

thorn /thôrn/ *n.* a sharp point that grows on the stems and branches of some plants. *He cut his finger on a thorn while he was trimming the rose bushes.*

though¹ /thō/ *adv.* however. *You must admit, though, that she was partly right.*

though² /thō/ *conj.* in spite of the fact that; although. *Though it was getting late, we kept playing for a while longer.*

threw /throo/ past tense of **throw**.

throw¹ /thrō/ *v.* (**throws, threw, thrown, throw•ing**) to toss or cast through the air. *Throw the ball to Angie.*

throw² /thrō/ *n.* an act of throwing; a toss. *The player made a bad throw to first base, and the runner was safe.*

thumb /thŭm/ *n.* **a.** the short, thick finger on the hand. *Little Jack Horner stuck his thumb into his pie.* **b.** something that covers the thumb. *Someone cut the thumbs off my mittens.*

thun • der /thŭn′ dər/ *n.* the loud noise caused by the violent expansion of air heated by lightning. *Thunder often comes before rain.*

ti • ger /tī′ gər/ *n.* a large cat with yellowish fur and black stripes. *Tigers live in Asia.*

time • ly /tīm′ lē/ *adj.* (**time•li•er, time•li•est**) happening at a good time; well-timed. *She planned her timely arrival so she didn't miss dinner.*

ti • tle /tīt′ l/ *n.* the name of a book, movie, painting, etc. *When I had finished reading the story, I couldn't remember its title.*

Pronunciation Key

ă	pat	ŏ	pot	th	thin
ā	pay	ō	toe	*th*	this
âr	care	ô	paw, for	hw	which
ä	father	oi	noise	zh	vision
ĕ	pet	ou	out	ə	about,
ē	be	oŏ	took		item,
ĭ	pit	ōo	boot		pencil,
ī	pie	ŭ	cut		gallop,
îr	pier	ûr	urge		circus

---

toad • stool /tōd′ stool′/ *n.* a particular type of mushroom, oftentimes poisonous. *The truffle is an edible toadstool.*

toast¹ /tōst/ *v.* to make crisp, hot, and brown by heat. *Would you like me to toast your bread?*

toast² /tōst/ *n.* sliced bread that is browned by heat. *I like toast for breakfast.*

to • day¹ /tə dā′/ *n.* this present day; the present time. *Today is the first day of spring.*

to • day² /tə dā′/ *adv.* on this present day. *Are you going to school today?*

to • ma • to /tə mā′ tō/ *n.* (**to•ma•toes** *pl.*) a commonly grown reddish fruit. *Please add a tomato to my salad.*

to • mor • row¹ /tə mŏr′ ō/ or / tə môr′ ō/ *n.* the day after today. *Tomorrow is the last day of school.*

to • mor • row² /tə mŏr′ ō/ or /tə môr′ ō/ *adv.* on the day after today. *We're going shopping tomorrow.*

tongue /tŭng/ *n.* a wide, flat organ in the mouth made of flesh and muscle and capable of easy movement. *The doctor looked at my tongue.*

to • night¹ /tə nīt′/ *n.* the night of the present day. *Tonight is a special night.*

to • night² /tə nīt′/ *adv.* on the night of the present day. *Let's go to a movie tonight.*

Spelling Dictionary

tractor

toot /t͞oot/ *n.* a short, sharp sound made by a horn or whistle. *They heard the toot of the tugboat whistle.*

tooth /t͞ooth/ *n.* (**teeth** *pl.*) one of the hard, bonelike parts in the jaw used for chewing. *The dentist filled a cavity in my tooth.*

tooth•paste /t͞ooth′ pāst′/ *n.* paste used to clean the teeth. *My dentist told me to use a toothpaste with fluoride in it.*

tore /tôr/ or /tōr/ past tense of **tear.**

tote /tōt/ *v.* (**totes, tot•ed, tot•ing**) *Informal.* to haul; to carry. *The farmer said he had to tote some hay up to the barn.*

town /toun/ *n.* **a.** a center of population that is larger than a village but smaller than a city. *Our cousins live in a small town in Kansas.* **b.** a city. *He decided that Chicago was his favorite town.*

trace /trās/ *v.* (**trac•es, traced, trac•ing**) to copy by placing transparent paper over a picture and following the lines of the picture with a pencil or pen. *We were told to draw a map, not to trace one.*

track /trăk/ *n.* **a.** a mark or a series of marks left by an animal, person, wagon, etc. *We saw the tire tracks on the snow.* **b.** a special path or course set up for racing. *A mile is four times around the track.* **c.** the metal rails on which trains run. *The railroad track runs through a tunnel.*

trac•tor /trăk′ tər/ *n.* a large machine on wheels, used for pulling trucks or farm equipment. *The farmer drove the tractor into the barn.*

trade¹ /trād/ *n.* **a.** the business of buying and selling goods. *Our company carries on trade with people all over the world.* **b.** an exchange of goods; a bargain. *I made a trade with him.*

trade² /trād/ *v.* (**trades, trad•ed, trad•ing**) **a.** to buy and sell goods. *Some companies trade with foreign countries.* **b.** to exchange. *I'll trade my pen for that book.*

trail¹ /trāl/ *n.* a path through mountains, a forest, etc. *The trail ended at the edge of the cliff.*

trail² /trāl/ *v.* to follow or pursue by following tracks or traces left behind. *The police trailed the suspect.*

train /trān/ *n.* a line of connected railroad or subway cars. *Many people take a train to work every day.*

trash /trăsh/ *n.* something that is no longer valuable; a useless thing; rubbish. *These old toys are trash; throw them out.*

tray /trā/ *n.* a flat holder or platform with a rim, used for holding or carrying something. *Put the dishes on a tray.*

treat¹ /trēt/ *v.* **a.** to handle; behave toward. *You must treat animals gently.* **b.** to try to cure or relieve. *The doctor treated me for the pain in my stomach.*

treat² /trēt/ *n.* anything that pleases or gives pleasure. *Seeing a movie at school was a special treat.*

tries /trīz/ a form of **try.**

trip¹ /trĭp/ *n.* a journey; a voyage. *They took a trip around the world last year.*

trip² /trĭp/ *v.* (**trips, tripped, trip•ping**) to lose one's balance by catching a foot on something. *I tripped on the edge of the rug.*

trout /trout/ *n.* (**trout** or **trouts** *pl.*) a freshwater fish that is closely related to salmon. *The rainbow trout has black speckles on its back and a pink stripe along each side.*

trunk /trŭngk/ *n.* **a.** the main stem of a tree apart from limbs and roots. *After they cut down the tree, all that was left was the trunk.* **b.** a large, hard box for moving clothes or other items. *My grandparents used this trunk when they came from Greece.* **c.** the luggage compartment of a car. *The stroller is in the trunk of the car.*

trust /trŭst/ *v.* **a.** to believe in; to depend or rely on. *We trust the doctor to do what is best for us.* **b.** to expect; to assume. *I trust you have finished your homework.*

try¹ /trī/ *v.* (**tries, tried, try•ing**) to attempt. *Try to answer all of the questions.*

try² /trī/ *n.* (**tries** *pl.*) an attempt; an effort to do something. *She hit the target on her first try.*

tube /tōōb/ or /tyōōb/ *n.* a long, hollow cylinder used to carry or hold liquids and gases. *A drinking straw is a tube.*

tu•na /tōō′ nə/ or /tyōō′ nə/ *n.* (**tu•na** or **tu•nas** *pl.*) a large fish. *The yellowfin tuna is a popular food.*

tur•key /tûr′ kē/ *n.* a large North American bird covered with thick feathers. *Turkeys can weigh more than thirty pounds.*

turn¹ /tûrn/ *v.* **a.** to move or cause to move around a center; to rotate. *Wheels turn.* **b.** to change directions. *Turn left at the post office.*

turn² /tûrn/ *n.* **a.** a change in direction or condition. *Make a right turn at the next street.* **b.** a time to do something. *Whose turn is it to bat?*

Pronunciation Key

ă	pat	ŏ	pot	th	thin
ā	pay	ō	toe	*th*	this
âr	care	ô	paw, for	hw	which
ä	father	oi	noise	zh	vision
ĕ	pet	ou	out	ə	about,
ē	be	ŏŏ	took		item,
ĭ	pit	ōō	boot		pencil,
ī	pie	ŭ	cut		gallop,
îr	pier	ûr	urge		circus

tur•tle /tûr′ tl/ *n.* an animal having four legs and a hard shell around its body. *A turtle can draw its head and legs into its shell.*

twen•ty-four /twĕn′ tē fôr′/ or /twĕn′ tē fōr′/ *n.* the next number after twenty-three; twenty plus four; 24. *In some places clocks go from one to twenty-four.*

twig /twĭg/ *n.* a very small branch of a tree or other plant. *We used twigs to get the campfire started.*

twirl /twûrl/ *v.* to turn rapidly. *The ice skater will twirl on one skate.*

twitch /twĭch/ *v.* (**twitch•es, twitched, twitch•ing**) to pull or move with sudden motion. *We watched the leaf twitch and then fall from the tree.*

ug•ly /ŭg′ lē/ *adj.* (**ug•li•er, ug•li•est**) unpleasant to any sense. *His mask was very ugly and scary.*

un•cle /ŭng′ kəl/ *n.* **a.** the brother of one's father or mother. *I have two uncles on my mother's side.* **b.** the husband of one's aunt. *We visited our aunt and uncle last spring.*

Spelling Dictionary

un•der /ŭn′ dər/ *prep.* **a.** below; beneath. *I found money hidden under a rock.* **b.** less than. *You can repair the broken window for under forty dollars.*

un•der•stand /ŭn′ dər **stănd′**/ *v.* (**un•der•stands, un•der•stood, un•der•stand•ing**) to get the meaning; to grasp the idea. *Do you understand all the test directions?*

un•friend•ly /ŭn frĕnd′ lē/ *adj.* not friendly. *I stayed away from the unfriendly dog.*

un•hap•py /ŭn hăp′ ē/ *adj.* (**un•hap•pi•er, un•hap•pi•est; un•hap•pi•ly** *adv.*) not happy; sad; full of sorrow. *When Maria was unhappy, we tried to cheer her up.*

United States *n.* a country in North America that lies between the Atlantic and Pacific oceans and between Canada and the Gulf of Mexico; it includes Hawaii and Alaska. *The flag of the United States is red, white, and blue.*

un•til[1] /ŭn tĭl′/ *prep.* **a.** up to the time of; till. *I slept until noon today.* **b.** before the time of. *He could not stop working until midnight.*

un•til[2] /ŭn tĭl′/ *conj.* **a.** up to the time that. *We waited for you until the show was about to begin.* **b.** before. *She would not serve dinner until everyone was seated.*

up•on /ə pŏn′/ or /ə pôn′/ *prep.* on. *Place the book upon the table.*

vac•cine /văk sēn′/ *n.* a mixture introduced into the body to protect against disease. *Most children receive the vaccine against polio when they are very young.*

veg•e•ta•ble /vĕj′ tə bəl/ or /vĕj′ ĭ tə bəl/ *n.* a plant or a part of a plant that is used as food. *Peas and beans are vegetables.*

ver•y /vĕr′ ē/ *adv.* greatly; extremely. *He was very unhappy when he lost his dog.*

voice /vois/ *n.* **a.** a sound made with the mouth, especially by talking or singing. *We heard her voice above all the others.* **b.** the type or quality of sound made with the mouth. *That singer has a pleasant voice.*

wag•on /wăg′ ən/ *n.* a four-wheeled vehicle for carrying loads usually pulled by a tractor, a horse, or a person. *Dad pulled us in the red wagon.*

waist /wāst/ *n.* the narrow part of the body between the ribs and the hips. *Belts are worn around the waist.*

walk[1] /wôk/ *v.* to go on foot at a normal rate. *Scott ran ahead, but the rest of us walked.*

walk[2] /wôk/ *n.* **a.** the act of walking. *Would you like to go for a walk with me?* **b.** the distance one has to walk. *It is just a short walk to the grocery store.*

wal•rus•es /wôl′ rəs əs/ or /wŏl′ rəs əs/ *n. pl.*(**wal•rus** *sing.*) large, arctic sea animals, related to seals, and having large tusks. *Walruses can live to be forty years old.*

war /wôr/ *n.* a fight or struggle between countries or parts of a country. *There are great losses of life and destruction of property in a war.*

warm[1] /wôrm/ *adj.* **a.** having a small amount of heat; neither hot nor cold. *Blankets keep us warm.* **b.** affectionate. *They gave us a warm greeting.*

warm[2] /wôrm/ *v.* to make warm; to heat. *Warm the food before you serve it.*

warn /wôrn/ *v.* to tell of coming danger. *The sirens will warn us of a tornado.*

warp /wôrp/ *v.* to bend or buckle from dampness. *Cover the wood so the rain doesn't warp it.*

wash•cloth /wŏsh′ klôth′/, /**wŏsh**′ klôth′/, or /**wôsh**′ klôth′/ *n.* a cloth used to wash a person's face or body. *Use a washcloth to wash your face.*

wasp /wŏsp/ or /wôsp/ *n.* a flying insect with a slender body and a painful sting. *Wasps build papery nests.*

watch¹ /wŏch/ *v.* **a.** to look at. *Did you watch television after school?* **b.** to pay attention to; to be careful. *Watch where you are going.*

watch² /wŏch/ *n.* (**watch•es** *pl.*) a small clock that is worn on the wrist or carried in a pocket. *I checked my watch before I left the house.*

wa•ter /wô′ tər/ or /wŏt′ ər/ *n.* the clear liquid that falls as rain. *Water becomes ice when it freezes.*

wave¹ /wāv/ *n.* **a.** a rising swell of water moving across the surface of a body of water. *The waves splashed against the rocks.* **b.** a signal made with the hand. *He gave a wave as he passed us.*

wave² /wāv/ *v.* (**waves, waved, wav•ing**) **a.** to move up and down or from side to side. *The branches waved in the wind.* **b.** to give a signal or greeting by moving the hand. *We waved good-bye.*

way /wā/ *n.* **a.** a path, road, or course. *The way was blocked by a fallen tree.* **b.** direction. *Come this way.* **c.** distance. *It's only a short way from here.* **d.** a manner. *She has a funny way of talking.* **e.** a detail or feature. *In many ways his plan seemed good.*

Pronunciation Key

ă	pat	ŏ	pot	th	thin
ā	pay	ō	toe	*th*	this
âr	care	ô	paw, for	hw	which
ä	father	oi	noise	zh	vision
ĕ	pet	ou	out	ə	about,
ē	be	ŏŏ	took		item,
ĭ	pit	ōō	boot		pencil,
ī	pie	ŭ	cut		gallop,
îr	pier	ûr	urge		circus

wear /wâr/ *v.* (**wears, wore, worn, wear•ing**) **a.** to have on the body. *People wear clothes.* **b.** to make or produce gradually as a result of rubbing, scraping, etc. *He wore a hole in the sleeve of his sweater.*

weath•er /wĕth′ ər/ *n.* outside conditions of temperature, humidity, etc. *We have had two weeks of cold weather.*

weav•ing /wēv′ ĭng/ *v.* (**weaves, wove, wov•en, weav•ing**) making by lacing threads, yarns, or strips under and over each other. *She is weaving a basket out of straw.*

weigh /wā/ *v.* **a.** to determine the weight of by using a scale. *Weigh the package before you mail it.* **b.** to have weight of a certain amount. *She weighs eighty pounds.*

wel•come /wĕl′ kəm/ *v.* (**welcomes, welcomed, welcom•ing**) to greet with pleasure. *The flight attendant will welcome us on the plane.*

were /wûr/ past tense of **be.**

we're /wîr/ we are. *We're too tired to play.*

were•n't /wûrnt/ or /**wûr**′ ənt/ were not. *The dog and the cat weren't in the house.*

west[1] /wĕst/ *n.* the direction in which the sun sets. *East and west are opposite directions.*

west[2] /wĕst/ *adj.* **a.** in the west; of the west; toward the west. *Cindy lives in the west part of town.* **b.** from the west. *A west wind was blowing.*

west[3] /wĕst/ *adv.* toward the west. *We walked west.*

whale /hwāl/ *n.* a huge sea mammal that looks like a fish and breathes air. *When a whale comes up for air, it blows a spout of water vapor.*

whale

what's /hwŏts/ or /hwŭts/ what is; what has.

wheel /hwēl/ or /wēl/ *n.* a round frame that turns on a central axis. *A bicycle has two wheels.*

where[1] /hwâr/ or /wâr/ *adv.* **a.** in or at what place. *Where will you be?* **b.** to what place. *Where did you go?*

where[2] /hwâr/ or /wâr/ *conj.* to the place that; in the place that. *Stay where you are.*

whirl /hwûrl/ or /wûrl/ *v.* to move in a circle with great force or speed. *The wind made the pinwheel whirl.*

whisk•ers /hwĭs′ kərz/ or /wĭs′ kərz/ *n. pl.* (**whisker** *sing.*) **a.** short hairs growing on the side and chin of a face. *My dad's whiskers feel rough.* **b.** long, stiff hairs that stick out near the mouth of a cat or other animal. *My pet mouse has black whiskers.*

whit•er /hwīt′ ər/ or /wīt′ ər/ *adj.* being more white than something else. *This paint makes the wall look whiter than before.*

whit•est /hwīt′ ĭst/ or /wīt′ ĭst/ *adj.* being the most white of anything else. *You have the whitest shirt I have ever seen.*

who's /hōōz/ who is; who has.

wide /wīd/ *adj.* (**wid•er, wid•est; wide•ly** *adv.*) **a.** covering or having much space from side to side; broad; not narrow. *Our new car has wide seats.* **b.** having a certain distance from side to side. *My room is ten feet wide.*

wild /wīld/ *adj.* not tamed; not cultivated; living or growing in a natural condition. *Wild flowers grew along the side of the road.*

wild•cat /wīld′ kăt′/ *n.* a large cat that is not tame. *The wildcat growled at the people at the zoo.*

will /wĭl/ *v.* (**would**) **a.** am, is, or are going to. *We will see you next week.* **b.** am, is, or are willing to. *I'll help if you will.*

win /wĭn/ *v.* (**wins, won, win•ning**) **a.** to gain a victory. *Do you think our team can win?* **b.** to get or earn. *Nina's pig may win a ribbon at the fair.*

win•dow /wĭn′ dō/ *n.* an opening in the side of a house, automobile, etc., usually covered with glass. *Windows let in light and air.*

wish•es[1] /wĭsh′ ĭs/ *v.* (**wish•es, wished, wish•ing**) wants; desires for. *She wishes she could have that watch.*

wish•es[2] /wĭsh′ ĭs/ *n.* (**wish** *sing.*) things wanted. *The genie granted the young boy three wishes.*

with•out /wĭth out'/ prep. **a.** not having; with no. *I left without my umbrella.* **b.** with a lack or neglect of. *I sometimes speak without thinking.*

wit•ty /wĭt' ē/ adj. (**wit•ti•er, wit•ti•est; wit•ti•ly** adv.) showing wit; clever and amusing. *The witty speaker made the audience laugh.*

wom•an /wŏŏm' ən/ n. (**wom•en** pl.) a grown female person. *Your mother is a woman.*

wom•en /wĭm' ĭn/ plural of **woman.**

won't /wōnt/ will not.

wool•ly /wool' ē/ adj. (**wool•li•er, wool•li•est**) consisting of wool. *He sheared the woolly sheep.*

word /wûrd/ n. a group of letters that make sense because they stand for a certain thing. *We use words when we speak and write.*

wore /wôr/ or /wōr/ past tense of **wear.**

work¹ /wûrk/ n. **a.** the use of strength or skill to make or do something; labor. *Building the dam was hard work for the beavers.* **b.** job; occupation; the thing one does to earn a living. *Her work is modeling clothes.*

work² /wûrk/ v. **a.** to have a job for pay in order to make a living. *He works in a big office.* **b.** to operate; to do as it should. *Does that machine work?*

work•er /wûr' kər/ n. a person who works; a person who works for money. *The factory needs more workers.*

worm /wûrm/ n. a slender animal with a soft, segmented body and no vertebrae. *An earthworm is a popular worm used for fishing bait.*

wor•ry¹ /wûr' ē/ or /wŭr' ē/ v. (**wor•ries, wor•ried, wor•ry•ing**) to be or cause to be restless, disturbed, or anxious about something. *I am worried about getting to the airport on time.*

wor•ry² /wûr' ē/ or /wŭr' ē/ n. (**wor•ries** pl.) a cause of anxiety or trouble. *Money is a constant worry to him.*

Pronunciation Key

ă	pat	ŏ	pot	th	thin
ā	pay	ō	toe	*th*	this
âr	care	ô	paw, for	hw	which
ä	father	oi	noise	zh	vision
ĕ	pet	ou	out	ə	about,
ē	be	ŏŏ	took		item,
ĭ	pit	ōō	boot		pencil,
ī	pie	ŭ	cut		gallop,
îr	pier	ûr	urge		circus

would /wŏŏd/ v. **a.** used to express what could have happened or been true. *I would have come if I had known you were sick.* **b.** used to make a polite request. *Would you carry this for me?* **c.** past tense of **will.**

wrap /răp/ v. (**wraps, wrapped, wrap•ping**) **a.** to enclose in something by winding or folding. *Wrap the baby in warm blankets.* **b.** to cover with paper. *Did you wrap the gift for your mother?*

wrapped /răpt/ v. (**wraps, wrapped, wrap•ping**) covered an object with paper or another material and taped or tied it up. *She wrapped the gift with pink paper.*

wrin•kle¹ /rĭng' kəl/ n. a small crease or fold. *Rosa ironed the wrinkles out of her skirt.*

wrin•kle² /rĭng' kəl/ v. to crease or crumple. *Your forehead wrinkles when you frown.*

wrist /rĭst/ n. the joint between the hand and the arm. *The wrist can move in any direction.*

write /rīt/ v. (**writes, wrote, writ•ten, writ•ing**) **a.** to form letters or words with a pen, pencil, or other instrument. *Most people learn to write in school.* **b.** to be the author of. *He wrote a story for the school newspaper.*

wrote /rōt/ past tense of **write.**

Spelling Dictionary

yawn•ing /yô′ nĭng/ v. opening the mouth wide as an involuntary reaction to being tired or bored. *Matt was yawning during the long movie.*

yel•low /yĕl′ ō/ n. the color of a lemon or of butter. *Yellow is a bright, sunny color.*

yes•ter•day¹ /yĕs′ tər dā/ or /**yĕs**′ tər dē/ n. the day before this day. *Today is Saturday and yesterday was Friday.*

yes•ter•day² /yĕs′ tər dā/ or /**yĕs**′ tər dē/ adv. on the day before this. *It snowed yesterday.*

yoke /yōk/ n. a wooden frame that connects two work animals at the neck. *The farmer put the yoke on the oxen.*

yolk /yōk/ n. the yellow part of an egg. *Linda added one yolk to the cake mix.*

your /yŏŏr/ or /yôr/ adj. of or belonging to you. *Is this your coat?*

you're /yŏŏr/ you are.

your•self /yŏŏr **sĕlf**′/, /yôr **sĕlf**′/, /yōr **sĕlf**′/, or /yər **sĕlf**′/ pron. (**your•selves** pl.) the pronoun referring to you. *Please help yourself to some snacks.*

ze•bra /zē′ brə/ n. a wild member of the horse family that has stripes of black or dark brown on a light background. *Zebras are difficult to tame.*

zip•per /zĭp′ ər/ n. a fastening device with two rows of tiny teeth that can be closed together by a sliding tab. *My boots close with a zipper.*

USING THE Thesaurus

The **Writing Thesaurus** gives synonyms, or words that mean the same or nearly the same, and antonyms, or words that mean the opposite, for your spelling words. Use this sample to learn about the different parts of each thesaurus entry.

- **Entry words** are given in alphabetical order and are shown in boldface type.
- The abbreviation for the **part of speech** of each entry word follows the boldface entry word.
- The **definition** of the entry word explains the word's meaning. A **sample sentence** shows you how to use the word.
- Each **synonym** of the entry word is listed under the entry word. Again, a sample sentence shows the correct use of the synonym.
- Sometimes, an **antonym** for the entry word is listed at the end of the entry.

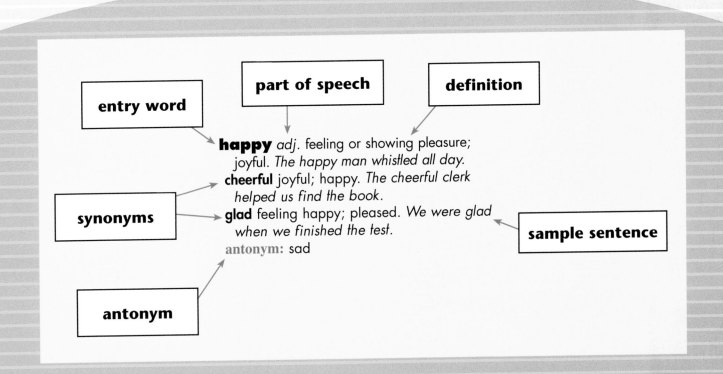

entry word

part of speech

definition

happy *adj.* feeling or showing pleasure; joyful. *The happy man whistled all day.*
cheerful joyful; happy. *The cheerful clerk helped us find the book.*
glad feeling happy; pleased. *We were glad when we finished the test.*
antonym: sad

synonyms

sample sentence

antonym

A

about *adv.* somewhere near. *She guessed it was about seven o'clock.*
almost nearly; just about. *That bus is almost on time; it is only two minutes late.*
nearly almost; not quite. *We were nearly finished with our homework.*
roughly somewhat like. *The houses looked roughly alike.*

afraid *adj.* frightened; filled with fear. *Some people are afraid of falling from high places.*
alarmed filled with sudden fear. *The man was alarmed by the loud noise.*
fearful showing fear. *The fearful kitten raced to its mother.*
frightened full of fright. *The frightened child hid from the very scary creature.*

after *prep.* following. *Don't forget that you come after me in the parade.*
behind farther back. *We will march behind the clowns.*
following coming after. *The parade will take place the following day.*
next following at once. *You will have the next turn.*

always *adv.* all the time; constantly. *At the North Pole, it is always cold.*
ever at any time. *Have you ever traveled to Europe?*
forever for always. *People want to be healthy forever.*

B

badly *adv.* poorly; in a bad manner. *He plays the piano well but sings badly.*
awfully in an awful manner; terribly. *Usually the clowns are funny, but they acted awfully rowdy today.*
dreadfully in a dreadful manner. *The actor played his part dreadfully.*

poorly in a poor manner. *The football team played poorly today.*

band *n.* any flat strip of material used for holding something together. *Put a rubber band around each newspaper.*
sash long, broad strip of cloth worn around the waist. *The dress has a red flowered sash.*
strap a thin strip of leather or another type of material. *I put a strap around the suitcase.*

better *adj.* higher in quality; more excellent; finer. *Does anyone have a better place?*
improved made better. *The mayor told about the improved condition of the city budget.*
superior very good; above average. *She did superior work as an officer.*

blow *v.* to move rapidly. *We could hear the wind blow.*
blast to blow up; tear apart. *They had to blast the rocks for the new roadway.*
toot to give a short blast. *The horn will toot at lunchtime.*

bright *adj.* shining; giving light; reflecting light. *See how bright the car is when it is polished.*
brilliant sparkling; shining brightly. *A brilliant light shone in the sky.*
clear bright; light. *You could see the plane fly across the clear sky.*
light clear; bright. *It is as light as day in here.*
shiny bright; shining. *The shiny vase sparkled in the sunlight.*

C

care *n.* protection; close attention. *A baby needs loving care.*
concern interest; attention. *Our main concern was using the right words.*
interest a feeling of taking part in or wanting to know. *The students had an interest in space travel.*

worry a cause of anxiety or trouble. *Money is a constant worry to him.*

carry *v.* to take from one place to another. *Will you carry this package home?*
  conduct to carry or transfer. *The wires conduct electricity from the wall to the lamp.*
  transport to carry from one place to another. *A truck was used to transport the new cars.*

catch *v.* to get; take and hold onto; seize. *Watch the boy catch the ball!*
  capture to take by force. *The zookeeper will capture the runaway animal.*
  seize to grasp; take hold of. *The happy child tried to seize the big balloon.*

change *v.* to make or become different. *She will change her mind.*
  alter to make different. *We can alter our plans for the trip to the zoo.*
  vary to change; become different. *I will vary the colors in the picture.*

choose *v.* to pick out. *Choose the kind of toy you want.*
  elect to choose for an office by voting. *Who did the group elect as class president?*
  pick to make a choice. *I will pick the winner of the contest.*
  select to choose; pick out. *The teacher will select a book about the stars.*

close *v.* to shut. *Close the door when you leave.*
  bolt to fasten with a bolt. *She will bolt the door each night.*
  seal to close tightly; shut. *He tried to seal the box with tape.*
  shut to close; to prevent entrance. *We shut the door to the gym.*

cost *n.* price that is to be paid. *The cost of meals in restaurants is going up.*
  amount the value; sum. *The amount on the bill was twenty dollars.*
  charge price for service; cost. *A delivery charge will be added to the furniture bill.*
  price the cost in money; the amount of money for which something is sold. *The price should be clearly labeled.*

·D·

dawn *n.* the first appearance of light in the morning. *Dawn came at six o'clock this morning.*
  daybreak time when light appears in the morning. *The rooster crowed at daybreak.*
  sunrise time when the sun appears in the sky. *The campers got up at sunrise.*

digging *v.* making a hole in the ground; breaking up the soil. *The dog was digging in the backyard.*
  burrowing making a hole in the ground. *We caught a rabbit burrowing under the fence.*
  tunneling making a way under the ground. *Moles are tunneling under the whole backyard!*

draw *v.* to make a design, picture, etc. *The artist will draw an outline before he paints the picture.*
  design to make a sketch or a plan. *She will design a new skirt.*
  outline to give a sketch; plan. *We must outline our ideas for the report.*
  sketch to make a rough drawing. *The builder will sketch the plans.*

dream *n.* the thoughts, feelings, and pictures that occur in a person's mind as he or she sleeps. *Her dream was about flying in an airplane.*
  nightmare a very troubled dream. *The terrible nightmare made him scream.*
  vision something seen in one's imagination, dreams, or thoughts. *He had a vision that he was the new captain.*

drop *v.* to fall or let fall. *I will try not to drop a dish as I dry it.*
  fall to drop from a higher place. *The leaves fall from the trees.*
  lower to put down. *Use the rope to lower the flag.*

dull *adj.* uninteresting; boring. *It was such a dull book that I fell asleep reading it.*
boring dull; tiresome. *The boring play had no exciting action in it.*
tiresome tiring; boring. *Without any good jokes, the clown's act was very tiresome.*
uninteresting not interesting. *With no points scored, it was a very uninteresting game.*

E

early *adv.* sooner than usual; before the usual time. *I will have to get up early to go fishing tomorrow.*
shortly before long. *The parade will start shortly.*
soon in a short time; before the usual time; early. *The bus arrived much too soon.*
antonym: late

earn *v.* to deserve as a result of performing a service, doing work, etc. *After we study for two hours, we will earn a break.*
merit to earn; deserve. *The careful workers merit the award for their excellent safety record.*
rate to consider, regard; put a value on. *We rate the movie the best science show of the year.*

F

fair *adj.* in keeping with the rules; according to what is accepted as right. *If you want to play on the team, you must learn fair play.*
equal of the same value, size, rank, amount, etc. *The two boys are of equal weight.*
just right; fair. *She received a just reward for her heroic deeds.*
reasonable not asking too much; just. *We paid a reasonable price for the bookcases.*
antonym: unfair

fight *v.* to try to overcome by force. *Boxers wear padded gloves when they fight.*
battle to take part in a fight or struggle. *The team will battle for first place.*
clash to disagree strongly; fight. *The report's viewpoint always seems to clash with ours.*

find *v.* to look for and get back a lost object. *We will find my watch.*
discover to find out; learn for the first time. *The hikers want to discover a new trail in the woods.*
locate to find the specific place. *The museum guide helped us locate the dinosaur display.*
antonym: lose

finish *v.* to come or bring to an end; complete or become completed. *The movie will finish at 9:30.*
complete to finish; get done. *We will complete the job before we go home.*
conclude to come or bring to an end. *The speaker will conclude by asking everyone to help with the book fair.*
end to stop; to come or bring to its last part. *Our story will end with a very clever surprise.*
antonyms: start, begin

flash *n.* a light that appears suddenly and briefly. *A flash of lightning appeared in the distance.*
gleam a flash or beam of light. *You could see the gleam of the car's lights through the fog.*
sparkle shine; glitter; flash. *The sparkle of the jewels caught my eye.*

float *v.* to stay or move in or on top of air, water, or liquid. *Ice will float in water.*
drift to carry or be carried along by air or water. *The wind made the balloons drift toward the trees.*
antonym: sink

flow *v.* to move in a stream, as water does. *A river can flow to the ocean.*
run to flow. *Water will run downhill.*
stream to flow, move. *The tears seemed to stream down his face.*

fool *v.* to trick or attempt to trick someone. *Her costume could not fool me into thinking she was someone else.*
deceive to mislead; trick. *The magician tried to deceive us with his magic tricks.*
trick to fool; cheat. *We will trick them into thinking the painting was real.*

fresh *adj.* newly made, grown, or gathered. *Mother baked fresh bread.*
new not having existed before. *We played with the new computer game.*
unusual not ordinary. *The book was an unusual size.*
antonym: stale

friend *n.* a person one likes. *Julio is a good friend.*
companion someone close to another; someone to share with. *Jane's dog is her favorite companion.*
comrade a close friend. *The officer and her comrade directed traffic.*
mate a fellow worker or companion. *My trusted mate helped with the work.*
pal a friend; comrade. *My pal and I like to play baseball.*

funny *adj.* strange; unusual; peculiar. *That is a funny way to act.*
curious odd; unusual. *We heard the curious noises from the haunted house.*
odd strange; peculiar. *The music was odd because it had no melody.*
peculiar unusual; strange. *Having a snake for a pet is somewhat peculiar.*

furry *adj.* covered with fur. *A mouse is a very small, furry animal.*
bushy thick; spreading. *The pirate's beard was very bushy.*
hairy covered with hair. *The dog has a hairy body.*
woolly covered with wool or something like it. *The sheep had a woolly coat.*

give *v.* to hand over to another as a present. *Please give me the watch.*
award to give; present. *He will award a prize to the best writer.*
donate to give help or money; contribute. *We will donate our time to clean the park.*
present to offer; give. *The track coach will present ribbons to the winning teams.*
antonym: take

grand *adj.* large; beautiful; impressive. *The queen lived in a grand palace.*
magnificent stately; grand. *The royal family lived in a magnificent castle by the river.*
majestic noble; grand. *The queen rode in a majestic carriage.*
splendid brilliant; grand. *The picture showed a splendid view of the palace.*

great *adj.* large in size or number; big. *A great crowd of people was at the carnival.*
enormous huge; very large. *The enormous crowd clapped for the clowns.*
immense very large; huge. *The immense elephant stood by the tiny mouse.*
large big. *A whale is large.*
vast very great; large. *The animals roamed through the vast jungle.*

hair *n.* the mass of thin threadlike strands that grow on a person's or animal's skin. *Elizabeth has beautiful hair.*
curl a lock of hair forming a ring. *She tucked a curl behind her ear.*
locks the hair on one's head. *She tied a ribbon around her curly locks.*

happy *adj.* feeling or showing pleasure; joyful. *The happy man whistled all day.*

cheerful joyful; happy. *The cheerful clerk helped us find the book.*

glad feeling happy; pleased. *We were glad when we finished the test.*

antonym: sad

high *adj.* tall; far above the ground. *Walnuts fell from a high branch.*

tall having great height. *The tall building could be seen for miles.*

towering very high. *They climbed up the towering mountain.*

antonym: low

hop *v.* to move by jumping. *Rabbits hop from place to place.*

bound to leap or spring. *The sheep bound from rock to rock.*

leap to jump. *The tiger can leap over the fallen tree.*

spring to jump; to leap. *The fox will spring at the rabbit.*

hurry *v.* to act quickly; move fast. *Hurry or you'll be late.*

fly to move quickly, swiftly. *We were so busy that the time seemed to fly.*

hustle to move fast; hurry. *We had to hustle to get to the bus stop on time.*

hurt *v.* to cause pain to. *The sting of the bee hurt his arm.*

ache to be in pain; hurt. *His arm must ache after he fell off his bike.*

pain to suffer; hurt. *The sore finger seemed to pain her when she wrote.*

smart to feel sharp pain. *His eyes will smart from the dust in the air.*

ice *n.* water that has been frozen solid by cold. *Ice keeps food and drinks cold.*

glaze a smooth, glossy coating. *The glaze is what makes the dishes shine.*

hail small pieces of ice falling like rain. *The hail beat on the windows.*

sleet snow or hail mixed with rain. *The sleet covered the town with a shiny coat of ice.*

jelly *n.* a food made by boiling fruit juices and sugar. *I like grape jelly.*

jam food made by boiling fruit and sugar until thick. *The jam was full of purple grapes.*

preserves fruit cooked with sugar and sealed in containers. *We put strawberry preserves on our toast.*

join *v.* to put together; to connect. *They will join the caboose to the last car of the train.*

combine to put two or more things together. *The chef will combine the meat and vegetables for the stew.*

link to connect or join. *The chain will link the gate and the fence.*

kind *adj.* gentle and caring. *They are always very kind to animals.*

gentle kindly; friendly. *The teacher spoke with a gentle voice.*

good-hearted caring; generous. *The good-hearted neighbor helped.*

last *adj.* coming after all others; final. *The last train leaves at six o'clock.*

concluding bringing to an end. *The concluding question asked for the name of the president.*

final at the end; coming last. *The final act of the play was exciting.*

lastly *adv.* at the end; finally. *Lastly, pour the batter into a cake pan and put it into the oven.*

finally at last; at the end. *We finally found the missing ring.*

learn *v.* to gain skill or knowledge in. *We learn spelling in school.*

acquire to obtain. *She wants to acquire the skills to read another language.*

master to become skillful; to learn. *He can master the addition facts.*

study to try to learn by thinking, reading, and practicing. *We study many subjects in school.*

leave *v.* to go away; to go from. *The train will leave in ten minutes.*

abandon to leave and not return. *The people were told to abandon the ship.*

desert to leave without notice. *The officer will not desert her post.*

antonym: arrive

lesson *n.* something to be taught or learned. *My brother is taking his violin lesson.*

exercise something that gives practice. *The assignment was a math exercise.*

lecture a planned speech on a topic. *The lecture was on safety.*

letter *n.* a symbol for a sound. *Z is the twenty-sixth letter in our alphabet.*

character letter, mark, or sign used in writing. *What is the Chinese character for "happy"?*

symbol something that stands for something else. *The + sign is a symbol used in math.*

lift *v.* to raise from a lower to a higher position. *This box is too heavy for me to lift.*

elevate to raise up; lift. *The worker used the crane to elevate the heavy beam to the top of the building.*

hoist to raise; lift up. *The sailors will hoist the sails to begin the trip.*

raise to put up; lift up. *We had to raise our hands if we wanted a turn.*

list *v.* to write or print in a column. *List the spelling words on your paper.*

enter to write or print in a book. *You need to enter the addresses by the names.*

record to write or put in some form. *The scorekeeper will record each score.*

little *adj.* small. *An elephant is big and an ant is little.*

brief lasting a short time; little. *A brief meeting was held.*

small not large; little. *The hummingbird is a very small bird.*

tiny very little; wee. *The tiny ladybug sat on the leaf.*

antonyms: big, large

load *n.* something that is carried. *The load was too heavy for the small car.*

cargo goods sent by plane or ship. *The cargo was unloaded from the plane.*

freight goods carried by plane, truck, ship, or train. *The dock worker sent the freight by truck.*

shipment goods sent together to a company or person. *The shipment arrived this morning.*

mail *v.* to send by mail; to place in a mailbox. *Did you mail my letter?*

send to cause or order to go. *The principal might send the children home early because of the storm.*

transmit to send; to pass along. *The clerk will transmit the order by computer.*

maybe *adv.* perhaps. *Maybe he hasn't left the train yet, and we can still find him.*
perhaps could be; maybe. *Perhaps you will get the first ticket.*
possibly perhaps; by a possibility. *Possibly that is the winning number.*

mild *adj.* not harsh; not severe; warm rather than cold. *We had a mild winter last year.*
calm still; quiet. *Without any wind, the water was calm.*
easy smooth and pleasant. *Her quiet, easy way made everyone around her feel comfortable.*
gentle not rough or violent; mild. *A gentle breeze blew through the trees.*

morning *n.* the earliest part of the day, ending at noon. *We eat breakfast every morning.*
forenoon part of day from sunrise to noon. *We spent the forenoon in the park.*
antonym: evening

news *n.* information; things that a person has not heard about. *What is the news about your brother's new job?*
information knowledge about some fact or event. *The information contains a description of the space launch.*
report information about something seen, heard, done, or read. *The report had many interesting details.*

night *n.* the time between evening and morning; the time from sunset to sunrise when it is dark. *The stars shine at night.*
evening early part of night. *Each evening we eat dinner.*
nighttime time between sunset and morning. *Nighttime begins at dark.*
antonym: day

oil *n.* a greasy liquid obtained from animals, plants, or minerals. *Olive oil is used for salads.*
lubricant oil or grease put on parts of machines to help them move or slide easily. *The mechanic put a lubricant in the engine.*
petroleum a dark liquid found in the earth's crust. *Gasoline is made from petroleum.*

page *n.* one side of a sheet of paper in a book, magazine, newspaper, or letter. *Kurt knew from the first page that he would like the book.*
leaf one sheet of paper. *Each side of a leaf is called a page.*
sheet one piece of paper. *He used one sheet of paper.*

pail *n.* a round bucket with a handle. *He put water in the pail.*
bucket a pail made of plastic, metal, or wood. *The water was in a big bucket.*
scuttle a bucket for carrying or storing coal. *A scuttle was used to store the coal by the old cookstove.*

paint *v.* to cover a surface with paint. *They will paint the fence.*
color to give color; put color on. *He wants to color the fire engine red.*
draw to make a design, picture, etc. *The artist will draw an outline before he paints the picture.*

pair *n.* two things of the same kind that go together; a set of two. *Carlos has a new pair of shoes.*
  couple two of anything; a pair. *We saw a couple stumble during the lively dance.*
  double person or thing like another. *A person who looks like and can act for an actor is called a double.*
  mate a pair. *He could not find the mate to his glove.*

peace *n.* quiet and calm; stillness. *We like the peace of the country.*
  calm stillness; quiet. *There was a strange calm before the storm hit.*
  quiet stillness; peace. *I need quiet to be able to study.*
  serenity calmness; peace and quiet. *We enjoyed the serenity of the countryside.*
  antonym: war

people *n.* human beings; persons; men, women, boys, and girls. *People of all ages attended the fair.*
  folks people or group of people. *The city folks come to work by bus.*
  population number of people in a specific place. *The population of our town is 3,500 people.*
  public all the people. *The public was invited to the free concert.*

place *n.* a certain point; a spot. *The coolest place is near the river.*
  location place or position. *This is a good location for a repair shop.*
  point place or spot. *The race starts at this point.*
  spot place. *This is the spot where we can set up the tent.*

place *v.* to put in a particular position; to set. *Place your pencil on the desk.*
  put to set at a particular place. *I put the books back on the bookshelf.*
  rest to set or place. *He can rest the ladder against the tree.*
  set to put in some place or position. *I set the dishes in the sink.*

plain *adj.* simple; not fancy in appearance. *Tracey wore a plain dress.*
  modest humble; not bold. *The modest child did not brag about her talent.*

point *v.* to aim. *He meant to point his arrow at the target.*
  aim to point or direct. *We tried to aim the telescope at the moon.*
  beam to send out; direct. *The machine will beam the light at the sign.*
  direct to point or aim. *Direct the light at the sign.*
  level to keep even; to aim. *The soldier will level his weapon at the target.*
  train to point or aim. *He tried to train the light on the actor.*

pool *n.* a tank filled with water and used for swimming. *Peter swam across the pool.*
  basin very shallow water area. *The boats docked in the basin of the harbor.*
  lagoon pond or small lake. *The boat was anchored in the lagoon.*
  pond a very small lake. *The ducks swam across the pond.*

pretty *adj.* lovely; pleasing; pleasant to look at or to hear. *The garden was filled with pretty flowers.*
  attractive pleasing; lovely. *The attractive person modeled new fall clothes.*
  beautiful very pretty; pleasing. *The beautiful queen wore a blue dress.*
  lovely very pretty; beautiful. *The lovely flowers filled the room with color.*

prize *n.* a thing won in a contest. *Tony won the prize for spelling the most words correctly.*
  award prize; something given after careful selection. *The award went to the student with the best test score.*
  medal prize; award. *The best swimmer won a gold medal.*
  reward payment offered for the return of property or a person. *We got a reward for finding the ring.*

proud *adj.* having satisfaction and pleasure. *The proud mother watched her daughter graduate.*

exalted filled with pride and joy. *Everyone was exalted by the victory of their beloved king.*

lofty very high; proud. *The group had set lofty goals for the safety project.*

real *adj.* actual; true; not imagined; not made up. *My uncle told us a real story about his trip to Brazil.*

actual real; made of facts. *The book tells of actual events in history.*

factual true; consisting of facts. *She wrote a factual report.*

true real; genuine. *This is a true story of the life of the queen.*

ribbon *n.* a narrow strip of fabric, especially one used as a decoration. *She wore a yellow ribbon in her hair.*

braid a narrow band of fabric used to trim clothing. *The uniform is trimmed with a gold braid.*

tape a narrow strip of material. *The seams had tape on the edges.*

right *adj.* correct; true; accurate. *Allan's answers were all right.*

accurate exact; correct. *The man gave a very accurate description of the football game.*

correct right; without errors. *I gave you the correct answer.*

proper fitting; right for the occasion. *This is not proper behavior at a wedding.*

round *adj.* shaped like a circle. *Our swimming pool is square, but theirs is round.*

circular round like a circle. *The building has a circular tower.*

ringlike like a circle. *The bracelet had ringlike links in it.*

sad *adj.* unhappy. *We were sad when our team lost.*

joyless sad; without joy. *The joyless group waited for news about the fire.*

unhappy sad; without cheer. *The clown wore a very unhappy face.*

sail *v.* to move swiftly, especially in air or on the water. *The ship can sail down the river.*

boat to go in a boat. *We want to boat down the river to fish.*

cruise to sail from place to place. *The ship will cruise to the islands.*

sand *n.* tiny bits of stone in large amounts, found in the desert and on shores along oceans, lakes, and rivers. *This beach has smooth sand.*

dust fine, dry earth. *The dust settled all over the road.*

grit fine bits of sand or gravel. *The boat was covered with grit.*

powder dust made from grinding, crushing, or pounding a solid. *The rocks were ground into fine powder.*

scent *n.* an odor; a smell. *The dogs followed the scent of the wolf.*

aroma strong odor; fragrance. *The aroma of flowers filled the air in the garden.*

fragrance pleasant odor or smell. *The new fragrance smelled like fresh flowers.*

smell an odor; a scent. *The smell of fresh bread filled the air.*

sharp *adj.* having a fine point or a thin edge for cutting. *The knife blade is sharp.*

fine sharp. *The scissors had a very fine cutting edge.*

keen sharp; cutting. *The knife had a keen edge.*

shoot v. to send out swiftly. *The archer will shoot an arrow at the target.*
bombard to attack. *The children always bombard us with questions.*
fire to shoot; discharge. *The officer tried to fire his gun at the target.*
launch to send out; throw. *NASA will launch the rocket on schedule.*

sight n. something that is seen. *The sunset last night was a lovely sight.*
scene view; picture. *The snow on the mountain peaks made a pretty scene.*
spectacle sight; something to see. *The fireworks were a beautiful spectacle.*
view something seen; scene. *She painted a scenic view of the hillside.*

sign n. something that stands for something else; symbol. *The sign for adding is +.*
mark a symbol. *Writers put a question mark at the end of a question.*
symbol something that stands for something else. *The + is a symbol used in math.*

sled n. a low platform on runners that slides over ice and snow. *It is fun to coast down a hill on a sled.*
bobsled a long sled on runners with steering wheel and brakes. *He won an Olympic medal as brakeman for the second American bobsled.*
sleigh cart on runners. *The horse pulled the sleigh over the snow.*

slow adj. not fast or quick. *The turtle makes slow but steady progress.*
leisurely without hurry. *We took a leisurely stroll around town.*
poky moving slowly. *The poky old camel took forever to get there.*
antonym: fast

smooth adj. having no bumps or rough spots. *The smooth highway made driving a pleasure.*
even level; flat. *The road is even with no holes or ruts.*
level flat; even. *The grass was level as far as we could see.*
antonym: rough

soft adj. quiet; gentle; mild. *She has a soft voice.*
gentle low; soft. *He has a gentle way of playing the piano.*
mild not harsh; not severe. *She had a very mild manner.*
antonym: hard

soil n. ground; earth; dirt. *Plants grow in rich, dark soil.*
dirt earth; soil. *We put some dirt into the flowerpot.*
earth ground; soil. *Plant these seeds in black earth.*
ground soil; earth. *The ground in the field is rich and fertile.*

splash v. to make wet or dirty. *The car tried to splash me with mud as it sped past.*
splatter to splash. *The rain will splatter the windows.*
sprinkle to scatter or spray with small drops. *Use the can to sprinkle water on the flowers.*

stick n. a long, thin piece of wood or other material. *We used a stick to stir the paint.*
pole a long piece of wood. *The wires went to the telephone pole.*
rod a thin stick. *The clothes were hung on a metal rod.*
stake a stick pointed at one end. *The stake held up the corner of the tent.*

stop v. to halt or come to a halt. *The car will stop if we don't get more gas.*
cease to come to an end; stop. *The treaty meant all fighting would cease.*
halt to stop. *They had to halt the parade until the mayor arrived.*
pause to stop for a short time. *We will pause for a short rest.*
quit to stop. *The men quit working because of the rain.*

story *n.* a tale or account of an adventure or happening. *Mr. Lee told us a story about his grandfather.*
account a detailed statement about an event. *Each witness gave an account of the accident.*
legend a story of the past that might be based on real events. *The story of Robin Hood is a legend of old England.*
tale a made-up story. *The tale was about the magic of the sea creatures.*

street *n.* a road in a city or town. *This street is always crowded during rush hour.*
avenue a wide street. *Trees lined both sides of the avenue.*
boulevard a broad street. *The boulevard was named after a president.*
road a way for cars, trucks, etc., to travel. *The road went from town to the farm.*

summer *n.* the warmest season of the year. *Summer comes between spring and fall.*
midsummer the middle of the summer season. *The fair always came to town midsummer.*
summertime summer; the summer season. *We loved to swim in the summertime.*

sunshine *n.* the light from the sun. *Our cat loves to nap in the sunshine.*
sunlight the light of the sun. *The plants needed sunlight to grow.*

take *v.* to accept or receive; to grasp. *Take one; they're free.*
grab to seize suddenly; to take. *The man tried to grab the paper before it could fly away.*
grasp to hold; to seize. *She had to grasp the railing to walk down the stairs.*
seize to take hold of; to grasp. *He tried to seize the paper before we could read what it said.*
antonym: give

test *v.* to try; to examine; to put to a test. *Our teacher will test us in history next week.*
check to examine; to prove true or right. *The quiz will check how well we add numbers.*
examine to test skills or knowledge. *This assignment will examine your understanding of today's math lesson.*
quiz to give a short test. *The teacher needed to quiz the students on the chapter they had read.*

think *v.* to have in the mind as an opinion, idea, etc.; to believe. *She tried to think of the answer.*
believe to think something is true or real. *I believe you know the rules.*
expect to think something will occur. *I expect our team to win the game.*
imagine to picture in one's mind. *I like to imagine that elves did the work.*

track *n.* a mark or series of marks left by an animal, person, wagon, etc. *We saw a bicycle track in the snow.*
mark a line, spot, or dot made by something on an object. *That mark was made by the cat's claws.*
pattern a guide to make something. *Use the pattern to make the star.*

treat *v.* to handle; behave toward. *You must treat animals gently.*
handle to touch or use with the hands. *He meant to handle the vase carefully.*
manage to guide or handle. *She can manage the workers very well.*

under *prep.* below; beneath. *I found the money hidden under a rock.*
below lower than; under. *The sign is hanging below the branches.*
beneath below; under. *The light was placed beneath the window.*

until *prep.* up to the time of; till. *I slept until noon today.*
  till until; up to the time of. *The game lasted till five o'clock.*

very *adv.* greatly; extremely. *He was very unhappy when he lost his dog.*
  exceedingly unusually; greatly. *The report was done exceedingly well.*
  extremely greatly; strongly. *She was extremely busy at work today.*
  greatly in a great manner. *She was greatly pleased by the award.*

war *n.* a fight or struggle between countries or parts of a country. *There are great losses of life and destruction of property in a war.*
  fight a struggle; contest. *The fight was scheduled for Tuesday.*
  struggle a conflict; fight. *The struggle for freedom took many years.*

warm *v.* to make warm; to heat. *Warm the food before you serve it.*
  cook to prepare with heat. *The stew must cook for several hours.*
  heat to make or become warm. *The furnace will heat the house.*

wave *v.* to move up and down or from side to side. *The branches began to wave in the wind.*
  flap to move up and down. *The bird needed to flap its wings to get off the ground.*
  flutter to wave back and forth quickly. *The flag will flutter in the wind.*

wide *adj.* covering or having much space from side to side; broad; not narrow. *Our new car has wide seats.*
  broad large across; wide. *The broad road had four lanes in each direction.*
  extensive far-reaching; large. *There were extensive changes in the plans for the new building.*
  antonym: narrow

without *prep.* not having; with no. *I left without my umbrella.*
  less without; with something taken away. *The group was less two people.*
  minus less; decreased by. *Five minus two leaves three.*

woman *n.* a grown female person. *Your mother is a woman.*
  female woman; girl. *The new judge is a female.*
  lady a well mannered woman. *Everyone thinks of her as a real lady.*

work *n.* job; occupation; the thing one does to earn a living. *Her work is modeling clothes.*
  business work; occupation. *Their cleaning business can be found in the shopping mall.*
  job piece of work. *The plumber did a good job of fixing the shower.*
  occupation job; work. *Her occupation was bank manager.*

work *v.* to have a job for pay in order to make a living. *He likes to work in a big office.*
  labor to work hard; toil. *The gardener will have to labor many hours in the spring.*
  toil to work hard. *The farmer needs to toil in the field for many long hours.*

worry *n.* a cause of anxiety or trouble. *Money is a constant worry to him.*

anxiety fears about what might happen; worries. *She felt great anxiety over her test.*

nervousness anxiety; jumpiness. *His nervousness was caused by his fear of heights.*

wrap *v.* to enclose in something by winding or folding. *Wrap the baby in warm blankets.*

bundle up to wrap up. *He needed to bundle up in a heavy coat.*

envelop to wrap, cover, or hide. *The caterpillar will envelop itself in a cocoon.*